MATHEMATICS: A Second Start

S. G. PAGE, M.A., M.Sc., B.Sc.
formerly Lecturer in Mathematics
University of Bradford

ELLIS HORWOOD LIMITED
Publishers · Chichester

Halsted Press: a division of
JOHN WILEY & SONS
New York · Chichester · Brisbane · Toronto

Mathematics and its Applications

Series Editor: G. M. BELL, Professor of Mathematics, King's College (KQC), University of London

Statistics and Operational Research

Editor: B. W. CONOLLY, Professor of Operational Research, Queen Mary College, University of London

Mathematics and its applications are now awe-inspiring in their scope, variety and depth. Not only is there rapid growth in pure mathematics and its applications to the traditional fields of the physical sciences, engineering and statistics, but new fields of application are emerging in biology, ecology and social organisation. The user of mathematics must assimilate subtle new techniques and also learn to handle the great power of the computer efficiently and economically.

The need of clear, concise and authoritative texts is thus greater than ever and our series will endeavour to supply this need. It aims to be comprehensive and yet flexible. Works surveying recent research will introduce new areas and up-to-date mathematical methods. Undergraduate texts on established topics will stimulate student interest by including applications relevant at the present day. The series will also include selected volumes of lecture notes which will enable certain important topics to be presented earlier than would otherwise be possible.

In all these ways it is hoped to render a valuable service to those who learn, teach, develop and use mathematics.

Mathematics and its Applications

Series Editor: G. M. BELL, Professor of Mathematics, King's College (KQC), University of London

Artmann, B. — **The Concept of Number***
Balcerzyk, S. & Joszefiak, T. — **Commutative Rings***
Balcerzyk, S. & Joszefiak, T. — **Noetherian and Krull Rings***
Baldock, G.R. & Bridgeman, T. — **Mathematical Theory of Wave Motion**
Ball, M.A. — **Mathematics in the Social and Life Sciences: Theories, Models and Methods**
de Barra, G. — **Measure Theory and Integration**
Bell, G.M. and Lavis, D.A. — **Co-operative Phenomena in Lattice Models Vols. I & II***
Berkshire, F.H. — **Mountain and Lee Waves**
Berry, J.S., Burghes, D.N., Huntley, I.D., James, D.J.G. & Moscardini, A.O. — **Teaching and Applying Mathematical Modelling**
Burghes, D.N. & Borrie, M. — **Modelling with Differential Equations**
Burghes, D.N. & Downs, A.M. — **Modern Introduction to Classical Mechanics and Control**
Burghes, D.N. & Graham, A. — **Introduction to Control Theory, including Optimal Control**
Burghes, D.N., Huntley, I. & McDonald, J. — **Applying Mathematics**
Burghes, D.N. & Wood, A.D. — **Mathematical Models in the Social, Management and Life Sciences**
Butkovskiy, A.G. — **Green's Functions and Transfer Functions Handbook**
Butkovskiy, A.G. — **Structural Theory of Distributed Systems**
Cao, Z-Q., Kim, K.H. & Roush, F.W. — **Incline Algebra and Applications**
Chorlton, F. — **Textbook of Dynamics, 2nd Edition**
Chorlton, F. — **Vector and Tensor Methods**
Crapper, G.D. — **Introduction to Water Waves**
Cross, M. & Moscardini, A.O. — **Learning the Art of Mathematical Modelling**
Cullen, M.R. — **Linear Models in Biology**
Dunning-Davies, J. — **Mathematical Methods for Mathematicians, Physical Scientists and Engineers**

Eason, G., Coles, C.W. & Gettinby, G. **Mathematics and Statistics for the Bio-sciences**
Exton, H. **Handbook of Hypergeometric Integrals**
Exton, H. **Multiple Hypergeometric Functions and Applications**
Exton, H. ***q*-Hypergeometric Functions and Applications**
Faux, I.D. & Pratt, M.J. **Computational Geometry for Design and Manufacture**
Firby, P.A. & Gardiner, C.F. **Surface Topology**
Gardiner, C.F. **Modern Algebra**
Gardiner, C.F. **Algebraic Structures: with Applications**
Gasson, P.C. **Geometry of Spatial Forms**
Goodbody, A.M. **Cartesian Tensors**
Goult, R.J. **Applied Linear Algebra**
Graham, A. **Kronecker Products and Matrix Calculus: with Applications**
Graham, A. **Matrix Theory and Applications for Engineers and Mathematicians**
Griffel, D.H. **Applied Functional Analysis**
Griffel, D.H. **Linear Algebra***
Hanyga, A. **Mathematical Theory of Non-linear Elasticity**
Harris, D.J. **Mathematics for Business, Management and Economics**
Hoksins, R.F. **Generalised Functions**
Hoskins, R.F. **Standard and Non-standard Analysis***
Hunter, S.C. **Mechanics of Continuous Media, 2nd (Revised) Edition**
Huntley, I. & Johnson, R.M. **Linear and Nonlinear Differential Equations**
Jaswon, M.A. & Rose, M.A. **Crystal Symmetry: The Theory of Colour Crystallography**
Johnson, R.M. **Theory and Applications of Linear Differential and Difference Equations**
Kim, K.H. & Roush, F.W. **Applied Abstract Algebra**
Kosinski, W. **Field Singularities and Wave Analysis in Continuum Mechanics**
Krishnamurthy, V. **Combinatorics: Theory and Applications**
Lindfield, G. & Penny, J.E.T. **Microcomputers in Numerical Analysis**
Lord, E.A. & Wilson, C.B. **The Mathematical Description of Shape and Form**
Marichev, O.I. **Integral Transforms of Higher Transcendental Functions**
Massey, B.S. **Measures in Science and Engineering**
Meek, B.L. & Fairthorne, S. **Using Computers**
Mikolas, M. **Real Function and Orchogonal Series**
Moore, R. **Computational Functional Analysis**
Müller-Pfeiffer, E. **Spectral Theory of Ordinary Differential Operators**
Murphy, J.A. & McShane, B. **Computation in Numerical Analysis***
Nonweiller, T.R.F. **Computational Mathematics: An Introduction to Numerical Approximation**
Ogden, R.W. **Non-linear Elastic Deformations**
Oldknow, A. & Smith, D. **Learning Mathematics with Micros**
O'Neill, M.E. & Chorlton, F. **Ideal and Incompressible Fluid Dynamics**
O'Neill, M.E. & Chorlton, F. **Viscous and Compressible Fluid Dynamics***
Page, S. G. **Mathematics: A Second Start**
Rankin, R.A. **Modular Forms**
Ratschek, H. & Rokne, J. **Computer Methods for the Range of Functions**
Scorer, R.S. **Environmental Aerodynamics**
Smith, D.K. **Network Optimisation Practice: A Computational Guide**
Srivastava, H.M. & Karlsson, P.W. **Multiple Gaussian Hypergeometric Series**
Srivastava, H.M. & Manocha, H.L. **A Treatise on Generating Functions**
Shivamoggi, B.K. **Stability of Parallel Gas Flows***
Stirling, D.S.G. **Mathematical Analysis***
Sweet, M.V. **Algebra, Geometry and Trigonometry in Science, Engineering and Mathematics**
Temperley, H.N.V. & Trevena, D.H. **Liquids and Their Properties**
Temperley, H.N.V. **Graph Theory and Applications**
Thom, R. **Mathematical Models of Morphogenesis**
Toth, G. **Harmonic and Minimal Maps**
Townend, M. S. **Mathematics in Sport**
Twizell, E.H. **Computational Methods for Partial Differential Equations**
Wheeler, R.F. **Rethinking Mathematical Concepts**
Willmore, T.J. **Total Curvature in Riemannian Geometry**
Willmore, T.J. & Hitchin, N. **Global Riemannian Geometry**
Wojtynski, W. **Lie Groups and Lie Algebras***

Continued at back of book

First published in 1986
and Reprinted in 1988 by
ELLIS HORWOOD LIMITED
Market Cross House, Cooper Street,
Chichester, West Sussex, PO19 1EB, England
The publisher's colophon is reproduced from James Gillison's drawing of the ancient Market Cross, Chichester.

Distributors:
Australia and New Zealand:
JACARANDA WILEY LIMITED
GPO Box 859, Brisbane, Queensland 4001, Australia
Canada:
JOHN WILEY & SONS CANADA LIMITED
22 Worcester Road, Rexdale, Ontario, Canada
Europe and Africa:
JOHN WILEY & SONS LIMITED
Baffins Lane, Chichester, West Sussex, England
North and South America and the rest of the world:
Halsted Press: a division of
JOHN WILEY & SONS
605 Third Avenue, New York, NY 10158, USA
South-East Asia
JOHN WILEY & SONS (SEA) PTE LIMITED
37 Jalan Pemimpin # 05–04
Block B, Union Industrial Building, Singapore 2057
Indian Subcontinent
WILEY EASTERN LIMITED
4835/24 Ansari Road
Daryaganj, New Delhi 110002, India

British Library Cataloguing in Publication Data
Page, S. G.
Mathematics: a second start
1. Mathematics — 1961 —
I. Title
510 QA37.2

ISBN 0–7458–0116–1 (Ellis Horwood Limited — Library Edn.)
ISBN 0–7458–0127–7 (Ellis Horwood Limited — Student Edn.)
ISBN 0–470–20752–3 (Halsted Press)

Printed in Great Britain by The Camelot Press, Southampton

CONTENTS

INTRODUCTION

This book is intended for the student 'who never could do maths', the student who for one reason or another missed his or her way at school, either by absence from some of the O-level course, or by having too many changes of masters or schools. Such a student has lost confidence in his own ability to tackle the subject. It is intended for the student whose knowledge extends only to O-level mathematics, probably obtained several years ago, but who would now like to be able to communicate with mathematicians, i.e. to know what is meant when one talks about 'an integral' or 'a differential equation'. It is based on a course of tutorials and discussions with students of this type, to whom I am indebted for their patient endeavours and encouragement.

So let us begin at the beginning. The student who does not require the elementary work, nevertheless, is advised to see that the examples at the end of each chapter are worked through conscientiously, as each step depends on the previous steps being fully understood. One must be completely competent in dealing with mathematical 'shorthand', i.e. the method of expressing an idea in as neat a way as possible, so that it can be handled easily and quickly.

PART I EASY ALGEBRA

Chapter 1

Learning the language

You will know that the area of a rectangle is found by multiplying the length by the breadth, or more shortly

$A = L \times B$
or $A = L.B$
or $A = LB$

This simple shorthand is expressing the fact that 'if you multiply the length of a rectangle by the breadth, both being expressed in the same unit, then the result gives the area of the rectangle in square units'.

This is algebra, and the first fact emerges:

When two symbols are written side by side with no sign in between, **the sign understood is multiplication.** Multiplication is the only sign which can be omitted between two symbols and then only between letters or a letter and a number but not between two numbers.

$a \times b = ab$
But 2×3 is obviously not 23

We also know the shorthand way of writing

$2 \times 2 \times 2 \times 2 \times 2$ is 2^5
Similarly
$a \times a \times a \times a \times a = a^5$
Now we can distinguish
2a from a^2

2a means $2 \times a$
a^2 means $a \times a$ } THIS IS VERY IMPORTANT

i.e. if a = 5, 2a = 10 but $a^2 = 25$

Similarly 3b means $3 \times b$
but b^3 means $b \times b \times b$

Exercise 1.

1. Write down the shorthand form for:

(i) $a \times a \times a \times a$
(ii) $4 \times a$
(iii) $2 \times a \times b \times c$
(iv) $3 \times a \times b \times b \times c \times c \times c$

2. If a = 2 and b = 3, find the value of

(i) a^2, $3a$
(ii) b^2, $2b$
(iii) ab
(iv) $3a^2b$
(v) $4ab$
(vi) $2a + 3b$

INDICES

Knowing the meaning of a^2, a^3, a^4, etc., we can now multiply powers of the same letter (or number) together.

e.g. $a^4 \times a^3$ means $(a \times a \times a \times a)$ multiplied by $(a \times a \times a)$
i.e. $(a \times a \times a \times a) \times (a \times a \times a) = a \times a \times a \times a \times a \times a \times a$
Therefore $a^4 \times a^3$ is a^7.

So we ADD THE INDICES when multiplying powers of the same letter or number.

THIS IS THE FIRST RULE OF INDICES

This helps us to do quickly what we know by common sense is the meaning of a^4 and a^3 and we can imagine a row of seven a's all multiplied together. There is no mystery about this rule.

Similarly $a^6 \div a^2$ means $\dfrac{a \times a \times a \times a \times a \times a}{a \times a}$

Whatever number the a's represent, they all stand for the same number in the same question, so that two of the a's cancel out giving:

$$\frac{\overset{1}{\cancel{a}} \times \overset{1}{\cancel{a}} \times a \times a \times a \times a}{\underset{1}{\cancel{a}} \times \underset{1}{\cancel{a}}} = \frac{1\,a^4}{1} = a^4$$

This illustrates the rule of division of powers of the same letter or number, i.e. we SUBTRACT THE INDEX of the bottom line from that of the top line.

Exercise 2. Simplify:

1. $a^6 \times a^2$
2. $a^2 \times a^2 \times a$ (note a is the same as a^1)
3. $a^5 \times a \times a^3$
4. $a^7 \div a^3$
5. $a^9 \div a^3$ (be careful!)
6. $a^{10} \div a^5$
7. $ab^4 \times a^2b^2$ (multiply the a's and then the b's)
8. $a^2b^3 \times a^2b^2 \div ab$

(Write No.8 out in full, cancel and then simplify).

Some Common Errors

We must distinguish between the meanings of $2a^2$ and $(2a)^2$. The former is 'two a-squared' and the latter is 'two-a all squared', and the difference is fundamental.

For example:

if 'a' represents the number 4
$2a^2$ (which is $2 \times a \times a$) means $2 \times 4 \times 4 = 32$
but $(2a)^2$ (meaning $2a \times 2a$) means $8 \times 8 = 64$, i.e. $(2a)^2 = 4a^2$

so that the 'square' only affects the letter or number on which it stands, but when a bracket is squared, everything inside is squared.

Exercise 3. Simplify:

1. $(2a)^3$ 2. $(3ab)^2$ 3. $(ab)^3 \times (a^2b)^2$

ADDITION AND SUBTRACTION

Having coped with multiplication and division, let us add and subtract. We know that three 2's are 6 and four 2's are 8 and 6 + 8 = 14 = seven 2's, so that three 2's + four 2's make seven 2's.

This is a particular case of $3a + 4a = 7a$

3 x (a particular thing) + 4 x (the same kind of thing)
= 7 x (the same kind of thing)

Don't make the mistake of saying $3a + 4a = 7a^2$ which is a common error.

3 apples + 4 apples = 7 apples (not apples squared)

In the same way:

10 apples – 4 apples = 6 apples

i.e. $10a - 4a = 6a$

Now we can add and subtract in algebra. It is as simple as this.

$12a + 3a + a = 16a$ (a is the same as 1a)

and $5y + 3y - 2y = 6y$

Exercise 4. Write down the results of the following additions and subtractions:

1. $2x + 7x$
2. $5x - 2x$
3. $14x - 11x$
4. $9x + 2x - x$
5. $12a + 5a - 7a$
6. $13x^2y + 2x^2y - 5x^2y$

NEGATIVE NUMBERS

Now consider $5a - 7a$.
This is not the same as $7a - 5a$ (though $5a + 7a$ is the same as $7a + 5a$, both equalling $12a$).

We can consider $5a - 7a$ in several different ways. One popular way is the 'thermometer scale' method (Fig.1.1).

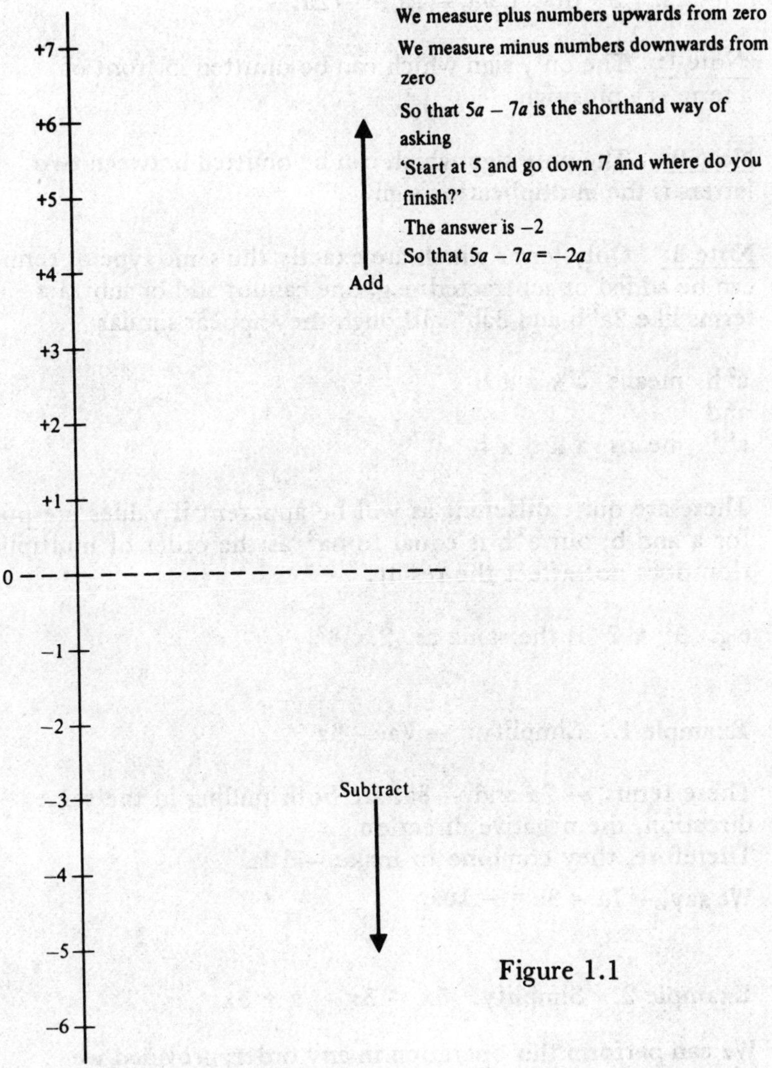

+7

+6

+5

+4

+3

+2

+1

0

−1

−2

−3

−4

−5

−6

We measure plus numbers upwards from zero

We measure minus numbers downwards from zero

So that $5a - 7a$ is the shorthand way of asking

'Start at 5 and go down 7 and where do you finish?'

The answer is −2

So that $5a - 7a = -2a$

Add

Subtract

Figure 1.1

or

One can think of *plus* terms pulling one way and *minus* terms pulling the opposite way (Fig.1.2).

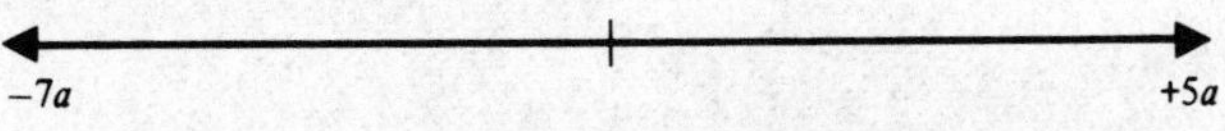

Figure 1.2

So that $+ 5a$ and $- 7a$ are pulling in opposite directions giving the result that the negative term 'wins'. And by how much? $- 2a$. So that $+ 5a - 7a = - 2a$.

Note 1: The only sign which can be omitted in front of a term is a plus sign.

Note 2: The only sign which can be omitted between two letters is the multiplication sign.

Note 3: Only terms which are exactly the same type of term can be added or subtracted: e.g. one cannot add or subtract terms like $2a^2b$ and $3ab^2$ although they appear similar.

a^2b means $a \times a \times b$
and
ab^2 means $a \times b \times b$

These are quite different as will be apparent if values are put in for a and b, but a^2b is equal to ba^2 as the order of multiplication does not affect the result:

e.g. $3^2 \times 2$ is the same as 2×3^2

Example 1. Simplify: $- 7a - 3a$

These terms, $- 7a$ and $- 3a$, are both pulling in the same direction, the negative direction.
Therefore, they combine to make $- 10a$.
We say, $- 7a - 3a =$ **$- 10a$.**

Example 2. Simplify: $5x - 3x - x + 3x$

We can perform this operation in any order, provided we remember that **the sign IN FRONT OF a term belongs to the term.**

Hence $5x - 3x - x + 3x$

$= 2x - x + 3x$

$= x + 3x$

$= 4x$

or $5x - 3x - x + 3x$

$= +8x - 4x$ Combining the plus terms and the minus terms first.

$= 4x$

Exercise 5. Collect like terms in the following:

(Example: $-2a - 3b + 4c + a - 6b + 5c = -a - 9b + 9c$)

1. $3a - 4b + 2c - 6b + 2a - 5c$
2. $5x + 2y - 9z - 7x - 5y + 12z$
3. $11x^2y + 2x^2y - 6x^2y - 12x^2y$
4. $-6pq + 11pq - 3pq$
5. $6a - 7b + 2a - 7b + 14b - 8a$
6. Add up the following columns:

(a)
$$\begin{array}{r} 2x - 3y + 7z \\ -2x - 2y - 3z \\ 6x + y - z \\ \hline \\ \hline \end{array}$$

(b)
$$\begin{array}{r} 3x^2 - 2x + 4 \\ -3x^2 - 5x - 1 \\ -6x^2 + 3x - 5 \\ \hline \\ \hline \end{array}$$

Worked Examples on Chapter 1. Simplify:

(i) $1\frac{1}{4}y \times 8$

$= \frac{5}{\not{4}_1} \times \frac{y}{1} \times \frac{\not{8}^2}{1}$

$= 10y$ (after cancelling by 4)

(ii) $\frac{4x^2}{9} \div \frac{2x^2}{3}$

$= \frac{{}^2\not{4}x^2}{\not{9}_3} \times \frac{\not{3}^1}{\not{2}x^2_1}$ (change ÷ to x and invert the second fraction)

$= \frac{2x^2}{3x^2}$ (after cancelling by 2 and 3)

$= \frac{2}{3}$ (after cancelling by x^2)

(iii) $\frac{p}{q} \times \frac{q}{r} \times \frac{r}{s} \div \frac{p}{s}$

$= \frac{{}^1\not{p}}{{}_1\not{q}} \times \frac{{}^1\not{q}}{{}_1\not{r}} \times \frac{{}^1\not{r}}{{}_1\not{s}} \times \frac{{}^1\not{s}}{{}_1\not{p}}$

$= \frac{1}{1}$ (everything cancels)

$= 1$ *

(* Don't make the error and say that 'everything cancels out ∴ the answer is nought').

<u>Exercise 6.</u> Simplify:

1. $3\frac{1}{3}ab \times 9$

2. $\frac{2a}{b} \times \frac{c}{4a} \times \frac{6b}{c}$

3. $\frac{6a^2}{5} \div \frac{3ab}{10}$

4. $\frac{a}{b} \times \frac{2a}{b} \div \frac{3a}{2c}$

5. $\frac{5a}{b} \times \frac{3b}{4c} \div \left(\frac{2a}{3} \times \frac{b}{10c}\right)$

6. $\frac{6}{5p} \times \frac{2q^2}{3q} \div \frac{q}{10r^2}$

Chapter 2
Useful tools

EXPRESSIONS INVOLVING BRACKETS

You are probably familiar with the guide to simplifying complicated expressions in arithmetic - B,O,D,M,A,S, meaning that the order of simplification is:

1. Brackets and 'Of'
   then
2. Division and Multiplication
   and lastly
3. Addition and Subtraction

Our only concern here is that **brackets have priority over other operations,** meaning that the contents of a bracket must be simplified if possible before any other operation is performed.

In algebra it is not always possible to simplify the contents of a bracket. Therefore we have to find other ways of removing the bracket without changing the value of the expression.

Example. How do we simplify $2(a + b) + 3(2a + 4b)$?
Let us consider $2(3 + 7)$
We know that this means $2 \times (3 + 7)$
(The only sign that can be omitted between two things is the multiplication sign)
So that $2 \times (3 + 7) = 2 \times 10 = 20$
Can we get the same answer any other way?

Can we split up the expression $2 \times (3 + 7)$?
Let us try $(2 \times 3) + 7$. This gives $6 + 7 = 12$, which is *incorrect.*

BUT (2 x 3) + (2 x 7) gives 6 + 14 = 20, i.e. the correct answer.
This suggests that everything INSIDE the bracket must be multiplied by the quantity OUTSIDE the bracket.

Let us consider another case: 5(60 – 3 + 5)
By conventional arithmetic this is 5 x 62 = 310
Let us try the other method, multiplying each number inside by 5 separately:
(5 x 60) – (5 x 3) + (5 x 5)
= 300 – 15 + 25
= **310**
It gives the correct answer although it is a longer method.

BRACKETS IN ALGEBRA

Following the same rule, for our first example:
2(a + b) + 3(2a + 4b)
gives 2a + 2b + 6a + 12b, multiplying the first bracket by 2 and the second by 3
= **8a + 14b**

Similarly 5(6p + 4q) + 2(p – 3q)
= 30p + 20q + 2p – 6q
= **32p + 14q**
And 4(a + b + c) + (2a – 3b – 6c)
= 4(a + b + c) + 1(2a – 3b – 6c)
= 4a + 4b + 4c + 2a – 3b – 6c
= **6a + b – 2c**
Note: If there is NO NUMBER OR TERM OUTSIDE a bracket, the number is understood to be 1.

NEGATIVE QUANTITIES OUTSIDE A BRACKET

Let us consider the value of
3 x (4 + 1) – 2 x (2 + 4)
= 3 x 5 – 2 x 6
= 15 – 12
= **3**

By the long method, would the following give the correct answer?

$(3 \times 4) + (3 \times 1) - (2 \times 2) + (2 \times 4)$

Simplifying: $12 + 3 - 4 + 8$

$= 23 - 4$

$= 19$ *wrong*

Note the change of sign her

Let us try again: $(3 \times 4) + (3 \times 1) - (2 \times 2) - (2 \times 4)$

$= 12 + 3 - 4 - 8$

$= 3$ *correct*

This seems to indicate that a NEGATIVE SIGN OUTSIDE THE BRACKET REVERSES the signs INSIDE when the bracket is removed.

Let us try another example:

$3 \times (4 - 1) - 2 \times (4 - 2)$

$= (3 \times 3) - (2 \times 2) \quad = 5$

Using the long way and changing the sign on removing the second bracket:

$3 \times (4 - 1) - 2(4 - 2)$ — Note the change

$= 3 \times 4 - 3 \times 1 - 2 \times 4 + 2 \times 2$ of sign here.

$= 12 - 3 - 8 + 4 \quad = 5$ correct.

This gives the following:

RULES FOR THE REMOVAL OF SIMPLE BRACKETS

1. **Every term INSIDE** the bracket must be multiplied by the number or quantity **OUTSIDE** the bracket.
2. If the sign in **FRONT** of the bracket is **POSITIVE** the signs **INSIDE** the bracket are **unchanged.** (Note: No sign in front of the bracket implies that it is positive).
3. If the sign in **FRONT** of the bracket is **NEGATIVE all the signs INSIDE are changed** from positive to negative or negative to positive.

Exercise 7. Remove brackets from the following and collect like terms:

1. $3(a + b) + 4(5a + b)$
2. $3(a - b) + 4(2a + b)$
3. $6(a + 2b - c) + (a - b + c)$
4. $2(3a - 4b) - (a + b) + 2(a + b)$
5. $3(a - 2b + 3c) - 2(b + 4c)$
6. $-4(a - 3b) - 3(-3a - b)$

7. $2p(q + r) - p(3q - 2r)$
8. $11a(2b + c) - 3a(3b - 2c)$
9. $a(a + b - c) - b(a - b + c)$ Remember ab is the same as ba
10. $a(b + c) - b(c + a) + c(a + b)$

SUBTRACTION IN COLUMNS

We shall need to be able to perform the following type of operation:

From $2a + 4b - 3c$ (1)
Subtract $a - 2b + 6c$ (2)

This is only another way of writing down:
$(2a + 4b - 3c) - (a - 2b + 6c)$ (3)
the brackets implying that the whole of the second line (2) has to be subtracted from line (1).
We know how to do this: line (3) can be simplified to:
$2a + 4b - 3c - a + 2b - 6c$ (changing signs on removing second bracket)
$= a + 6b - 9c$

We note that we can obtain this answer from the columns above by mentally **changing the signs on the lower line and adding to the top line.** (A check is obtained by adding the answer and the lower line which must equal the top line.)

Example:

From $3x - 2y + 4z$
Subtract $-x - 3y + 7z$
$\mathbf{4x + y - 3z}$

Check: Adding these two lines gives $3x - 2y + 4z$

The reasoning goes something like this:

1. Look at the 'subtract' line
2. Change the sign of minus x (mentally) giving +x. Add this to 3x above giving +4x.
3. Next, change the sign of $-3y$ to give $+3y$ add to $-2y$ to give $+y$
4. Lastly, change the sign of $+7z$ to give $-7z$ add to $+4z$ to give $-3z$

5. Check by adding the lower two lines, which should give the top line

e.g. From $3x$

Subtract $-x$ ⌉ Add: $4x - x = 3x$

$4x$ ⌋

Thus adding the two lower lines gives the top line.

Exercise 8. Complete the following:

1. From $2a + 3b + c$
   Subtract $a + b + c$

2. From $a + b - c$
   Subtract $2a + 3b + c$

3. From $6x - 2y + 3z$
   Subtract $2x + 3y - z$

4. From $-11xy - 2yz + 4zx$
   Subtract $-4xy + yz - 6zx$

5. From $5x + y - 2z$
   Subtract $-2x + 3y - 3z$

6. From $-a - 2b - 7c$
   Subtract $-3a - 4b - 8c$

(N.B. Add your answer to the second line and it should equal the first line.)

MULTIPLICATION AND DIVISION OF POSITIVE AND NEGATIVE NUMBERS

(i) It is obvious that $(+2) \times (+3) = +6$
i.e. two **positive** numbers multiplied together give a **positive** answer.

(ii) Also $+2 \times (-3)$ by our previous rules about brackets $= -6$, the sign inside the bracket being unchanged by the plus sign outside, rule 2 (page 12)
and $-2 \times (+6)$
$= -12$, the sign inside the bracket being changed by the negative sign outside the bracket, rule 3 (page 12)
i.e. a **positive** quantity multiplied by a **negative** quantity or vice versa gives a **negative** answer.

(iii) Also $-4 \times (-3) = +12$, the sign inside the bracket being changed by the negative sign in front of the bracket, rule 3 (page 12)
i.e. a **negative** quantity multiplied by a **negative** quantity gives a **positive** answer.

Summary

We say briefly two LIKE signs multiplied together give a POSITIVE result.
Two UNLIKE signs multiplied together give a NEGATIVE result.
This is merely another way of stating rules 2 and 3 on page 12.

Exercise 9. Using the facts that

$(+) \times (+) = +$ $\quad (-) \times (-) = +$

$(+) \times (-) = -$ $\quad (-) \times (+) = -$

simplify the following:

1. $(-2) \times (+3)$
2. $(+3) \times (-4)$
3. $(-5) \times (-2)$
4. $(-3)^2$
5. $5 \times (-2)$
6. $(-1)^3$
7. $(-2) \times (-3) \times (+2)$
8. $(-6a) \times (-2a^2)$
9. $(4xy) \times (-2x)$
10. $(-3a) \times (+2b) \times (-c)$

Using the fact that the rules for division of signs are exactly the same as those for multiplication simplify:

11. $(+6) \div (-2)$
12. $(-12) \div (-3)$
13. $\frac{-4}{+2}$
14. $\frac{-7}{+2}$
15. $\frac{-4}{-4}$
16. $\frac{10}{-1}$

Exercise 10. Revision Examples on Chapter 2.

Write down shorter forms for:

1. $x + x + x + x$
2. $a + a + a - a$
3. $5a + 7a$
4. $3a + a$
5. $9p - 2p$
6. $2p - 9p$
7. $-9p + 2p$
8. $-2p + 9p$
9. $10x - 5x + 5x$
10. $4x - 2y - 2y - y$
11. $6e + f - 2e - f + f$
12. $3x - 5y - 4z - 2x - y + z$

Simplify: multiply the numbers first and then the letters)

13. $3a^2 \times 6a$
14. $4b \times 4b$
15. $(6x)^2$
16. $2c \times 5d$
17. $2kh \times 3km$
18. $3xyz \times 2xz$
19. $5c \div c$
20. $2 \times \frac{3x}{4}$
21. $1\frac{1}{5}y \times 10$
22. $x^2y^2 \div xy$
23. $\frac{h}{h^2}$
24. $\frac{x}{xy^2}$
25. $\frac{p^2}{pq}$
26. $\frac{x}{2} \times 6x$
27. Add:

$$\begin{array}{r} 2x^2 + 3x^2y + 4x^2z \\ 5x^2 - 2x^2y - 2x^2z \\ -3x^2 - 4x^2y - 5x^2z \\ \hline \\ \hline \end{array}$$

Chapter 3

Easy equations

Perhaps it would help those students who dislike the sound of the word 'equations' if we could find another word to replace it, e.g. simple puzzles, the answers to which need to be found.

Take the following example:

Example 1. I am thinking of a number. I double it and add 3, and the answer is 11. What is the number I first thought of?

The reasoning behind this goes something like this:

The answer after adding 3 is 11.
Therefore before adding 3 it must have been 8.
But this was double the number first thought of.
Therefore the number must have been 4.
Checking this $(2 \times 4) + 3 = 11$
Now, in algebraic shorthand one says:
Think of a number , call it x
Double it　　　　　$2x$
Add 3　　　　　　$2x + 3$
The answer is 11, therefore $2x + 3$ must equal 11.
Here is the equation to solve: $2x + 3 = 11$

This is saying in algebraic shorthand exactly the same as the whole of the statement in example 1.
Now let us analyse our commonsense method of solving this. Each time we are instructed to 'double it' or 'add 3' or some such similar simple operation, we are making it more complicated, in the same way that tying a complicated knot in a piece of string is really a series of simple knots tied one after another. In order to untie a complicated knot, what do we do? We start with the last knot which was tied and undo that first and then proceed backwards, reversing the process step by step or knot by knot. In exactly the same way we reverse the operations in algebra to get rid of the complications.

Example 2

I think of a number — this gives x (say)
I subtract 4 — this gives $x - 4$
I then multiply it by 3 — this gives $3(x - 4)$
The answer is then 21
So that $3(x - 4) = 21$
Reversing the processes:
The last instruction was 'multiply by 3'
The reverse of multiplying by 3 is dividing by 3
Therefore before multiplying by 3, it must have been $21 \div 3$
i.e. 7
That is $x - 4 = 7$
The previous complication was 'I subtract 4'
So we must reverse this and ADD 4 to both sides
Therefore the unknown number must have been 11.

Check: If the number is 11
We subtract 4 giving 7 and multiply by 3 giving 21. Correct.

A QUESTION OF BALANCE

Another commonsense way of looking at an equation is to see it as a balance as with a pair of scales. The left-hand side balances the right-hand side and whatever we do to one side we must do exactly the same thing to the other in order to keep the balance.

For example, if a pair of scales is nicely balanced by objects or masses on one scale pan balancing objects on the other, then if I add equal masses to both sides, the scales will still balance. Similarly, if I subtract equal masses from both sides, it will still balance, or if I double the masses or objects on both sides or halve the masses or objects on both sides the balance is still maintained. Thus, the guide to dealing with equations is this:

Whatever you do to one side of an equation, you must do EXACTLY the same thing to the other.

Let us see how this works.

Suppose we have 4 equal objects of unknown mass, x grams each, on the left-hand pan and a mass of 2 grams . On the right-hand side we have 24 grams mass to keep it balanced (Fig. 3.1.)

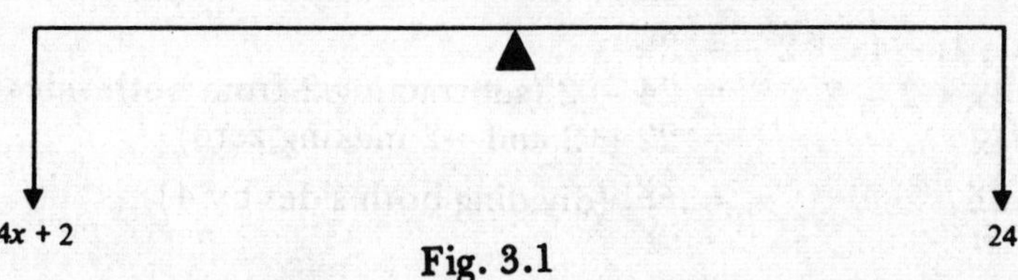

Fig. 3.1

Then 4x + 2 = 24, where x grams is the mass of each object. If we take off 2 grams from each side we are left with 4x on one side and 22 grams on the other, as in Fig.3.2.

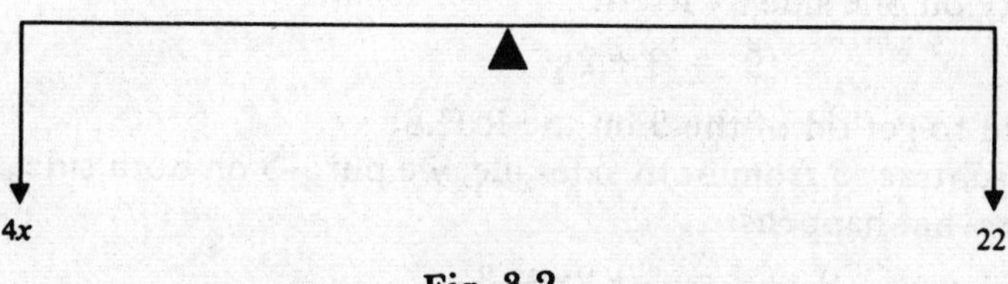

Fig. 3.2

That is 4x = 22

Now if we divide the L.H.S. by 4,[i.e. $\frac{4x}{4}$ = x] we get x

and if we divide the R.H.S. by 4 we get 5½ (Fig. 3.3)

Note: L.H.S. means 'left-hand side'; R.H.S. means 'right-hand side'.

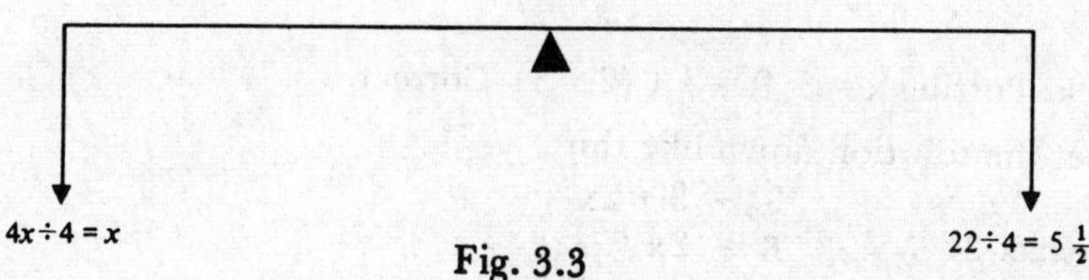

Fig. 3.3

Therefore x = 5½ Check: (4 x 5½) + 2 = 24 Correct.

This is the type of thing which is repeated step by step until a solution is obtained.
We put it down like this:

Example 1. $4x + 2 = 24$

$\therefore 4x + 2 - 2 = 24 - 2$ (subtracting 2 from both sides)

$\therefore 4x = 22$ (+2 and −2 making zero)

$\therefore \frac{4x}{4} = \frac{22}{4}$ (dividing both sides by 4)

$\therefore x = 5\frac{1}{2}$

Example 2. $9 = 3 + 2x$

It makes no difference which way round we write our equation. A pair of scales weigh equally well whether they are viewed from the front or the back. But the aim is to isolate the unknown quantity on one side by itself.

$$9 = 3 + 2x$$

We need to get rid of the 3 on the R.H.S.
So we subtract 3 from both sides, i.e. we put −3 on both sides and see what happens.

$$9 - 3 = 3 + 2x - 3$$

On the R.H.S. 3 and −3 cancel each other, so we are left with

$$6 = 2x$$

Now the 2 on the R.H.S. is multiplying the x, so we do the opposite: we divide both sides by 2, giving

$$\frac{6}{2} = \frac{2x}{2}$$

i.e. $3 = x$

or $x = 3$

Check: Putting $x = 3$; $9 = 3 + (2 \times 3)$ Correct.

We set the solution down like this:

$$9 = 3 + 2x$$

Subtract 3: $\therefore 6 = 2x$

Divide by 2: $\therefore 3 = x$

Example 3. $4x - 3 = x + 18$
This looks more difficult, but it is not fundamentally any more difficult than the previous examples.

The aim is to get the **unknown x's** to one side and the **known** quantities to the other. It does not matter which way round.

Let us try. $4x - 3 = x + 18$
Deal with the x's first: 4x on one side. x on the other
What can we do? Yes, take an x off both sides

$$\therefore \quad 4x - 3 - x = \not{x} + 18 - \not{x}$$
$$\therefore \quad 3x - 3 = 18 \quad (x - x \text{ making zero})$$

Now deal with the numbers. We wish to get rid of the −3 on the L.H.S. Therefore we ADD 3 to both sides, since the opposite of −3 is +3.

$$\therefore \quad 3x - 3 + 3 = 18 + 3$$ (the −3 and +3 cancelling each other on the R.H.S.)

$$\therefore \quad 3x = 21$$

Now on the L.H.S. x is multiplied by 3, so we divide both sides by 3.

$$\therefore \quad \frac{3x}{3} = \frac{21}{3}$$

Therefore $x = 7$

Check: Putting x = 7 on the L.H.S. of the original equation gives:
L.H.S. = (4 x 7) − 3 = 25
R.H.S. = 7 + 18 = 25 L.H.S. = R.H.S. Correct

This sounds very long, but it is necessary to make sure at each step that we are doing exactly the same thing to **both sides.**

Let us shorten it a little.

	$4x - 3 = x + 18$
subtract x:	$3x - 3 = 18$
Add 3:	$3x = 21$
Divide by 3:	$x = 7$

Example 4. $5 - 2x = x + 7$ (Always aim to make the x's positive)

∴ ADD 2x to both sides

$$5 - 2x + 2x = x + 7 + 2x$$
$$\therefore \quad 5 = 3x + 7$$

(Note that − 2x disappears from the L.H.S. but turns up as +2x on the R.H.S.)

Now get the numbers to the L.H.S. by subtracting 7.
Subtract 7:

$$5 - 7 = 3x + 7 - 7$$
$$\therefore \quad -2 = 3x$$

Divide both sides by 3 to give x:

$$\frac{-2}{3} = \frac{3x}{3}$$

$$\therefore \frac{-2}{3} = x$$

$$\therefore \quad x = -\frac{2}{3}$$

Check: Put $x = \frac{-2}{3}$ or $-\frac{2}{3}$

L.H.S. $= 5 - 2(-\frac{2}{3}) = 5 + \frac{4}{3} = 6\frac{1}{3}$

R.H.S. $= -\frac{2}{3} + 7 = 6\frac{1}{3}$

L.H.S. = R.H.S. Correct.

The work is shortened still further if we notice that a term which is positive on one side, when it is cancelled out by a negative term, reappears as a negative on the other side and vice versa. This is natural if we do the same operation on both sides.

We say, 'when a term is taken from one side of an equation to the other it changes sign'. But it is safer to keep asking oneself: 'Am I doing *exactly* the same thing to *both* sides?'

Example 5. $3(x + 4) = 2(x - 1) + 7$

(Work out the brackets)

$$3x + 12 = 2x - 2 + 7$$

Tidy up: $3x + 12 = 2x + 5$

(x's to L.H.S., numbers to R.H.S., changing signs as terms move across the equal sign):

$$3x - 2x = +5 - 12$$

Tidy up: $x = -7$

Exercise 11. Solve the following equations:

1. $3x - 4 = 5$
2. $5b - 7 = 8$
3. $5b + 7 = 8$
4. $9x - 5x + 3x = 28$
(Tidy up the L.H.S. first).
5. $4x - 3 = 2x + 3$
6. $7x + 1 = 1 + 6x$
7. $-5a + 1 = a - 11$
8. $2a = 7$
9. $x + 3 = 8$
10. $4a = a + 9$
11. $a - 3 = 2a - 14$
12. $7(a - 5) = 3(4 - a)$

EQUATIONS INVOLVING FRACTIONS.

Example l. Solve the equation:

$$\frac{3x+2}{5} - \frac{x+4}{2} = 4$$

Two precautions which should *always* be taken in dealing with such equations are these:

1. Any compound numerator or denominator should be put in brackets;

2. Any part of the equation, which appears without a denominator, e.g. the number 4 in the above equation, should be put over the denominator 1.

so $$\frac{(3x+2)}{5} - \frac{(x+4)}{2} = \frac{4}{1}$$

Now we know we can multiply or divide an equation by any number (other than zero) provided we do exactly the same to both sides.

Here, noting that the common denominator is 10

Multiplying through by 10:

$$\frac{10(3x+2)}{5} - \frac{10(x+4)}{2} = \frac{4 \times 10}{1}$$

$$\therefore \quad \frac{\overset{2}{\cancel{10}}(3x+2)}{\underset{1}{\cancel{5}}} - \frac{\overset{5}{\cancel{10}}(x+4)}{\underset{1}{\cancel{2}}} = \frac{4 \times 10}{1} \quad \text{Cancelling by 5 and 2}$$

$\therefore \quad 2(3x+2) - 5(x+4) = 40$

$\therefore \quad 6x + 4 - 5x - 20 = 40$

$\therefore \quad x - 16 = 40$

$\therefore \quad x = 56$

Example 2. Solve:

$$\frac{5x}{2} = \frac{3}{5}$$

Multiply by 10: $25x = 6$

$$\therefore\ x = \frac{6}{25}$$

Note: We get the same result by the following method:

$$\frac{5x}{2} = \frac{3}{5}$$

Cross multiply: $\frac{5x}{2} \times \frac{3}{5}$

$$\therefore\ 5x \times 5 = 3 \times 2$$

$$\therefore\ 25x = 6$$

$$\therefore\ x = \frac{6}{25}$$

BUT we can ONLY use this method when there is a single fraction on each side of the equation.

Example 3. Solve the equation:

$$1 - \frac{1}{6}(x + 5) = \frac{2x + 7}{3} - \frac{x}{4} + 2\frac{1}{2}$$

There are several points to note here. We rewrite the equation as follows:

$$\frac{1}{1} - \frac{(x + 5)}{6} = \frac{(2x + 7)}{3} - \frac{x}{4} + \frac{5}{2}$$

Multiply by 12 :

$$12 \times \frac{1}{1} - \cancel{12}^{2} \times \frac{(x+5)}{\cancel{6}_{1}} = \cancel{12}^{4} \times \frac{(2x+7)}{\cancel{3}_{1}} - \cancel{12}^{3} \times \frac{x}{\cancel{4}_{1}} + \cancel{12}^{6} \times \frac{5}{\cancel{2}_{1}} \; *$$

$$\therefore \; 12 - 2(x+5) = 4(2x+7) - 3x + 30$$
$$\therefore \; 12 - 2x - 10 = 8x + 28 - 3x + 30$$
$$\therefore \; -2x + 2 = 5x + 58$$
$$-58 + 2 = 5x + 2x$$
$$-56 = 7x$$
$$-8 = x$$

$$\therefore \; \mathbf{x = -8}$$

* This line may be omitted when the process is understood.

Exercise 12. Solve the following equations, taking note of the precautions mentioned at the beginning of the section:

1. $r + \frac{r}{2} - \frac{r}{3} = 2\frac{1}{3}$
2. $\frac{x}{2} - \frac{x}{3} = \frac{1}{5}$
3. $4x - \frac{(x+4)}{5} = 41$
4. $\frac{2a-1}{5} = 3 - \frac{3a-1}{4}$
5. $\frac{1+x}{2} = \frac{2x-1}{5} - 1$
6. $\frac{p+3}{5} = 8 - \frac{p-1}{4}$
7. $\frac{1}{3}(y+1) = \frac{1}{2}(y-1) + 1 + \frac{2y}{3}$
8. $\frac{2x-1}{5} - \frac{3x+1}{2} = \frac{2}{5}$
9. $\frac{3}{2x} - 4 = 3 - \frac{9}{x}$
(Multiply through by 2x)
10. $\frac{a+1}{2} - \frac{a-7}{5} = \frac{a+4}{3}$

Exercise 13. Solve the following by cross multiplication:

1. $\frac{x}{2} = \frac{3}{5}$
2. $\frac{3x}{4} = \frac{1}{2}$
3. $\frac{x-1}{5} = \frac{x+4}{2}$
4. $\frac{2a-1}{3} = \frac{1}{4}$
5. $\frac{1}{3x} = \frac{2}{9}$
6. $\frac{4a+3}{a} = 4\frac{1}{2}$

Chapter 4

Products, factors and quotients

Removal of Double Brackets.

We often need to work out brackets of a slightly more complex nature.

For example, here is a problem on areas.

A square has one side increased by 4 cm and the adjacent side increased by 5 cm as shown in Fig.4.1. These form the sides of a rectangle. If the final area of the rectangle is 380 cm^2 what is the length of the side of the original square?

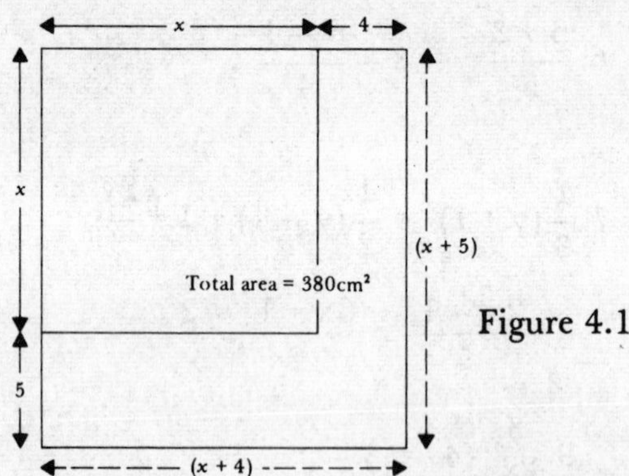

Figure 4.1

We tackle this in the following way:

Let the length of the side of the square = x cm (i.e. the thing we are trying to find). Then the sides of the rectangle are (x + 4) cm and (x + 5) cm long.

Therefore the area of the rectangle is (x + 4) cm multiplied by (x + 5) cm and this equals 380 cm^2.

We need to work out (x + 4) (x + 5) (omitting the multiplication sign).

Let us try some arithmetic again, to help us find a method, before returning to this problem.

Example 1.

What is the value of (3 + 4) x (3 + 5) ?

Simplifying the contents of each bracket, this is 7 x 8 = 56

By a longer method and realising that the whole of the first bracket must be multiplied by the whole of the second bracket we try as follows:

(3 + 4) (3 + 5)

= (3 x 3) + (4 x 5) + (4 x 3) + (3 x 5).

i.e. First pair, last pair, inside pair, outside pair.

= 9 + 20 + 12 + 15
= **56.** Correct.

Example 2.

(7 – 2) (12 – 4) .... [1]
= 5 x 8 (simplifying each bracket first)
= **40.**

Using the same order of multiplication as above:

[1] = (7 x 12) + (–2 x –4) + (–2 x 12) + (7 x –4)
= 84 + 8 – 24 – 28
= 92 – 52
= **40.** Correct

Examples 1 and 2 illustrate the method:

for 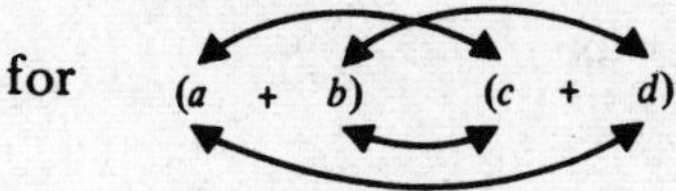

we get, following the arrows:

ac + bd + bc + ad (see Fig.4.2.)

Now we can work examples such as:

$(x + 4)(x + 5) = x^2 + 20 + 4x + 5x$ (Fig.4.3.)
$= x^2 + 9x + 20$ (collecting and rearranging)

We need to be very efficient at doing this operation.

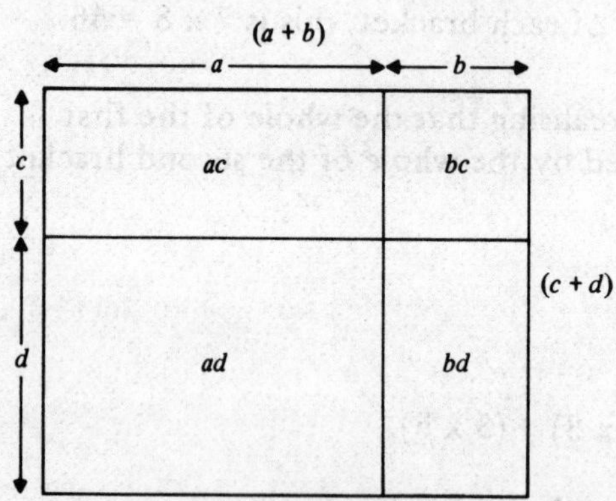

Fig. 4.2

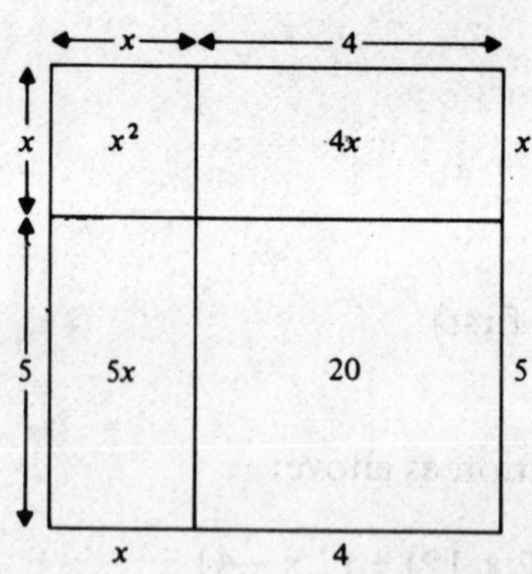

Fig. 4.3

Plenty of practice is needed.

Exercise 14. Simplify:

1. $(a + x)\ (b + x) = ab + x^2 + xb + ax$
2. $(3a + x)\ (2b + x)$
3. $(6a + b)\ (x + y)$
4. $(5a + b)\ (2c + 3d)$

In each of the questions in Exercise 15 we find two of the terms can be collected up.

For example, $(3a + 2)\ (4a - 1)$
$= 12a^2 - 2 + 8a - 3a$ (remembering the rules of signs)
$= 12a^2 + 5a - 2$ (collecting the 'a' terms)

Exercise 15. Simplify:

1. $(2a + 1)\ (3a + 4)$
2. $(a + 7)\ (a + 6)$
3. $(a - 7)\ (a + 6)$
4. $(a + 7)\ (a - 6)$
5. $(a - 7)\ (a - 6)$
6. $(2a + 1)\ (3a - 4)$
7. $(2a - 1)\ (3a - 4)$
8. $(2a - 1)\ (3a + 4)$
9. $(1 - b)\ (1 - b)$
10. $(2 - 3b)\ (2 + 3b)$
11. $(a + b)\ (a - b)$
12. $(a + b)\ (a + b)$
13. $(a - b)\ (a - b)$
14. $(2a - 3b)^2$
15. $(3a - 1)\ (3a + 1)$
16. $(2a + 3)\ (2a - 3)$
17. $(x - 10)\ (x + 10)$
18. $(ab - 2)\ (ab + 2)$
19. $(5a - 2b)\ (5a + 2b)$
20. $(2a - 9)\ (2a + 9)$

In numbers 15 - 20: (a) Why does the middle term disappear? (b) What is special about these examples?

Important Expansions

Three of the expansions in the last exercise are worth remembering:

(i) $(a + b)^2 = a^2 + 2ab + b^2$
(ii) $(a - b)^2 = a^2 - 2ab + b^2$
(iii) $(a + b)\ (a - b) = a^2 - b^2$

In words:

(i) The square of the sum of two terms is equal to the sum of their squares **plus** twice their product;

(ii) The square of the difference of two terms is equal to the sum of their squares **minus** twice their product;

(iii) The product of the sum and difference of two terms is equal to the difference of their squares.

THE REVERSE PROCESS - FACTORISATION.

When we wish to reverse the process, i.e. split an expression up into factors, we usually use a trial and checking process as follows:

Question. What are the factors of $x^2 + 8x + 7$?

Method. We try putting the expression into two brackets reversing the operation in the previous examples,

i.e. $x^2 + 8x + 7 = (\ ?\ )\ (\ ?\ )$

Obviously we try x and x at the beginning of each bracket, giving

$$(x \quad)\ (x \quad)$$

Also we take the factors of 7, i.e. 7 and 1, and put these in so that we get:

$$(x \quad 7)\ (x \quad 1)$$

Then since all the signs are positive in the given expression we get:

$(x + 7)\ (x + 1)$ which checks on multiplying out.

Therefore $x^2 + 8x + 7 = (x + 7)\ (x + 1)$
Similarly $x^2 - 8x + 7 = (x - 7)\ (x - 1)$, since $(-1) \times (-7) = +7$
and $x^2 + 6x - 7 = (x + 7)\ (x - 1)$, since $(+7) \times (-1) = -7$
and $x^2 - 6x - 7 = (x - 7)\ (x + 1)$, since $(-7) \times (+1) = -7$

Exercise 16. Factorise the following expressions:

1. $x^2 + 4x + 4$
2. $x^2 - 4x + 4$
3. $x^2 + 5x + 4$
4. $x^2 - 5x + 4$
5. $x^2 + x - 12$
6. $x^2 - x - 12$
7. $x^2 + 6x + 8$
8. $x^2 - 6x + 8$
9. $x^2 - 2x - 8$
10. $x^2 + 2x - 8$
11. $x^2 + 9x + 8$
12. $x^2 - 9x + 8$
13. $x^2 - 7x - 8$
14. $x^2 + 7x - 8$

The Difference of Two Squares.

Since $a^2 - b^2 = (a - b)\ (a + b)$
then $x^2 - 16 = (x - 4)\ (x + 4)$
and $49a^2 - 9 = (7a - 3)\ (7a + 3)$

Each of the expressions on the left-hand side is called a 'difference of two squares'. This type of expression is easy to identify since the terms involved are always the squares of other terms, and **one** of the two terms is **negative.**

Example 1. $25x^2 - 16y^2z^2 = (5x - 4yz)(5x + 4yz)$

Example 2. $-1 + 100x^2 = 100x^2 - 1$
$= (10x - 1)(10x + 1)$

Exercise 17. Factorise the following:

1. $x^2 - 9$
2. $4x^2 - 25$
3. $9x^2 - 1$
4. $100a^2 - 9b^2$
5. $16x^2 - 121y^2$
6. $49 - y^2$

Note: Since $(a + b)(a + b) = a^2 + 2ab + b^2$
$(a - b)(a - b) = a^2 - 2ab + b^2$
and $(a - b)(a + b) = (a + b)(a - b) = a^2 - b^2$

it follows that $a^2 + b^2$ has no real factors.
Hence the sum of two squares does not factorise.

FURTHER PROCESSES IN ALGEBRA.

Long Multiplication.

Example 1. Multiply $2x^2 - 3x + 2$ by $4x - 1$

$2x^2 - 3x + 2$	.... [1]
$4x - 1$	
$8x^3 - 12x^2 + 8x$	Multiply line [1] by 4x
$-2x^2 + 3x - 2$	Multiply line [1] by – 1 and place like terms below like
$8x^3 - 14x^2 + 11x - 2$	Add

Example 2. Multiply $a^2 + 2ab + b^2$ by $a + b$.

$a^2 + 2ab + b^2$	[1]
$a + b$	
$a^3 + 2a^2b + ab^2$	Multiply line [1] by a
$a^2b + 2ab^2 + b^3$	Multiply line [1] by b
$a^3 + 3a^2b + 3ab^2 + b^3$	Add

Since $(a+b)^2 = a^2 + 2ab + b^2$, this result showes that

$$(a+b)^3 = a^3 + 3a^2b + 3ab^2 + b^3 \qquad [1]$$

Similarly it can be proved that

$$(a-b)^3 = a^3 - 3a^2b + 3ab^2 - b^3 \qquad [2]$$

By multiplying [1] by $(a+b)$ and [2] by $(a-b)$ we obtain:

$$(a+b)^4 = a^4 + 4a^3b + 6a^2b^2 + 4ab^3 + b^4 \qquad [3]$$
$$(a-b)^4 = a^4 - 4a^3b + 6a^2b^2 - 4ab^3 + b^4 \qquad [4]$$

Long Division.

Example 3. Divide $2x^3 - 25x + 22$ by $x^2 + 2x - 8$.

$$\begin{array}{rl}
 & 2x - 4 \\
x^2 + 2x - 8 \,\big)\, & 2x^3 \qquad\quad - 25x + 22 \\
 & \underline{2x^3 + 4x^2 - 16x} \\
 & \qquad -4x^2 - 9x + 22 \\
 & \qquad \underline{-4x^2 - 8x + 32} \\
 & \qquad\qquad \underline{- x - 10}
\end{array}$$

(Note the gap left for any x^2 terms)
(Multiplying the divisor by 2x) and
(Subtracting and bringing down the next term)
(Multiplying the divisor by –4)

∴ Remainder = $-x - 10$ (Subtracting)

The quotient is **2x – 4** and the remainder is **–x – 10.**

Example 4. Divide $a^3 - b^3$ by $a - b$

$$\begin{array}{rl}
 & a^2 + ab + b^2 \\
(a-b) \,\big)\, & a^3 \qquad\qquad - b^3 \\
 & \underline{a^3 - a^2b} \\
 & \quad + a^2b \\
 & \quad \underline{+ a^2b - ab^2} \\
 & \qquad\quad + ab^2 - b^3 \\
 & \qquad\quad \underline{+ ab^2 - b^3} \\
 & \qquad\qquad \cdot \quad \cdot \quad \cdot
\end{array}$$

(Note the gaps left for a^2b and ab^2 terms)

The quotient is $a^2 + ab + b^2$ and there is no remainder.

Exercise 18.

Multiply:

1. $x^2 + 3x - 1$ by $x - 4$
2. $a^2 - ab + b^2$ by $a + b$
3. $3x^2 - x + 4$ by $2x - 1$

Divide:

4. $x^3 + x^2 - 5x - 6$ by $x + 2$
5. $x^4 + x^3 - 8x^2 - 11x - 3$ by $x^2 - 2x - 3$
6. $x^3 + 3x - 2$ by $x^2 - 4x + 4$

Simplify:

7. $(x - 1)(x + 2)(3x - 7)$

(Hint: Simplify $(x - 1)(x + 2)$ mentally and then multiply by $(3x - 7)$)

Chapter 5
Quadratic equations. Further indices

QUADRATIC EQUATIONS.

Now let us look at our problem on the square and the rectangle once more (see page 26). The total area is given as 380 cm^2 (Fig.5.1).

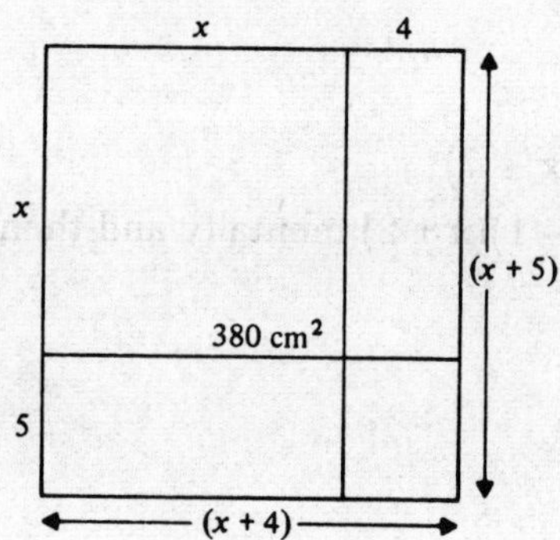

Fig. 5.1

We are told:

$$
\begin{aligned}
&(x+4)(x+5) &= 380 \\
\therefore\ &x^2+9x+20 &= 380 \quad \text{(working out the brackets)} \\
\therefore\ &x^2+9x-360 &= 0
\end{aligned}
$$

This equation which involves x^2, as well as terms in x and numbers, is called a 'quadratic equation' and we need to know how to solve this type of equation.

There are two well-known ways to solve a quadratic equation, namely:

1. by factors;
2. by formula.

The solution of quadratic equations by factors.

This is the simplest method if the factors are fairly obvious, but many quadratic equations cannot be solved in this way.

Let us try to solve the equation above.

i.e. $x^2 + 9x - 360 = 0$
(Note: We always take all terms to one side of the equation to leave zero on the other.)

We need to express the L.H.S. as the product of two brackets, as in Exercise 16.

i.e. $(\quad ? \quad) (\quad ? \quad) = 0$

Obviously the first term in each bracket must be x to give x^2 when multiplying out.

Therefore we require $(x \pm ?)(x \pm ?) = 0$ (Read ± as 'plus or minus'.)

Also the numbers at the end of each bracket must have a product of 360. But there are several pairs of factors of the number 360.

e.g. 36 x 10 or 18 x 20 or 9 x 40.

Let us try $(x \pm 36)(x \pm 10)$
$(x \pm 18)(x \pm 20)$
and $(x \pm 9)(x \pm 40)$

None of these pairs of factors would give 9x as the middle term on multiplying out the brackets.
For speed in finding correct factors we often arrange the work as follows:

x ± 36	x ± 18	x ± 9
╳	╳	╳
x ± 10	x ± 20	x ± 40

Cross-multiplying gives: $\pm 36x \pm 10x$; $\pm 18x \pm 20x$; $\pm 9x \pm 40x$

[1] [2] [3]

[1] can only give ± 46x or ± 26x
[2] can only give ± 38x or ± 2x
[3] can only give ± 49x or ± 31x

Is there another pair of factors of 360?
Yes, 15 x 24.

So let us try: $(x \quad 15)(x \quad 24) = 0$

We note one of the signs must be positive and one negative to give −360, when we multiply out, but to give + 9x in the middle we must choose

$$(x - 15)(x + 24) = 0$$

Here we have two brackets multiplied together giving zero as the product. When this happens, is there anything special about these quantities?

When two things are multiplied together and the answer is zero, one or other or both MUST be zero: non-zero numbers multiplied together cannot give zero.

e.g. $3 \times 0 = 0$
and $0 \times 7 = 0$
∴ In this case:
either $x - 15 = 0$ <u>or</u> $x + 24 = 0$
Therefore $x = +15$ <u>or</u> $x = -24$
But the number x represents the length of the side of a square. Therefore it cannot be −24 cm, and in this case the length of the side of the square must be 15 cm.

Check: the sides of the rectangle must be (15 + 4) and (15 + 5) cm
i.e. 19 cm and 20 cm

Therefore the area of the rectangle $= 19 \times 20 \text{ cm}^2$
$= 380 \text{ cm}^2$ Correct.

Example 1. Solve: $x^2 - 9 = 0$
Factorise: $(x - 3)(x + 3) = 0$ (Factors of a difference of two squares)
Therefore <u>either</u> $(x - 3) = 0$ <u>or</u> $(x + 3) = 0$
i.e. $x = 3$ <u>or</u> $x = -3$

Example 2. Solve: $x^2 - 9x = 0$ (this has a simple common factor x)

Giving $x(x - 9) = 0$

Again, <u>either</u> $x = 0$ <u>or</u> $(x - 9) = 0$

$\therefore$ <u>either</u> $x = 0$ <u>or</u> $x = 9$

Example 3. Solve: $4x^2 - 8x + 3 = 0$

By trial $(2x - 1)(2x - 3) = 0$

Note: One usually tries combinations of various pairs of factors of the first and last terms. In this case these are $4x^2$ and +3 to give $-8x$ in the middle (cross multiplying the pairs)
There are several combinations here,

e.g.
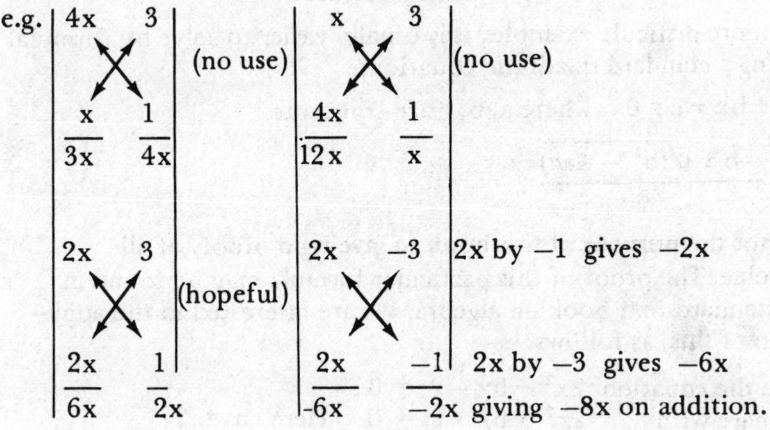

$\therefore$ The factors are $(2x - 1)(2x - 3)$

$\therefore$ <u>either</u> $2x - 1 = 0$ (Note that we get two simple equations
<u>or</u> $2x - 3 = 0$ replacing the original difficult quadratic)

$\therefore$ <u>either</u> $2x = 1$ <u>or</u> $2x = 3$

$\therefore$ <u>either</u> $x = \frac{1}{2}$ <u>or</u> $x = \frac{3}{2}$

Note: There are **ALWAYS TWO SOLUTIONS TO EVERY QUADRATIC EQUATION**! These may be two different numbers or both equal or even both zero, but there must be TWO solutions.

Example 4. Solve: $x^2 = 0$

$x = 0$ (twice)

Example 5. Solve: $x^2 + 2x = 15$

$\therefore \quad x^2 + 2x - 15 = 0$

N.B. We must have zero on one side of the equation.

$\therefore \quad (x + 5)(x - 3) = 0$

$\therefore \quad \mathbf{x = -5 \text{ or } +3}$

Exercise 19. Solve the equations:

1. $x^2 + 3x - 10 = 0$
2. $x^2 - 7x + 6 = 0$
3. $x^2 - 5x + 6 = 0$
4. $x^2 - 16 = 0$
5. $x^2 - 16x = 0$
6. $x^2 = 100$

(N.B. You must obtain two solutions).

Solution of quadratic equations by formula.

For more difficult examples it is usually easier to solve by formula. Taking a standard quadratic equation,

$ax^2 + bx + c = 0$ where a, b, c are constants

then

$$x = \frac{-b \pm \sqrt{(b^2 - 4ac)}}{2a}$$

It is not the purpose of this book to give rigid proofs of all formulae. The proof of this particular formula may be found in any standard text book on algebra. We are interested in the application of this, as follows:

Solve the equation $2x^2 + 5x - 2 = 0$

Compare with $ax^2 + bx + c = 0$ Here $a = 2$, $b = 5$, $c = -2$

Substituting in $x = \dfrac{-b \pm \sqrt{(b^2 - 4ac)}}{2a}$

We get
$$x = \frac{-5 \pm \sqrt{(25 - (4)(2)(-2)}}{4}$$

$$= \frac{-5 \pm \sqrt{(25 + 16)}}{4} \text{ since } (-) \times (-) = +$$

$$= \frac{-5 \pm \sqrt{41}}{4}$$

$\sqrt{41} = 6.403$ from tables or calculator.

Therefore
$$x = \frac{-4 \pm 6.403}{4}$$

Therefore $x = \dfrac{-4 + 6.403}{4}$ or $\dfrac{-4 - 6.403}{4}$

$= \dfrac{2.403}{4}$ or $-\dfrac{10.403}{4}$

$= 0.60$ or -2.60 to two decimal places (2 d.p.)

Exercise 20. Solve the following quadratic equations by formula (give answers correct to 2 d.p.):

1. $2x^2 - 5x - 3 = 0$
2. $2x^2 - 7x - 1 = 0$
3. $3x^2 - 2x - 6 = 0$
4. $3x^2 + 2x - 1 = 0$
5. $4x^2 + 5x - 2 = 0$
6. $4x^2 + 6x - 1 = 0$
7. $2x^2 - 5x + 1 = 0$
8. $3x^2 + 8x + 2 = 0$
9. $4x^2 - 6x = -1$
10. $5x^2 + 8x = -2$
11. $2x^2 = 6x - 3$
12. $5x^2 + 3 = 9x$

(9–12: Remember to take all terms to one side of the equation.)

FURTHER INDICES.

a^4 means a x a x a x a
a^3 means a x a x a
$\therefore \quad a^4 \times a^3 = (a \times a \times a \times a) \times (a \times a \times a)$
$= a^7$.

This illustrates the rule that:

1. When MULTIPLYING together powers of the same letter or number ADD the indices i.e. $a^m \times a^n = a^{m+n}$

Similarly:

a^5 means a x a x a x a x a
a^2 means a x a

$$\therefore \quad a^5 \div a^2 = \frac{\overset{1}{\cancel{a}} \times \overset{1}{\cancel{a}} \times a \times a \times a}{\underset{1}{\cancel{a}} \times \underset{1}{\cancel{a}}}$$

$= a^3$.

This illustrates the rule that:

2. When DIVIDING powers of the same letter or number SUBTRACT the index of the denominator from the index of the numerator

i.e. $a^m \div a^n = a^{m-n}$

Also:

$(a^2)^3$ means $a^2 \times a^2 \times a^2 = a^6$.

This illustrates the rule that:

3. When a power of a number or letter is RAISED TO A FURTHER POWER, MULTIPLY the indices together

i.e. $(a^m)^n = a^{mn}$.

Conversely: Since $a^6 = a^2 \times a^2 \times a^2$ cf. $27 = 3 \times 3 \times 3$

$\sqrt[3]{a^6} = a^2$ $\therefore \sqrt[3]{27} = 3$

This illustrates the rule that:

4. When taking the SQUARE ROOT (or cube root) of a power of a letter or number, DIVIDE the power by 2 (or 3)

In general $\sqrt[n]{a^m} = a^{\frac{m}{n}}$

To deduce meanings for a^0, a^{-1}, $a^{-\frac{1}{2}}$, $a^{\frac{2}{3}}$, etc.

Since $a^0 \times a^2 = a^{0+2} = a^2$ adding the indices, a^0 has not altered the a^2. Therefore it can only have the value 1, since the only number which can multiply another number and leave it unaltered is 1.

$\therefore$ **$a^0 = 1$**

Giving the rule ANYTHING TO THE POWER NOUGHT EQUALS 1

e.g. $10^0 = 1$; $59^0 = 1$;

$(a^{\frac{2}{3}} \times {}^{\frac{5}{9}} \times a^{-6})^0 = 1.$

$\underline{a^{-1}}$ **Consider** $\dfrac{a^2}{a^3}$

This equals $\dfrac{\overset{1}{\cancel{a}} \times \overset{1}{\cancel{a}}}{\underset{1}{\cancel{a}} \times \underset{1}{\cancel{a}} \times a} = \dfrac{1}{a}$

But by the second rule of indices (subtracting the indices)

$$\frac{a^2}{a^3} = a^{2-3} = a^{-1}$$

$\therefore a^{-1}$ must mean $\frac{1}{a}$, if our rules are to be consistent.

Similarly $\frac{a^2}{a^4} = \frac{1}{a^2}$ or $a^{2-4} = a^{-2}$

$\therefore a^{-2}$ must mean $\frac{1}{a^2}$

$\underline{a^{1/2}}$ Since $a^{1/2} \times a^{1/2} = a^{1/2+1/2} = a^1$ cf. $3 \times 3 = 9$

then $a^{1/2}$ must be $\sqrt[2]{a^1}$ gives $3 = \sqrt[2]{9}$

$\underline{a^{\frac{2}{3}}}$ $a^{\frac{2}{3}} \times a^{\frac{2}{3}} \times a^{\frac{2}{3}} = a^2$ $4 \times 4 \times 4 = 64$

$\therefore a^{\frac{2}{3}}$ must be $\sqrt[3]{a^2}$ $\therefore$ $4 = \sqrt[3]{64}$

All these statements can be stated in symbols:

1. $a^m \times a^n = a^{m+n}$
2. $a^m \div a^n = a^{m-n}$
3. $(a^m)^n = a^{mn}$
4. $a^{\frac{m}{n}} = \sqrt[n]{a^m}$
5. $a^{-n} = \frac{1}{a^n}$
6. $a^0 = 1$

Exercise 21. Simplify the following:

1. $a^4 \times a^2 \div a$
2. $a^{10} \div a^5$
3. (i) $\sqrt[2]{a^6}$; (ii) $\sqrt[2]{a^5}$; (iii) $\sqrt[3]{a^7}$

4. $(a^6)^2$

5. $a^6 \times a^2$

6. (i) 10^0; (ii) a^0; (iii) $(2a^5)^0$

7. (i) a/a^{10}; (ii) a^6/a^7; (iii) $a^7/a^{\frac{3}{2}}$

8. Express the following with positive indices:

Examples. $a^{-2} = \frac{1}{a^2}$; $\frac{a^2}{a^{2\frac{1}{2}}} = \frac{1}{a^{\frac{1}{2}}}$; $\frac{1}{a^{-3}} = a^3$

(i) a^{-1} ; (ii) $\frac{1}{a^{-1}}$; (iii) $\frac{a^4}{a^6}$; (iv) 3^{-2} ; (v) a^{-2}

9. Express as powers of x :

(i) the cube roots of x^{12}, x^{10}, x ;
(ii) the square roots of x^3, x^{-2}, x ;
(iii) $\sqrt[3]{x}$, $\sqrt[4]{x^3}$, $\sqrt[3]{x^4}$

Write down the values of:

10. $16^{\frac{1}{2}}$

11. $27^{\frac{1}{3}}$

12. $81^{\frac{1}{4}}$

13. 90^0

14. 2^{-1}

15. 3^{-2}

16. $9^{-\frac{1}{2}}$

17. $81^{-\frac{1}{4}}$

18. $32^{\frac{2}{5}}$
(find $32^{\frac{1}{5}}$ first and then square it)

19. 3^{-3}

20. $32^{-\frac{2}{5}}$

Chapter 6

Calculus - the mathematics of change

Many of the terrors of so called 'advanced' mathematics are associated with a study of calculus, probably because it is so different in approach from that of 'ordinary' mathematics. The language of mathematics is a shorthand way of saying something which is usually quite simple. For example, in this chapter we shall talk about $\delta x, \delta y, \delta t$, etc. This symbol δ (the Greek letter delta) merely means 'a little bit of' and we say 'delta x' or 'delta y' or 'delta t' meaning 'a little bit of x', 'a little bit of y' 'a little bit of t'. Mathematicians refer to it as 'an element of. . .' or 'an increment in. . .'.

For instance, if we were thinking of x as a distance in miles, then δx could be an inch or ½ inch or even $\frac{1}{100}$ of an inch, but always something small in relation to the whole. BUT, OBVIOUSLY, THE SUM OF ALL THESE LITTLE δx's MAKES A WHOLE x. We say $\Sigma \delta x = x$ (sigma delta x = x). The sign sigma, Σ, is the shorthand way of saying 'the sum of'.

WHAT IS SMALLNESS?

In calculus we often have to deal with different degrees of smallness. We all know that smallness is relative. To a millionaire a tip of £1 for a service would be small, but most likely to you or me it would not be small.

Suppose we think of some other examples.
Relative to a week, a minute is small, i.e. it is minute, hence its name, but relative to the time man has been on earth, a week is small, and a minute is then a small part of a small part. That is, it is of a second degree of smallness.

We could say that a new penny is small in value in comparison with a £5 note, but a £5 note is small in comparison with the latest win of £¼ million on the pools, so that relative to this sum a new penny is negligible.

But we must always remember that small bits, if multiplied by a large enough number, can be large. Even a small coin becomes considerable if we take a few thousand of them.

What are the meanings of:

$$\frac{0}{\text{something}} \quad ; \quad \frac{\text{something}}{0} \quad ; \quad \frac{0}{0} \ ?$$

This sounds a silly thing to talk about, and we might get several answers if we put these questions to different people.

Let us approach it this way:

1. $\frac{0}{4}$ for example means 'if we divide nothing into 4 equal parts, what is the value of each part?' I think we would all say 'nothing'. So far so good.

2. $\frac{4}{0}$, for example, means 'how many times can I take nothing out of 4?' The answer is of course as many times as I like, i.e. as large a number as I can possibly think of.

OR, we can approach it this way:
What is 4 ÷ by a small fraction?

e.g. $4 \div \frac{1}{10}$

$= 4 \times \frac{10}{1}$ (change the division sign to multiply and invert the following fraction)

$= 40$

What is 4 ÷ a smaller fraction, e.g. $\frac{1}{100}$?

$4 \div \frac{1}{100}$

$= 4 \times \frac{100}{1}$

$= 400$

Similarly $4 \div \frac{1}{1000} = 4000$

$4 \div \frac{1}{1,000,000} = 4,000,000$ etc.

In other words, a number divided by a very small fraction is very large.

Now we still have not reduced our denominator to zero, but we can see that the smaller the fraction we divide by, the bigger the answer. So that by dividing by a fraction small enough we can get an answer with as many noughts on the end as we like. What does this imply? It implies that however big a number we can think of, 4 ÷ a very small number, can be made bigger than this.

INFINITY

We have a symbol for this thing which is always beyond any number we can think of. We call it 'infinity' and write it ∞ like an 8 on its side.

We say that a finite number divided by another number, which is approaching zero, gives a result which approaches infinity, and we write

Limit of $\frac{n}{x}$ as $x \to 0$ is ∞ **(Read: 'Limit of n over x as x approaches nought is infinity')**

provided n is not zero also.

What about $\frac{0}{0}$? Is it 0 ? Is it 1 ? Is it ∞ ?

In the same way that we were unable to answer the previous question directly we have to look at this from another angle.

Let us consider $\frac{x^2 - 4}{x - 2}$ as x approaches 2.

If we put x = 2 in the above we get $\frac{4 - 4}{2 - 2} = \frac{0}{0}$, so we get no further.

Now take it another way, i.e. in factors,

$$\frac{x^2 - 4}{x - 2} = \frac{{}^{1}\cancel{(x - 2)}(x + 2)}{\cancel{(x - 2)}_{1}} = (x + 2) \quad \text{(cancelling by } (x - 2)\text{)}$$

Whatever the value of x, (x – 2) is the same in both the numerator and the denominator and we can cencel by it (provided $x - 2 \neq 0$) giving (x + 2) as the result.

Now what is the value of (x + 2) as $x \to 2$? (But does not quite equal 2)

This value approaches 4.

So that the ratio of two quantities both approaching zero works out in this case to be approaching 4, and can be made as close as we like to the value 4.

We say $\underset{x \to 2}{\text{Lim}} \dfrac{x^2 - 4}{x - 2} = 4$ (Read the limit of $\dfrac{x^2 - 4}{x - 2}$ as x approaches 2, is 4)

Take another case:

Consider $\underset{x \to 3}{\text{Lim}} \dfrac{x^2 - 9}{x - 3} = \dfrac{(x + 3)\overset{1}{\cancel{(x - 3)}}}{\underset{1}{\cancel{(x - 3)}}}$

$= (x + 3)$ provided $x \neq 3$

$\underset{x \to 3}{\text{Lim}} = 3 + 3 = 6$

This is another answer for the ratio of two things both approaching zero.
And we could go on like this.

One more example. I am sure you can make others up for yourself.

Consider $\underset{x \to 0}{\text{Lim}} \dfrac{x^2 + 3x}{x} \left[\to \dfrac{0}{0} \right]$

$= \dfrac{\overset{1}{\cancel{x}}(x + 3)}{\underset{1}{\cancel{x}}}$ (taking out the common factor x)

$= x + 3$ (cancelling by x)
$= 0 + 3$
$= 3$

We see that the question 'What is nought ÷ nought' is silly. There is no answer.
We can only say 'What is the limit of $\dfrac{a}{b}$ as both a and b approach zero?' And the answer depends on the values of a and b. We say that the limit is **indeterminate** and it is the study of this limit with which we are concerned in differential calculus.

Now we need a few definitions, most of which you probably know already.

FUNCTIONS AND LIMITS

Definitions

A constant is a number or physical quantity whose value is fixed. These are usually denoted by a, b, c, at the beginning of the alphabet.

A variable is a number or physical quantity whose value can change, usually denoted by x, y, z, at the end of the alphabet.

An independent variable is one whose value does not depend on one or more other variables.

A dependent variable is said to be a **function** of the variable (or variables) on which it depends.

For example:

1. **The area of a circle is a function of its radius, $A = \pi R^2$**
2. **The volume of a cylinder is a function of its height and radius,** $V = \pi R^2 h$
3. **The interest on a sum of money invested in a Building Society is a function of the time invested and also of the rate per cent.**

Functional Notation

A function of x is often denoted by f(x). (Read 'eff-x' or 'eff of x')

The value of f(x) when x = 2 is denoted by f(2).
The value of f(x) when x = 0 is denoted by f(0)
The value of f(x) when x = a is denoted by f(a), etc.

Limits

A function of x may not have a value when x = a, but may nethertheless approach a value when x approaches the value a, and we write it

$$\lim_{x \to a} f(x)$$

and we say 'the limit of eff-x as x approaches a.'

Example. If $f(x) = \dfrac{x^2 - 100}{x + 10}$ find $\lim\limits_{x \to -10} f(x)$

$$f(x) = \frac{x^2 - 100}{x + 10}$$

$$= \frac{(x - 10)(x + 10)}{(x + 10)}$$

$$= (x - 10) \text{ (cancelling } (x + 10)\text{, provided } x \neq -10.)$$

$$\therefore \lim_{x \to -10} f(x) = -10 - 10$$

$$= -20$$

Try the following examples.

Exercise 22. Find the limits of the given functions as x approaches the given values:

1. $\dfrac{x^2 - 1}{x - 1}$ $(x \to 1)$
2. $\dfrac{x^2 + x}{x}$ $(x \to 0)$
3. $\dfrac{x^2 - 9}{x + 3}$ $(x \to -3)$
4. $\dfrac{x^2 - a^2}{x - a}$ $(x \to a)$
5. $\dfrac{10x}{x^2 + 3x}$ $(x \to 0)$

SUMMARY: We now realise that $\dfrac{0}{0}$ is indeterminate but that the fraction $\dfrac{A}{B}$ can approach a definite limit as both A and B approach zero.

Chapter 7
Beginnings of relative growth

Now we can start to study how one quantity changes when we change another, i.e. how things grow relative to each other. Many children in primary schools deal with this quite early in their school careers.

They start by studying how a square 'grows,' by adding more squares around the edges (Fig.7.1.)

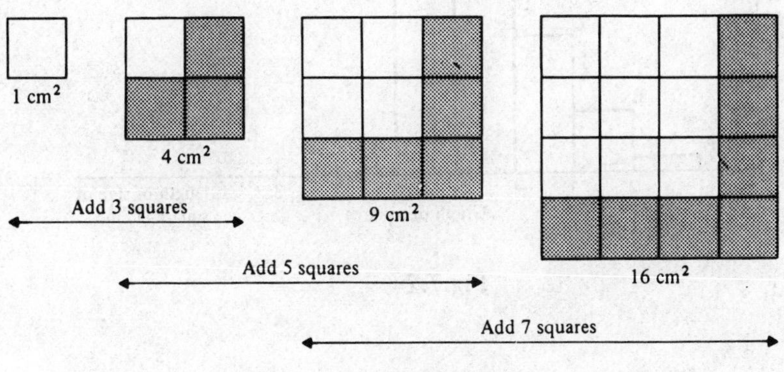

Figure 7.1

Perhaps one can see the pattern of increase here and make a guess at the number of small squares to be added for the next square of side 5cm. Would it be 9 squares?

You can check this yourself.

Thus, we can see that when the SIDE of the square is increasing steadily, 1cm, 2cm, 3cm, 4cm, that is, growing in steps of 1 cm, the area of the corresponding square does not increase in the same way. The *rate of increase* gets larger and larger.

We could put these results on a graph as in Fig. 7.2.which is a simple graph showing

$$\text{area} = (\text{length})^2$$
$$\text{or } A = l^2$$

and also the increases (or increments) needed to step up the areas from one stage to the next. This shows that the rate of increase is changing from one step to the next. It is an *increasing rate of change.*

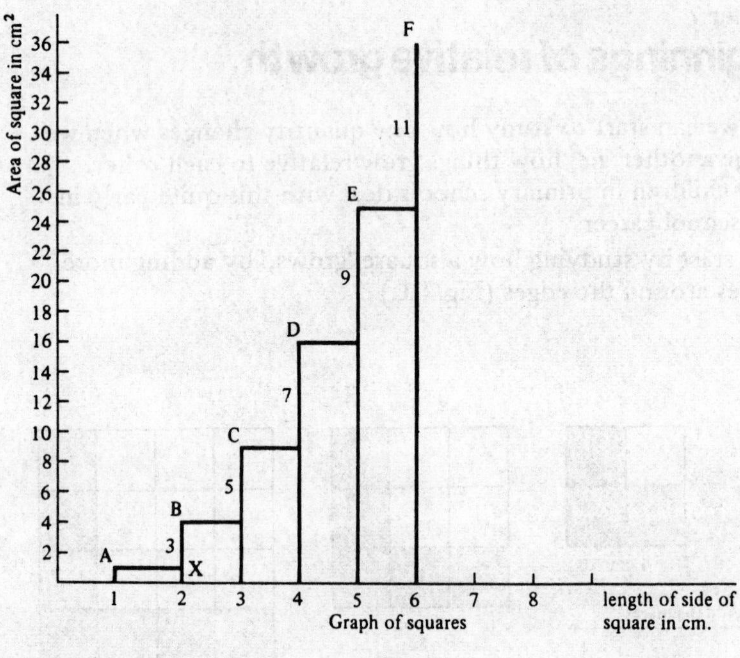

Fig.7.2

In the same way we can draw the graph of cubes (Figs. 7.3 & 7.4).

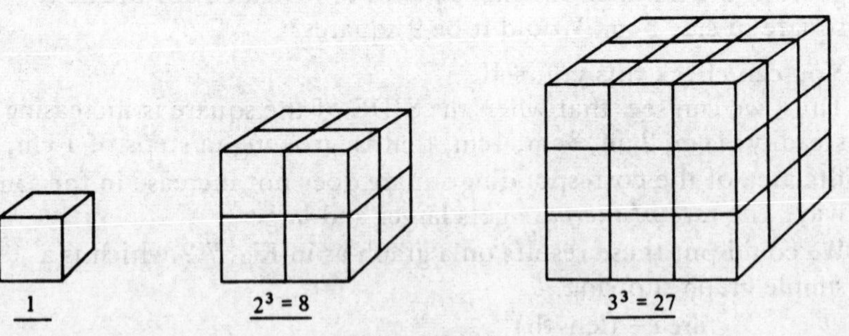

Fig.7.3

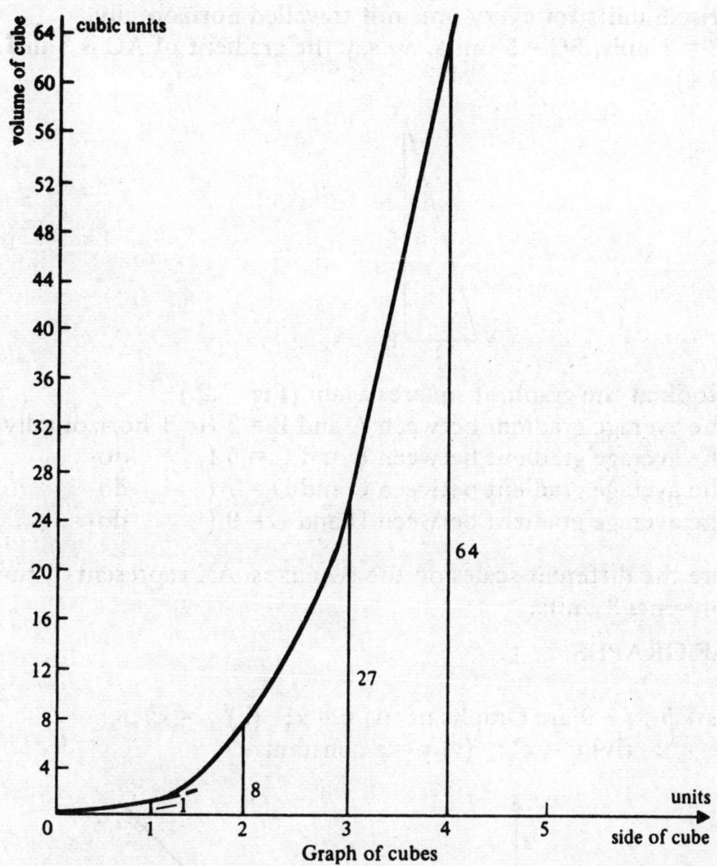

Fig.7.4

Here we see a much more rapid rate of increase. If we join the points by a curve, we see that the curve becomes rapidly steeper as the side of the cube is increased.

GRADIENTS

We all have a general idea of the meaning of a gradient. For example, we speak of the gradient of a road as being 1 in 10, or 10%, or 1 : 10. In this respect we mean that, for every 10 units we travel along the road we rise 1 unit (or drop 1 unit, according to whether we are travelling uphill or downhill). In mathematics we have a similar definition.

If we rise 3 units for every one unit travelled horizontally,
i.e. AB = 1 unit, BC = 3 units, we say the **gradient of AC is 3 in 1.**
(Fig. 7.4)

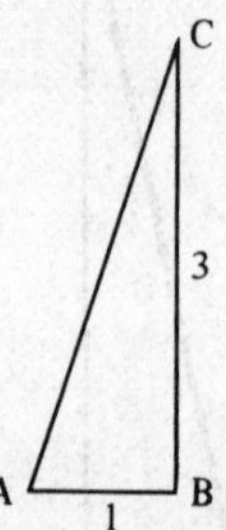

Let us look at the graph of squares again (Fig. 7.2.)
Then the average gradient between A and B = 3 (to 1 horizontally)*
Then the average gradient between B and C = 5 (-do-)
Then the average gradient between C and D = 7 (-do-)
Then the average gradient between D and E = 9 (-do-)

* Ignore the different scales on the two axes. AX represents 1 unit; BX represents 3 units.

SIMPLE GRAPHS.

Figures 7.5 to 7.9 are Graphs of (i) $y = x$; (ii) $y = x^2$; (iii) $y = x^3$; (iv) $y = x^4$; (v) y = a constant.

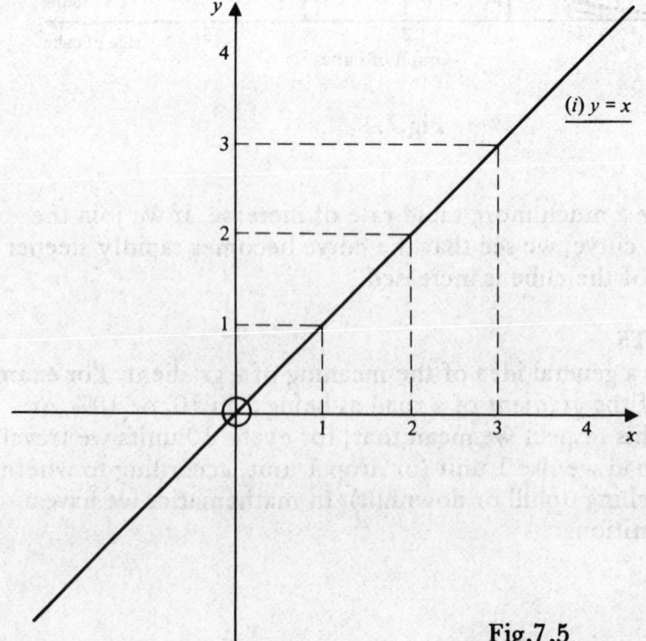

Fig.7.5

The graph of $y = x$ is a straight line at an angle of 45° to the x and y axes, if the scales on the x and y axes are the same.

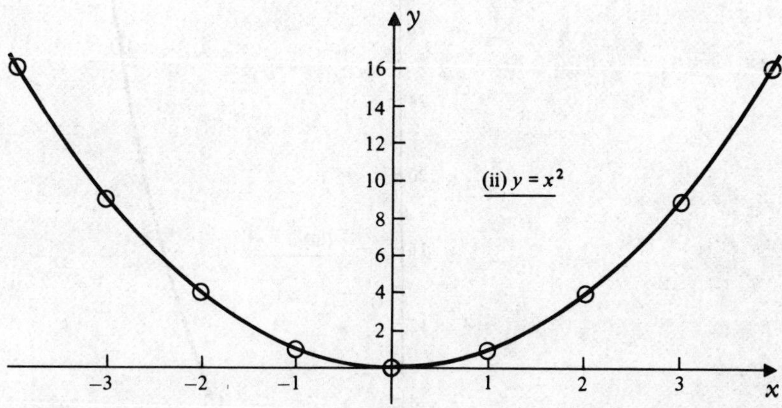

Fig.7.6

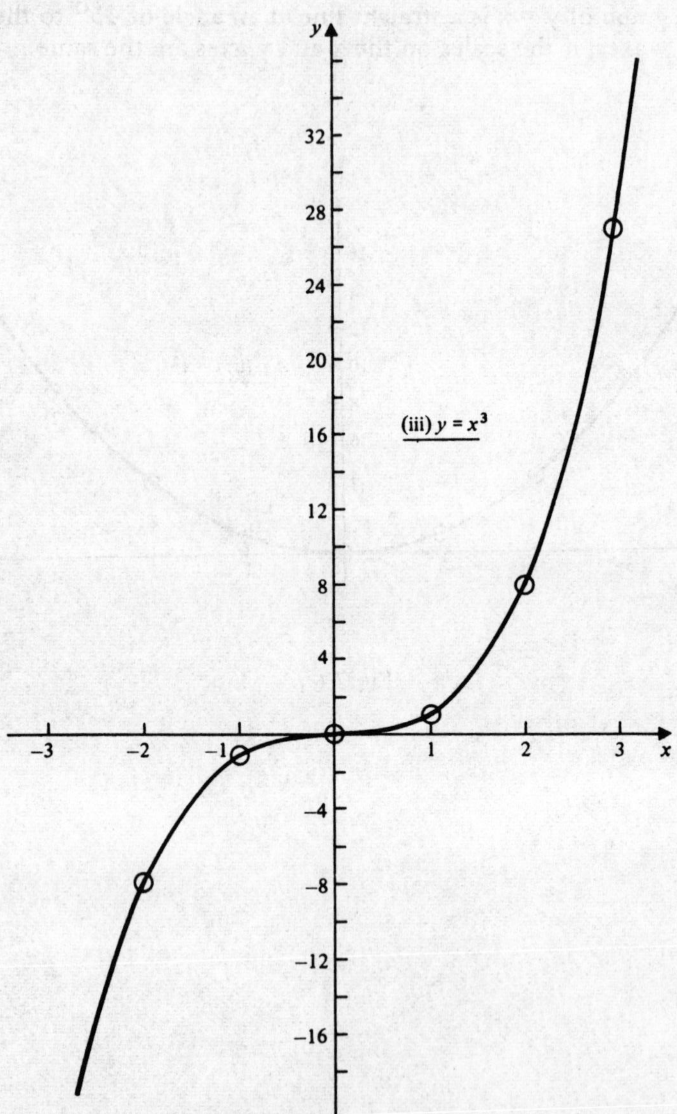

Fig.7.7

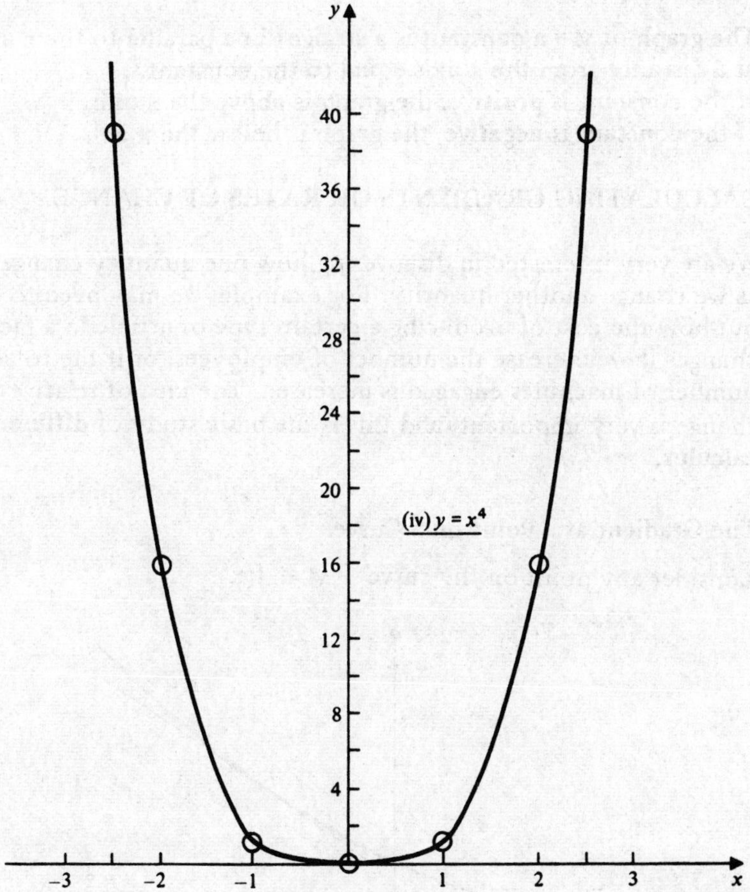

(iv) $y = x^4$

Fig.7.8

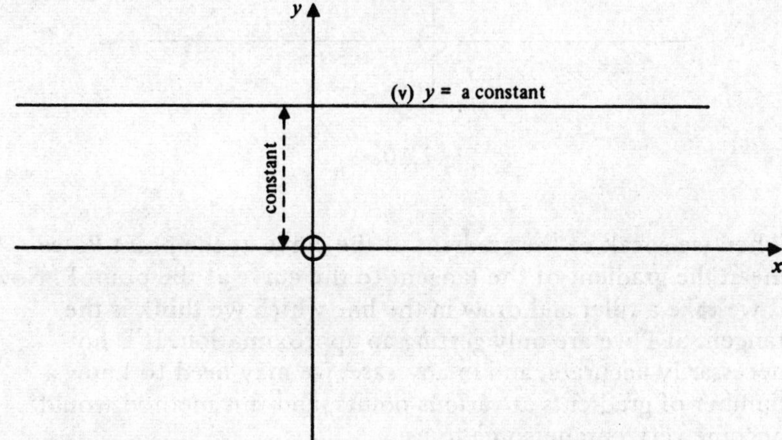

Fig.7.9

The graph of y = a constant is a straight line parallel to the x axis at a distance from the x axis equal to the constant.
If the constant is **positive**, the graph is **above** the x axis.
If the constant is **negative**, the graph is **below** the x axis.

CALCULATING GRADIENTS OR RATES OF CHANGE.

We are very interested in discovering how one quantity changes as we change another quantity. For example, we may need to find out how the cost of producing a certain type of article in a factory changes if we increase the number of employees, or if the total number of machines engaged is increased. The idea of relative change is very important, and this is the basic study of **differential calculus.**

The Gradient at a Point on a Curve.

Consider any point on the curve $y = f(x)$

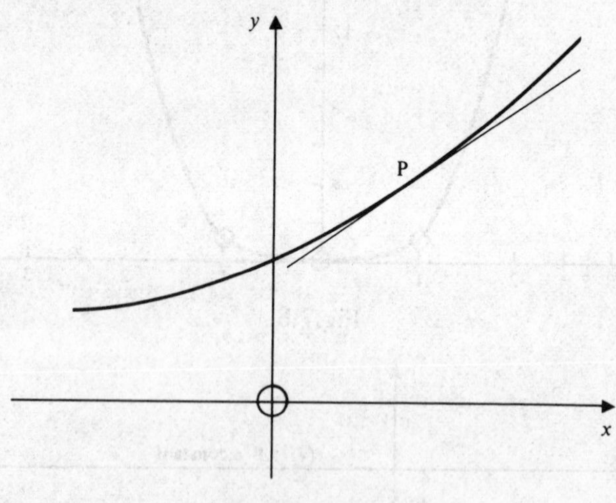

Fig.7.10.

When we speak of the gradient of the curve at the point P, we mean the gradient of the tangent to the curve at the point P. Now if we take a ruler and draw in the line which we **think** is the tangent at P we are only getting an approximation. It is not necessarily accurate, and in any case, we may need to know a number of gradients at various points, and this method would become very cumbersome to use.

The following method is much more useful (Fig.7.11)

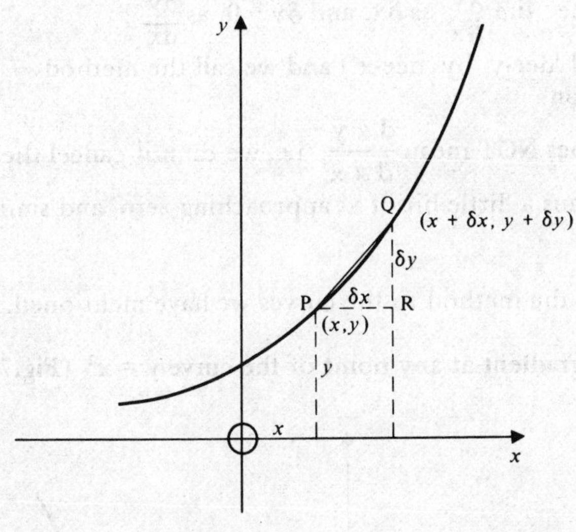

Fig. 7.11

Let P be the point (x,y) i.e. x horizontally, y vertically — We call (x,y) the co-ordinates of point P.

Let Q be a point $(x + \delta x, y + \delta y)$ i.e.

$(x + \delta x)$ horizontally - read: 'x plus delta x'
$(y + \delta y)$ vertically - read: 'y plus delta y'

So that in the Δ PQR in Fig.7.11.

$$PR = \delta x, \quad QR = \delta y$$

In Δ PQR the gradient of chord PQ $= \dfrac{\delta y}{\delta x} = \dfrac{\text{vertical step}}{\text{horizontal step}}$

Now let the point Q approach the point P, so that δx and δy get smaller, and the triangle PQR shrinks to a point at P.

What happens to the chord PQ? By putting in various positions for Q you will see that the chord approaches the position of the tangent at P, and in the limit when P and Q coincide, the chord becomes a tangent.

We say, the gradient of the tangent at P is the limit of $\dfrac{\delta y}{\delta x}$ as both δy and $\delta x \to 0$.

This is why we had to make a study of the ratio of very small quantities, both approaching zero

and we define $\lim \frac{\delta y}{\delta x}$ as δx and $\delta y \to 0$ as $\frac{dy}{dx}$

(pronounced 'dee-y by dee-x') and we call the method differentiation.

Note: $\frac{dy}{dx}$ does NOT mean $\frac{d \times y}{d \times x}$, i.e. we cannot cancel the d's.

The 'dx' means a 'little bit of x, approaching zero' and similarly for dy.

Let us apply the method to the curves we have mentioned.

To find the gradient at any point of the curve $y = x^2$ (Fig.7.12).

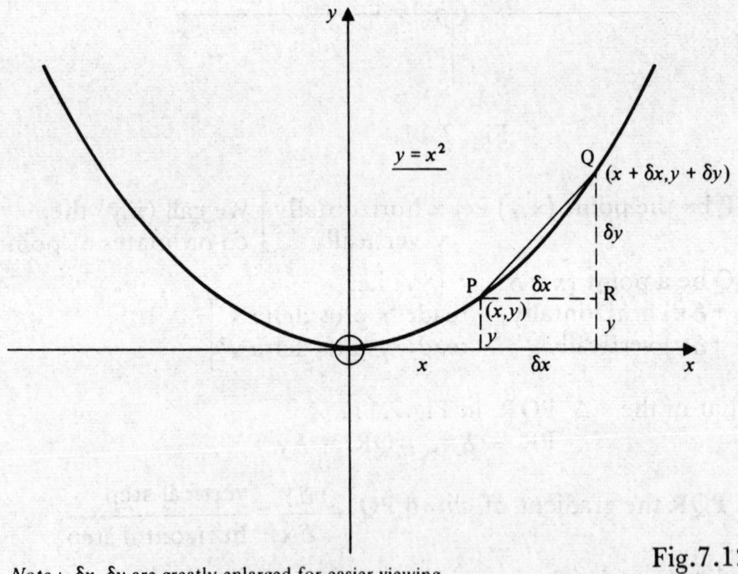

Note : δx, δy are greatly enlarged for easier viewing.

Fig.7.12.

Let $P \equiv (x,y)$

Let $Q \equiv (x + \delta x,\ y + \delta y)$

i.e. let x and y grow by small amounts $\delta x, \delta y$

Complete the Δ PQR

Then $PR = \delta x \quad QR = \delta y$

$\therefore$ Gradient of $PQ = \frac{\delta y}{\delta x}$

We evaluate this as follows:

Since the point (x,y) lies on the curve
then $y = x^2$ .... [1]
Since the point $(x + \delta x, y + \delta y)$ also lies on the curve
$y + \delta y = (x + \delta x)^2$ .... [2]

N.B. The square of the x value must always equal the y-value for any point on this curve $y = x^2$, i.e. the y-value = (x-value)^2

From [2] $y + \delta y = x^2 + 2x.\delta x + (\delta x)^2$ (Using $(a + b)^2 = a^2 + 2ab + b^2$)

From [1] $y = x^2$

Subtracting [1] from [2] : $\delta y = 2x\delta x + (\delta x)^2$

Divide by δx : $\dfrac{\delta y}{\delta x} = 2x + \delta x$

$\therefore$ Gradient of PQ $= 2x + \delta x$

As $\delta x \to 0$, Gradient of PQ $\to 2x$

$\therefore$ We say the gradient of the tangent at P = 2x,

i.e. $\dfrac{dy}{dx} = 2x$ for the curve $y = x^2$

This means that, where x = 1 the gradient of the tangent = 2 x 1 = 2
Similarly : where x = 2 the gradient of the tangent = 4
where x = 3 the gradient of the tangent = 6
where x = 3.1 the gradient of the tangent = 6.2
where x = −½ the gradient of the tangent = −1 etc.

i.e. the gradient of the curve at any point of the curve $y = x^2$ is always twice the x-value at that point.

To find the gradient at any point on the curve $y = x^3$ (Fig.7.13)

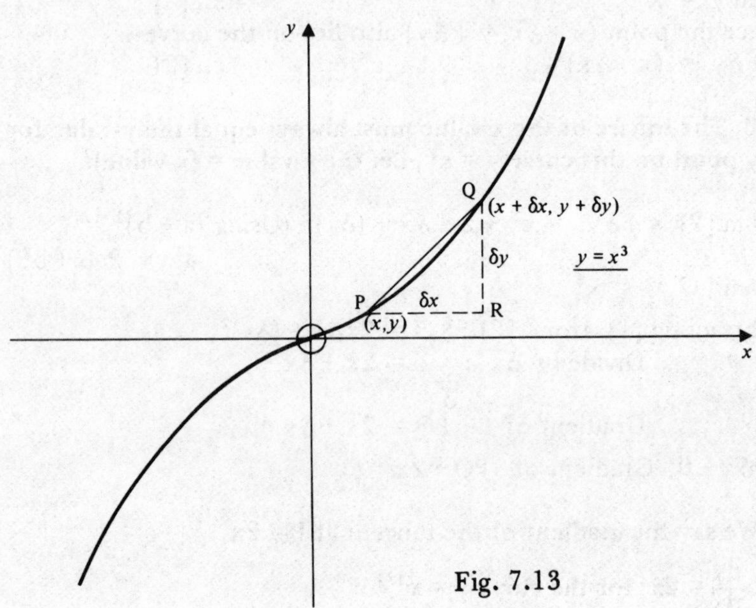

Fig. 7.13

Following the same procedure as before:

Let x and y both grow by small bits δx and δy.

Gradient of PQ $= \dfrac{\delta y}{\delta x}$

But since P lies on the curve:

$$y = x^3 \quad \text{.... [1]}$$

$$y + \delta y = (x + \delta x)^3 \quad \text{.... [2]}$$

$$\therefore y + \delta y = x^3 + 3x^2.\delta x + 3x(\delta x)^2 + (\delta x)^3 \quad \text{.... [3]}$$

[Using $(a + b)^3 = a^3 + 3a^2 b + 3ab^2 + b^3$ see page 32]

Subtracting [1] from [3]:

$$\delta y = 3x^2.\delta x + 3x(\delta x)^2 + (\delta x)^3$$

Divide through by δx:

$$\frac{\delta y}{\delta x} = 3x^2 + 3x.\delta x + (\delta x)^2$$

Now we know that δx is small, therefore, $(\delta x)^2$ is of the second degree of smallness, that is it is very small. (See p.43 'What is smallness?').

e.g. if $\delta x = 0.001$ $\quad (\delta x)^2 = 0.001 \times 0.001 = 0.000001$

$\delta x = 0.0001$ $\quad (\delta x)^2 = 0.0001 \times 0.0001 = 0.00000001$

It is therefore negligible in comparison with the other terms.

Let δx and $\delta y \to 0$. Then the gradient of the tangent at P is:

$$\frac{dy}{dx} = 3x^2 \text{ for the curve } y = x^3$$

Thus we can calculate the gradient of the tangent at any point on the curve by substituting the value of x in $\dfrac{dy}{dx} = 3x^2$

e.g. The gradient of tangent where x = 2 is $3 \times 2^2 = 12$

The gradient of tangent where x = $-1\frac{1}{2}$ is $3x(-\frac{3}{2}) \times (-\frac{3}{2}) = +\frac{27}{4}$

To find the gradient of the tangent to the curve $y = x^4$ (Fig.7.14).

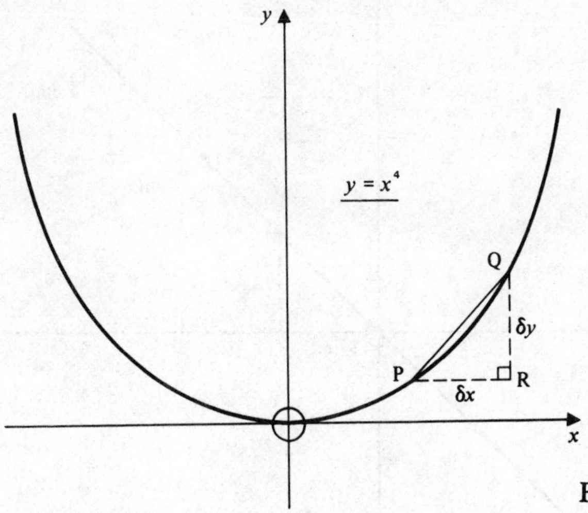

Fig.7.14.

Here we shall need the expansion

$(a + b)^4 = a^4 + 4a^3b + 6a^2b^2 + 4ab^3 + b^4$ (See p.32)

Proceed as in the previous examples.

Since P lies on the curve:

$$y = x^4 \qquad [1]$$

Since Q lies on the curve:

$$y + \delta y = (x + \delta x)^4 \qquad [2]$$

Expanding: $y + \delta y = x^4 + 4x^3.\delta x + 6x^2\ (\delta x)^2 + 4x(\delta x)^3 + (\delta x)^4$

From [1] : $y = x^4$

Subtracting : $\delta y = 4x^3.\ \delta x + 6x^2\ (\delta x)^2 + 4x\ (\delta x)^3 + (\delta x)^4$

$$\therefore \frac{\delta y}{\delta x} = 4x^3 + 6x^2\ \delta x + 4x(\delta x)^2 + (\delta x)^3$$

As δy and $\delta x \to 0$, $\text{Lim}\ \frac{\delta y}{\delta x} = 4x^3$

$\therefore \frac{dy}{dx} = 4x^3$ = the gradient of the tangent at P for the curve $y = x^4$

The simple case of y = x (Fig.7.15)

This has an obvious gradient of 1, by considering the horizontal and vertical steps.

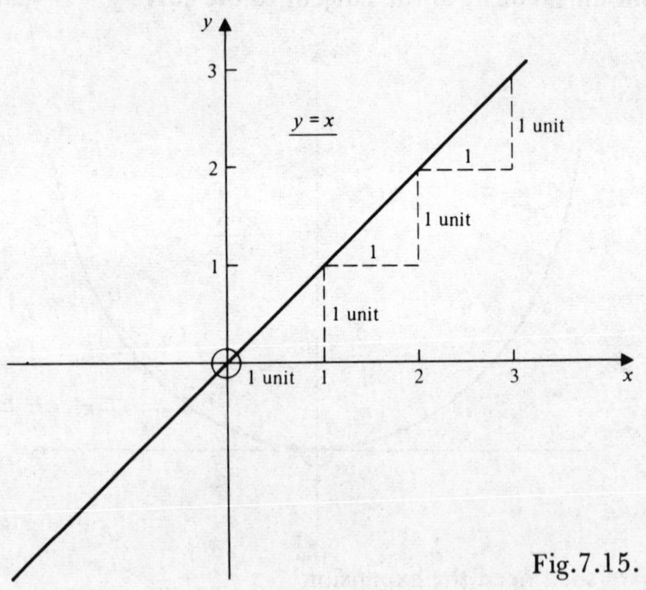

Fig.7.15.

$$\therefore \frac{dy}{dx} = 1 \text{ for the straight line } y = x$$

The case of y = a constant (Fig.7.16)

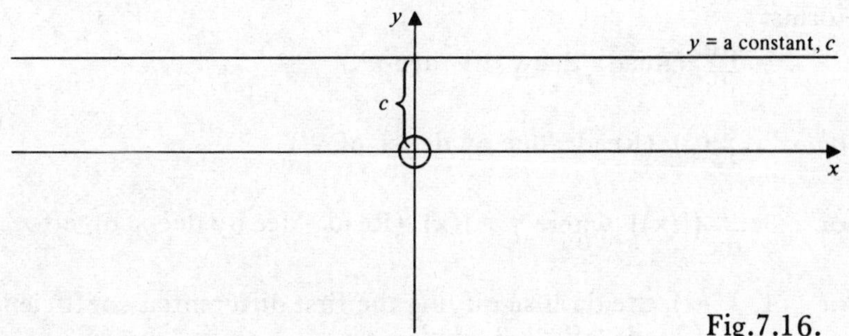

Fig.7.16.

This also is a simple case. Whatever the value of the constant, the graph is a line parallel to the x - axis, and therefore has zero gradient.

$$\therefore \frac{dy}{dx} = 0 \text{ for the straight line } y = \text{a constant}$$

In tabular form we have:

	y	$\frac{dy}{dx}$	
	x [or x^1]	1 [or $1x^0$]	since $x^0 = 1$
	x^2	$2x$	
	x^3	$3x^2$	
	x^4	$4x^3$	
Guessing the next:	x^5	$5x^4$	and so on.
In general:	x^n	nx^{n-1}	

So that if $y = x^n$

$$\frac{dy}{dx} = nx^{n-1}$$

Basic Formula

At this stage we do not prove this formally. It is the use of this formula which is of most importance. It is true for all values of n, positive, negative and fractional.

Notation.

The gradient of the tangent may be written in the following forms:

1. $\frac{dy}{dx}$ (Read: 'dee-y by dee-x'.)

or 2. $\frac{d}{dx}(y)$ (Read: 'dee by dee-x of y').

or 3. $\frac{d}{dx}(f(x))$ where $y = f(x)$ (Read: 'dee by dee-x of eff-x'.)

or 4. $f'(x)$, the dash signifying the first differential coefficient. (Read: 'eff-dash of x')

or 5. the rate of change of y with respect to x.

Negative Gradients: Zero Gradients

We note that the gradient of a curve can be positive or negative (Fig.7.17).

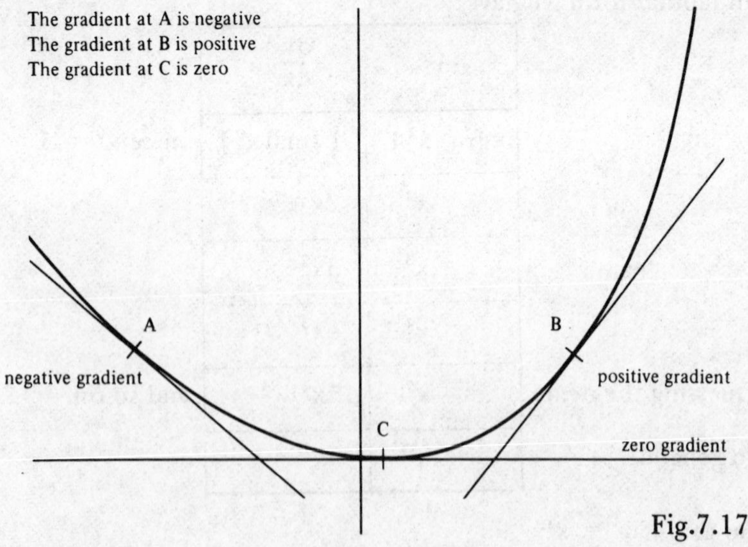

Fig.7.17.

A negative gradient implies that as x increases from left to right then y decreases.

How to deal with constants

Constants occur in two different ways, that is, there are two different types:

(i) the type which is added to (or subtracted from) other terms involving a variable; and

(ii) the type which multiplies a variable.

Added constants

An example will illustrate the way to deal with these.

Let $y = x^2 - 4$ .... [1]

In exactly the same way as previously, suppose x increases to $x + \delta x$, while y increases to $y + \delta y$.

Then from [1] $y + \delta y = (x + \delta x)^2 - 4$

$\therefore$ $y + \delta y = x^2 + 2x\,\delta x + (\delta x)^2 - 4$

Subtracting the original $y = x^2 - 4$

we get $\delta y = 2x\delta x + (\delta x)^2$

Divide by δx : $\dfrac{\delta y}{\delta x} = 2x + \delta x$

As δx and δy approach zero:

$$\text{Lim}\ \frac{\delta y}{\delta x} = 2x$$

$$\therefore\ \frac{dy}{dx} = 2x \quad \text{for} \quad y = x^2 - 4$$

In other words, the –4 has disappeared from the result. It has not affected the change in y. In the same way, whatever number we add to or subtract from x^2, the same thing will happen whether it is a whole number or a fraction, positive or negative - that is, any constant. Hence we say 'the differential of a simple constant is zero'. We could also see this result by drawing the graphs of $y = x^2$ and $y = x^2 - 4$; they are of the same shape, only the second one is 4 units vertically below the first. So for a given value of x they have the same gradient.

Multiplying constants

As a simple example consider

$$y = 5x^2$$

As before $y + \delta y = 5(x + \delta x)^2$

$$= 5(x^2 + 2x\,\delta x + (\delta x)^2)$$

$\therefore \quad y + \delta y = 5x^2 + 10x\,\delta x + 5(\delta x)^2$

Subtract $\quad y = 5x^2$

This gives $\quad \delta y = 10x\,\delta x + 5(\delta x)^2$

Divide by $\delta x \quad \dfrac{\delta y}{\delta x} = 10x + 5\,\delta x$

As δx and δy approach zero

$$\text{Lim} \quad \frac{\delta y}{\delta x} = 10x \quad \text{since } 5\,\delta x \to 0$$

$$\therefore \quad \frac{dy}{dx} = 10x \quad \text{for} \quad y = 5x^2$$

Thus to differentiate $5x^2$ we multiply the differential of x^2, which is $2x$, by 5 and we obtain $10x$.

In the same way if we differentiate

$$y = ax^2 \quad \text{where a is any constant}$$

we obtain $\quad \dfrac{dy}{dx}$ = a multiplied by 2x

$$\therefore \quad \frac{dy}{dx} = 2ax$$

This method holds for any power of x, but the general proof is beyond the scope of this book.

i.e. if $\quad y = ax^n$

$$\frac{dy}{dx} = anx^{n-1}$$

Sums and differences

How do we deal with several terms added or subtracted? The answer is quite simple. We treat each term separately. For example, consider

$y = x^4 + 3x + 6$

We know that if we increase x, x^4 will increase by a certain amount and 3x will increase by a different amount. The constant 6 will not change. Therefore it will not affect the change in y. Hence the total increase in y due to a change in x is the sum of the increases in x^4 and 3x. This means that the rate of increase of y is equal to the sum of the rates of increase of x^4 and 3x. A formal proof is as follows:

Let $y = u + v$ ... [1]

where u and v are both functions of x
(u corresponds to x^4 and v to 3x in the example above.)

If x increases by δx
then u will increase by δu (say)
v will increase by δv (say)
and y will increase by δy.

From [1] $y + \delta y = (u + \delta u) + (v + \delta v)$
Subtract [1] $y = u + v$
and we obtain $\delta y = \delta u + \delta v$
Divide by δx $\frac{\delta y}{\delta x} = \frac{\delta u}{\delta x} + \frac{\delta v}{\delta x}$

Let δx approach zero. Then $\delta u, \delta v$ and δy will approach zero.
Hence in the limit $\frac{dy}{dx} = \frac{du}{dx} + \frac{dv}{dx}$ for $y = u + v$

This method applies however many terms we have, whether positive or negative. **To differentiate a function consisting of sums and differences of terms, differentiate each term separately.**

Example 1. If $y = x^6$, find $\frac{dy}{dx}$

Here $n = 6$

$$\frac{dy}{dx} = 6x^{6-1}$$
$$= \mathbf{6x^5}$$

Example 2. If $y = 3x^2$ find $\frac{dy}{dx}$

$$\therefore \frac{dy}{dx} = 3 \times \text{differential of } x^2$$
$$= 3 \times 2x$$
$$= \mathbf{6x}$$

Example 3. If $y = 4x^3 - x + 6$ find $\frac{dy}{dx}$ and the gradients of the tangents at x = 2, 1, 0, –1

$$\frac{dy}{dx} = 4.3x^2 - 1 + 0 \text{ since } \frac{d}{dx}(6) = 0$$

$$\frac{dy}{dx} = 12x^2 - 1$$

When x = 2

$$\frac{dy}{dx} = 12.2^2 - 1$$

∴ Gradient of tangent = 47 at x = 2.

When x = 1

$$\frac{dy}{dx} = 12 - 1$$

∴ Gradient of tangent = 11 at x = 1.

When x = 0

$$\frac{dy}{dx} = -1$$

∴ Gradient of tangent = – 1 at x = 0

When x = – 1

$$\frac{dy}{dx} = 12(-1)^2 - 1$$

Gradient of tangent = 11 at x = – 1.

∴ **the gradients at x = 2, 1, 0, –1 are 47, 11, –1, 11 respectively.**

Example 4. Differentiate the following functions by rule:

(i) $(x + 3)^2$; (ii) $ax(a - x)$; (iii) $\frac{x^n + 1}{x}$; (iv) $\frac{1}{x^2}$; (v) $\frac{1}{x}$

(i) Let $y = (x + 3)^2$

$$= x^2 + 6x + 9$$

$$\frac{dy}{dx} = 2x + 6$$

(ii) Let $y = ax(a - x)$, [a = a constant]

$$= a^2x - ax^2$$

$$\frac{dy}{dx} = a^2 - a(2x)$$

$$= a^2 - 2ax$$

(iii) Let $y = \frac{x^n + 1}{x}$

$\therefore \quad y = x^{n-1} + \frac{1}{x}$

$= x^{n-1} + x^{-1}$

(iv) Let $y = \frac{1}{x^2} = x^{-2}$

$\therefore \frac{dy}{dx} = -2x^{-2-1}$

$= -2x^{-3}$

$= \frac{-2}{x^3}$

$\frac{dy}{dx} = (n-1)\,x^{n-2} + (-1x^{-1-1})$

$= (n-1)\,x^{n-2} - \frac{1}{x^2}$

(v) $\quad y = \frac{1}{\sqrt{x}} = \frac{1}{x^{+1/2}} = x^{-1/2}$ i.e. $= \frac{1}{x^{-1/2}} = x^{-1/2}$

$\frac{dy}{dx} = -\frac{1}{2}\,x^{-1/2-1}$

$= -\frac{1}{2}\,x^{-\frac{3}{2}}$

$= \frac{-\frac{1}{2}}{x^{\frac{3}{2}}}$

$= -\frac{1}{2.\sqrt[2]{x^3}}$

Now you know how to differentiate powers of x. It is all very easy, but before doing the next exercise, revise the rules dealing with fractional and negative indices, at the end of Chapter 5 (page 41)

Exercises in Simple Differentiation

In the following, use $\frac{d}{dx}(x^n) = nx^{n-1}$ to find $\frac{dy}{dx}$ i.e. the differential coefficient of y w.r.t. x. (The differential coefficient of y with respect to x).

Exercise 23. Find $\frac{dy}{dx}$ for the following functions:

1. $y = x^5$
2. $y = 3x^3$
3. $y = 5x$
4. $y = -x$
5. $y = \frac{1}{4}x^4$
6. $y = 6x^{\frac{1}{2}}$
7. $y = \sqrt[3]{x}$
8. $y = 2x^2 - 4$
9. $y = \frac{2}{x}$
10. $y = \frac{1}{2x}$
11. $y = x + \frac{1}{x}$
12. $y = \frac{3}{x} - \sqrt{x}$
13. $y = \frac{x^6}{6}$
14. $y = \frac{x^7}{7}$
15. $y = \frac{x^8}{8}$
16. $y = \frac{x^{n+1}}{n+1}$
17. $y = \frac{x^4 - 4}{x}$
18. $y = \frac{x^4 - 4}{x^5}$
19. $y = (x + 2)^2$
20. $y = 3x^2 + 2x - 1$
21. $y = ax^2 (a - x^2)$ (a, b and c are constan
22. $y = ax^2 + bx + c$

Exercise 24. Using the fact that $\frac{dy}{dx} = 1/\frac{dx}{dy}$, find $\frac{dy}{dx}$ in terms of y for the following functions (find $\frac{dx}{dy}$ first).

For example, $x = 3y^2 - 2y + 4$

$$\therefore \frac{dx}{dy} = 6y - 2$$

$$\therefore \frac{dy}{dx} = \frac{1}{6y - 2}$$

1. $x = 2y - y^2$ 2. $y^2 + 1 = x$ 3. $y^3 = x + 7$

RATES OF CHANGE WITH RESPECT TO TIME

Linear Velocity

Suppose a straight line is marked with an arrow to indicate a positive sense of direction along the line. (Fig. 7.18).

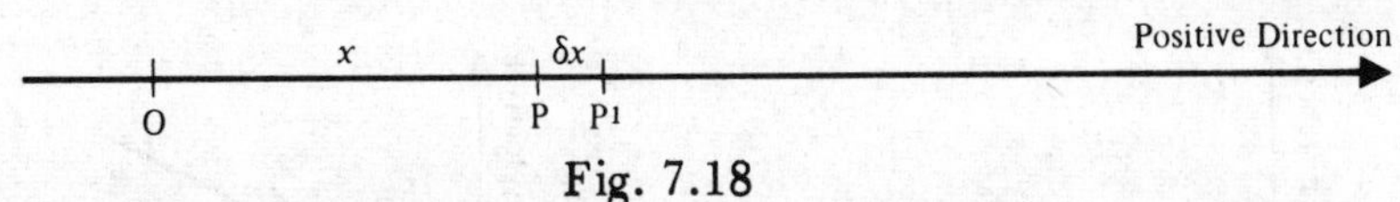

Fig. 7.18

Let 0 be a fixed point and P a variable point on the line, and let x be the distance of P from 0 at a given time t, the distance x being counted as positive or negative, according as the direction 0→P is the same as or opposite to the arrowhead. Then if P travels to an adjacent point P^1 where $PP^1 = \delta x$, in a time δt, then the average speed $= \frac{\delta x}{\delta t}$ during the interval δt.

N.B. Average Speed $= \frac{\text{distance}}{\text{time}}$

Then if δx and $\delta t \to 0$, the limit is the speed or velocity at the point P.

i.e. $\frac{dx}{dt}$ = velocity at P = v (say)

or, in words, the velocity at P is the rate of change of distance with respect to time.

Note 1: $\frac{dx}{dt}$ is **positive** when x is **increasing** with time, i.e. when P is moving in the positive direction.

$\frac{dx}{dt}$ is **negative** when x is **decreasing** with time, i.e. when P is moving in a negative direction.

Note 2: $v = \frac{dx}{dt}$ means that on the graph of distance plotted against time,

The velocity is the gradient of the (t,x) graph.

Linear Acceleration

Let v denote the velocity at time t.

Then $\frac{dv}{dt}$ is the rate at which the velocity is changing at the instant t, or briefly, the **acceleration** at time t. If f denotes the acceleration

$$f = \frac{dv}{dt}$$

i.e. f is the gradient of the (t,v,) graph.

The acceleration is the gradient of the (t,v) graph.

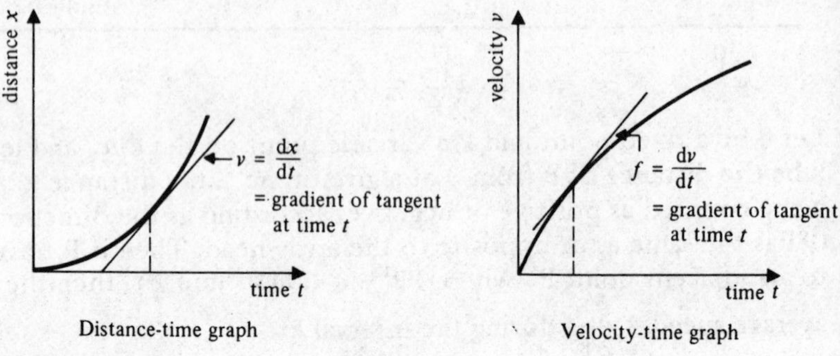

Fig. 7.19

Example 1. If x is measured in metres and t in seconds, and if

$x = \frac{1}{4}t^4 - 3t^2 + 2t$

find the velocity and acceleration when t = 3

$v = \frac{dx}{dt} = \frac{1}{4}.4t^3 - 3.2t + 2$ .... [1]

$= t^3 - 6t + 2$

$\therefore$ when t = 3 :

$v = 3^3 - 6(3) + 2$

$= 27 - 18 + 2$

v = 11 metres/second

Also $f = \frac{dv}{dt} = 3t^2 - 6$ from (1), differentiating

When t = 3 :

$f = 3(3)^2 - 6$

$= 27 - 6$

f = 21 metres/second^2

Note: metres/second^2 means 'metres per second per second', i.e. the increase in velocity (metres per sec) every second.

Example 2. If $x = t^3 - 9t^2 + 24t$ find the values of t at which the point is momentarily at rest.

$v = \frac{dx}{dt} = 3t^2 - 18t + 24$

When at rest, v = 0

i.e. $0 = 3t^2 - 18t + 24$

$0 = 3(t^2 - 6t + 8)$

$0 = 3(t - 4)(t - 2)$

$\therefore$ **t = 4 or 2**

Hence P is momentarily at rest after 2 seconds or 4 seconds.

Exercise 25

1. The distance, x metres, travelled by a car t seconds after the brakes are applied, is given by $x = 44t - 6t^2$

(i) what is the speed when the brakes are applied (i.e. $t = 0$)?
(ii) what is the retardation (i.e. the negative acceleration)?
(iii) how long does it take to come to rest?
(iv) how far does it travel before it comes to rest?

2. With the usual notation, find the velocity and acceleration at the given time for the following functions. Also find values of t when P is momentarily at rest.

(i) $x = 2t^3 - 9t^2 + 12t$ when $t = 2$
(ii) $x = t(3 - t)^2$ when $t = 2$
(iii) $x = t^2(4 - t^2)$ when $t = 1$

Chapter 8

More useful tools

BASIC CURVES AND THEIR RECOGNITION.

Here we discuss which type of curve is represented by a particular type of equation. First we deal with the special case of the straight line.

1. The Straight Line.

We have seen that the graph of $y = x$ is a straight line of gradient 1, passing through the origin (page 62).
Now we must study graphs of the type $y = mx + c$, where m and c are constants (Fig.8.1).
An example will suffice.

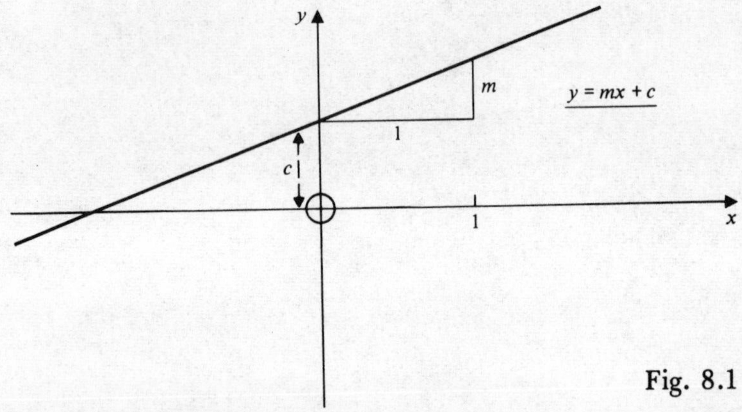

Fig. 8.1

Example. Draw the graph of $y = 3x + 2$
We make a table as follows taking several values of x and working the corresponding values of y.

x	0	1	2	3	−1	−2
3x	0	3	6	9	−3	−6
y = 3x + 2	2	5	8	11	−1	−4

Plotting the values of y against the values of x, we obtain the graph of Fig.8.2.

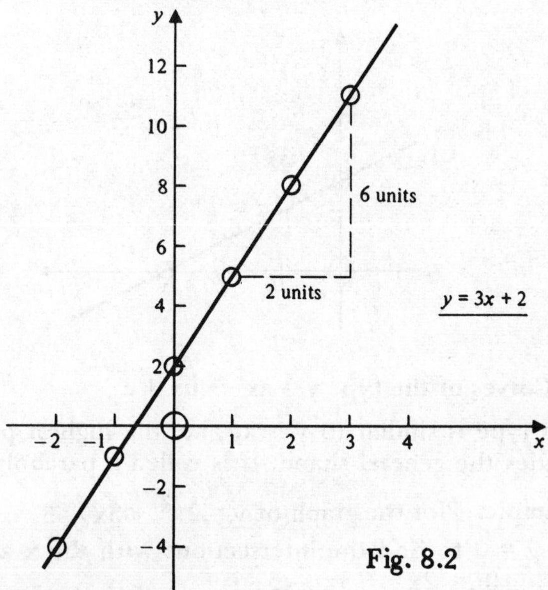

Fig. 8.2

We see that (i) the gradient of the line is 3;
and (ii) it cuts the y axis at the value 2.
Thus when we read the equation:
$y = 3x + 2$

we know: (i) **the coefficient of x gives the gradient;**
(ii) **the constant term gives the intercept** on the **y axis through the origin.**

Summary The graph of $y = mx + c$
is a **straight line of gradient m passing through the point (O, c).**
The student is advised to confirm this statement by drawing the graphs of similar equations, for example:

(i) $y = 2x + 1$
(ii) $y = 2x - 1$
(iii) $y = 6 - 3x$ (Hint: write this $y = -3x + 6$)

Example. Draw or sketch the graph of $2y = 3 - x$
(Note: "sketch" means that it is not necessary to plot points accurately.)
We write this in the form $y = mx + c$, to obtain

$$y = -\tfrac{1}{2}x + \frac{3}{2}$$

This tells us: (i) the gradient is $-\tfrac{1}{2}$;
(ii) the intercept on the y axis is $1\tfrac{1}{2}$.
The graph is shown in Fig. 8.3. Note that when $y = 0$, $x = 3$.

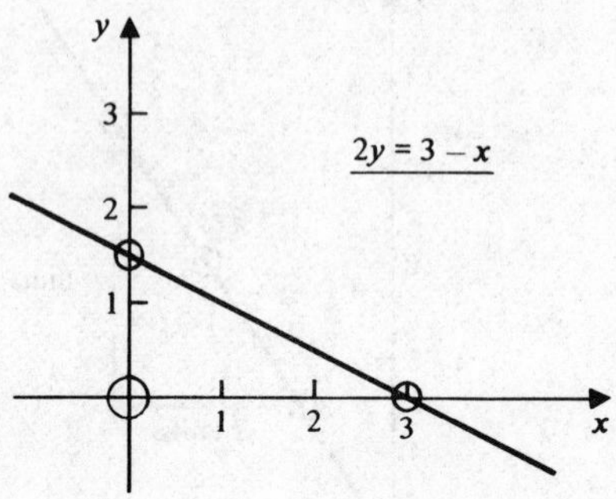

Fig. 8.3

2. Curves of the type $y = ax^2 + bx + c$

This type is similar to $y = x^2$, i.e. the highest power of x decides the general shape: It is called a parabola.

Example. Plot the graph of $y = 2x^2 + 3x - 5$

Put y = 0 to find the intersections with the x axis.

$$0 = 2x^2 + 3x - 5$$
$$\therefore 0 = (x - 1)(2x + 5)$$
$$\therefore x - 1 = 0 \text{ or } 2x + 5 = 0$$
$$\therefore x = 1 \text{ or } x = -\frac{5}{2}$$

How do we decide which range of values of x to choose? We must include both x = 1 and x = −2½

Suppose we choose an extra ½ or 1 unit at the ends of this range.(We could choose more than this, or less, but we must include the range −2½ to +1, not merely this range alone.)

Thus we make a table of values to plot the graph between x = –3 and x = +2 (Fig.8.4), as below:

$$y = 2x^2 + 3x - 5$$

x	–3	–2½	–2	–1	0	1	2	–¾ *
x^2	+9	$+\frac{25}{4}$	+4	+1	0	1	4	$+\frac{9}{16}$
$2x^2$	18	$\frac{25}{2}$	8	2	0	2	8	$\frac{9}{8}$
+3x	–9	$-\frac{15}{2}$	–6	–3	0	3	6	$-\frac{9}{4}$
–5	–5	– 5	–5	–5	–5	–5	–5	– 5
y	4	0	–3	–6	–5	0	9	$-6\frac{1}{8}$

Add these values ($2x^2$, +3x, –5) to give y.

Since $2x^2 + 3x - 5$ factorises we could in this case make our table of values as follows:

x	–3	–2	etc.	1	2	–¾ *
(x – 1)	–4	–3		0	1	$-\frac{7}{4}$
(2x + 5)	–1	+1		7	9	$\frac{7}{2}$
y = (x – 1)(2x + 5)	+4	–3		0	9	$-\frac{49}{8}$

Multiply these values ((x – 1), (2x + 5)) to give y

This is the easier method here but cannot always be used as most quadratic expressions do not factorise.

Note: *This extra value of y was taken (after plotting the other values) on observing the symmetry of the graph. The midpoint of the range on the x-axis is –¾, giving a value for y of $-6\frac{1}{8}$

This is the *minimum value* of y, and is of special importance as we shall see later.

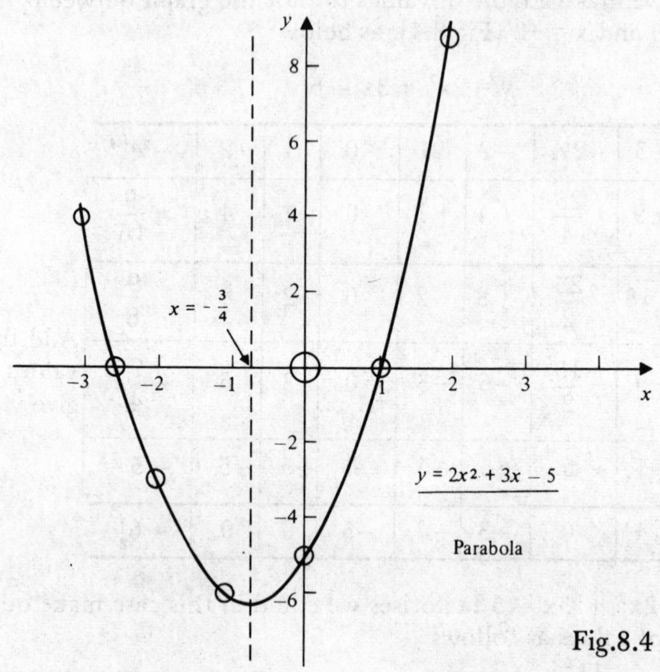

Fig.8.4

Note: If the coefficient of x^2 is negative, for example $y = 4 - x^2$, in which $a = -1$, then the curve is inverted as in Fig. 8.5.

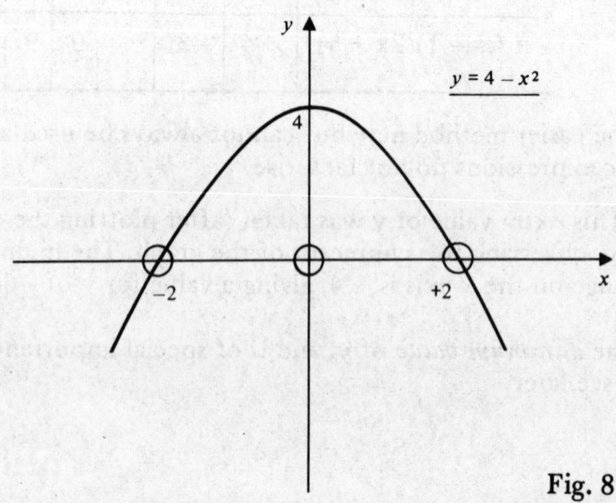

Fig. 8.5.

Exercise: Check that $y = 4 - x^2$ cuts the axes at the points indicated, by:

(i) putting $y = 0$ and finding x by factorising $x^2 - 4$;
(ii) putting $x = 0$ and finding y.

Note: **The highest power** of x determines the type of curve which is obtained.

Summary so far

Highest power of x	Example	Type of graph
Zero	$y = -2$	Straight line parallel to x-axis at distance 2 units below the x-axis
First	$y = 4 - 2x$	Straight line gradient -2 through point (0,4)
Second	$y = x^2 - 3x + 2$ $= (x-2)(x-1)$	Parabola, passing through points (1,0)(2,0) and (0,2)

3. Curves of the Type $y = ax^3 + bx^2 + cx + d$ where a,b,c,d, are constants. These are called cubic curves.

Example. Consider the curve $y = (x - 1)(x + 2)(3x - 7)$
The highest power of x, on working out the brackets, would be $3x^3$ obtained by multiplying all the x terms together.
So that it is a cubic curve.

If we put $\quad y = 0$

i.e. $\quad 0 = (x - 1)(x + 2)(3x - 7)$

we obtain the solutions $x = 1$ or -2 or $\frac{7}{3}$

∴ the curve cuts the x axis at these points.
It therefore looks like one of the curves of Fig. 8.6.

either (*a*)

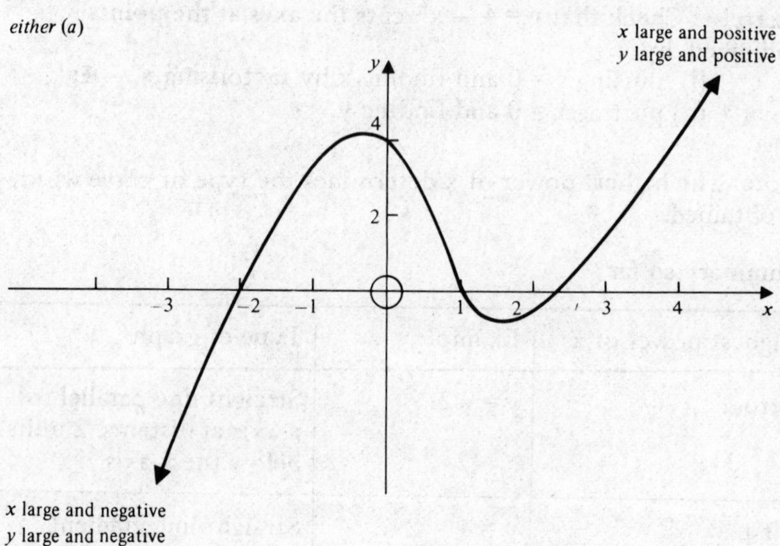

or (*b*) its mirror image in the *x* axis

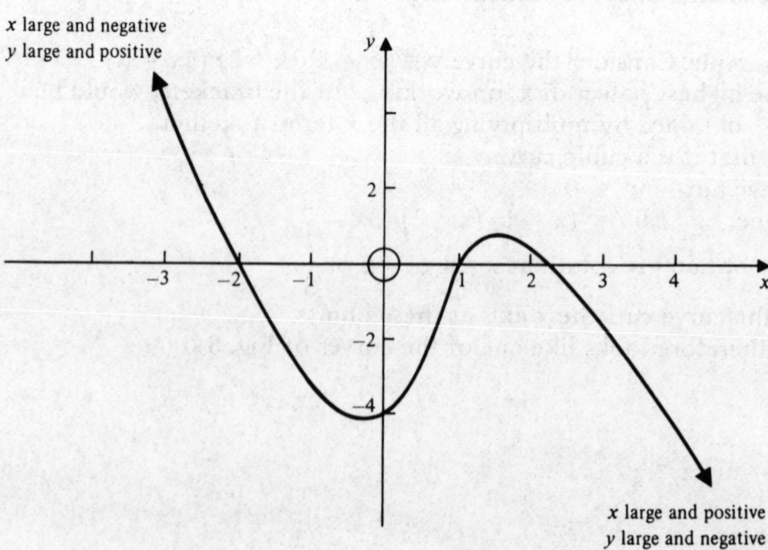

Fig. 8.6.

We can decide which of these is correct by asking ourselves the following questions:

1. If x is large and positive, what do we know about y? and
2. If x is large and negative, what do we know about y?

If x is large and positive,

using $y = (x - 1)(x + 2)(3x - 7)$
we get y = (a large positive number) x (a large positive number) x (a large positive number)
y = a large positive number.

If x is large and negative
y = (a large negative number) x (a large negative number) x (a large negative number)
y = a large negative number.

These two facts show that diagram (a) is the only possibility.

Note: **A cubic curve has two bends.**

Summary.

f(x)	Type of graph	Type of curve
$y = ax + b$	Straight line, gradient a, no turning points	
$y = ax^2 + bx + c$	Parabola, 1 turning point	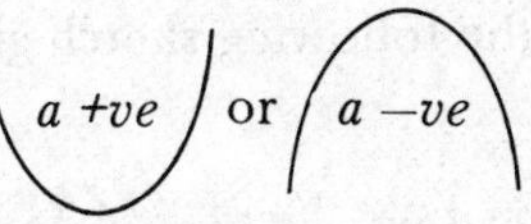 *a* +ve or *a* −ve
$y = ax^3 + bx^2 \ldots$	Cubic, 2 turning points	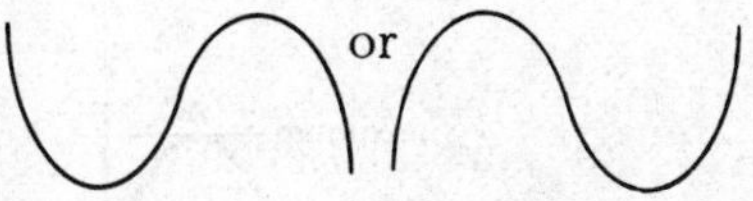 or
$y = ax^4 + \ldots$	Quartic, 3 turning points*	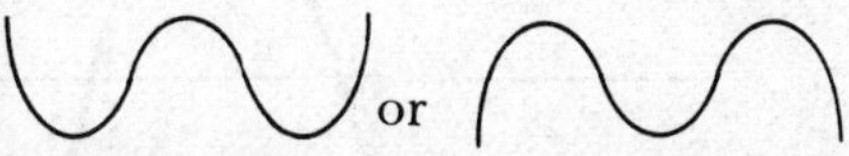 or

*We are making a reasonable guess here, but an example will check.

Note: In some special curves, two or more turning points may coalesce as in $y = x^3$ (Fig. 8.7).

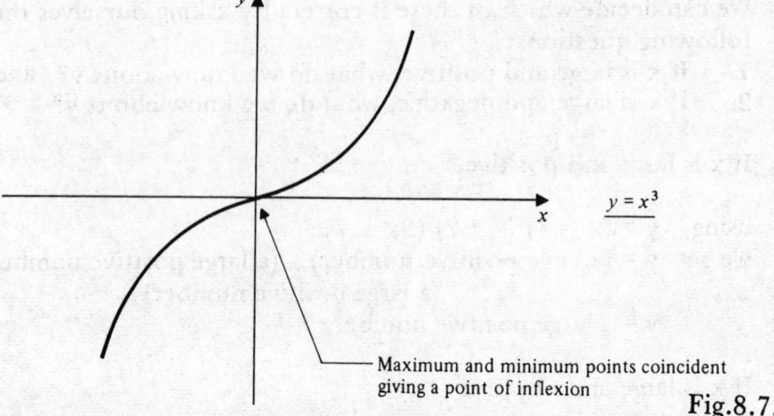

Fig.8.7.

In general, the number of turning points is one less than the highest power of the polynomial.

Expressions such as $1 + 2x + 5x^2$ and $3 + 4x - 2x^3 + x^4$ consisting of the sum of a number of positive whole number powers of the variable are called **polynomials.** The highest power of the variable which occurs is called the **degree** of the polynomial.

STATIONARY VALUES

We know that the graphs of many functions have turning points. It is often useful to be able to locate these without drawing an accurate graph. We now proceed to find a method for doing this.

Consider the following sketch-graphs (Fig.8.8).

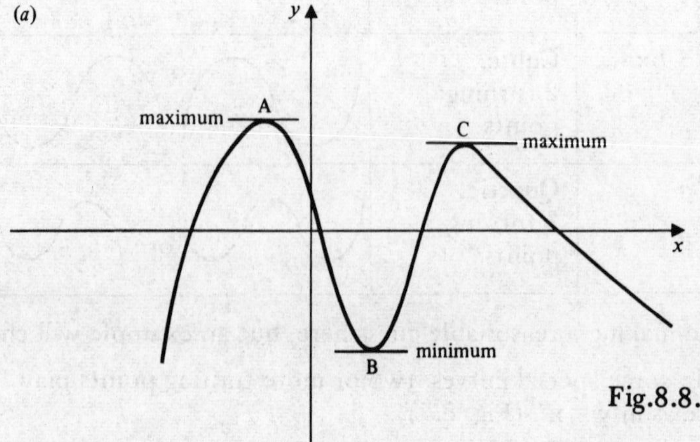

Fig.8.8.

(b)

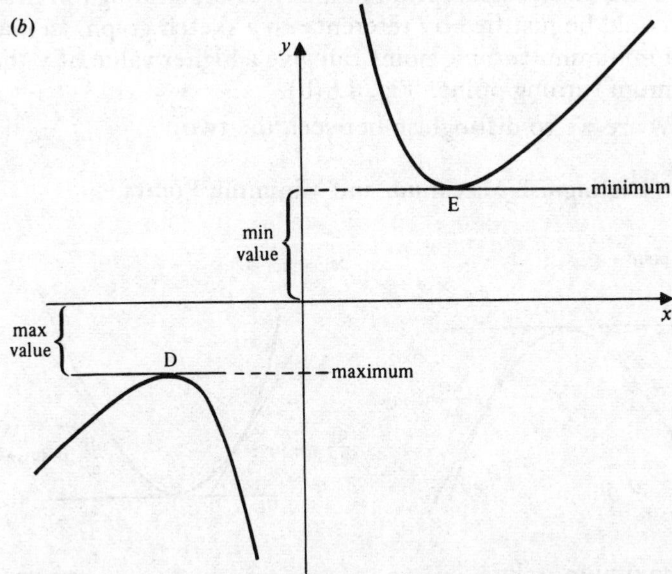

At A, C and D we have maximum turning points.
At B and E we have minimum turning points.

All these points have one thing in common, i.e. the tangents at all these points are horizontal and therefore the gradients of the curves at these points are all zero.

This means $\frac{dy}{dx} = 0$ is a condition for **maximum or minimum points.**

Let us see how we can make use of this fact.

Example. **Consider the curve** $y = 2x^3 + 3x^2 - 36x + 6$ ....(1)

Differentiating: $\frac{dy}{dx} = 6x^2 + 6x - 36$

For a turning point $\frac{dy}{dx} = 0$ i.e. $6x^2 + 6x - 36 = 0$

$\therefore 6(x^2 + x - 6) = 0$

$\therefore 6(x + 3)(x - 2) = 0$

$\therefore x = -3$ or $x = +2$

Substituting in (1): $y = 87$ or $y = -38$

We suspect that since we are studying a cubic curve, there will be a maximum and a minimum value (two turning points).

Can we assume, because y = + 87 at one of these and y = – 38 at the other, that the first of these gives the maximum value of y and the second gives the minimum value?

This is a dangerous assumption in many cases, although in this case it could be justified by reference to a sketch graph. In many cases, a minimum turning point can give a higher value of y than a maximum turning point, Fig. 8.8(b).
But how are we to distinguish between the two?

Tests to Distinguish Maximum and Minimum Points.

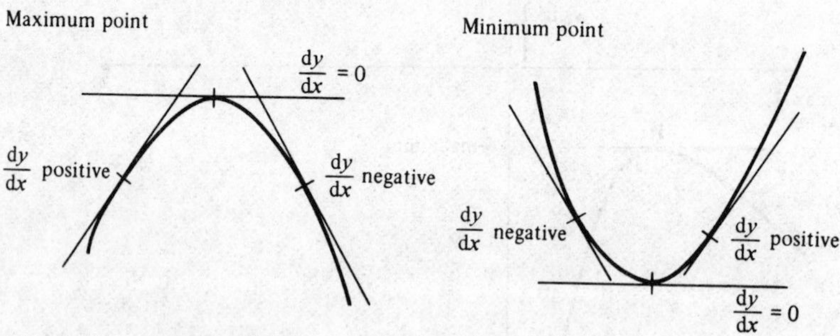

Fig.8.9.

For a maximum point:

On the left-hand side (L.H.S.) $\frac{dy}{dx}$ is positive (+ve)

On the right-hand side (R.H.S.) $\frac{dy}{dx}$ is negative (–ve)

So that $\frac{dy}{dx}$ changes from +ve → zero → –ve as the tangent rolls around the curve.
This means that $\frac{dy}{dx}$ is decreasing (+ve, zero, –ve).

For a minimum point:

On the L.H.S. $\frac{dy}{dx}$ is negative (–ve)

On the R.H.S. $\frac{dy}{dx}$ is positive (+ve)

So that $\frac{dy}{dx}$ changes from –ve → zero → +ve as the tangent rolls round the curve.
This means that $\frac{dy}{dx}$ is increasing (–ve, zero, +ve).
How do we express the fact that $\frac{dy}{dx}$ is decreasing (for a maximum point) or increasing (for a minimum point) ?

If any function is decreasing (or increasing) we know that its gradient, i.e. its differential, is negative (or positive). Hence the differential of $\frac{dy}{dx}$, which is itself a function of x, must be negative for a maximum point and positive for a minimum point.

Fig.8.10. illustrates what happens to $\frac{dy}{dx}$ at a maximum point (8.10(a)) and at a minimum point (8.10(b)).

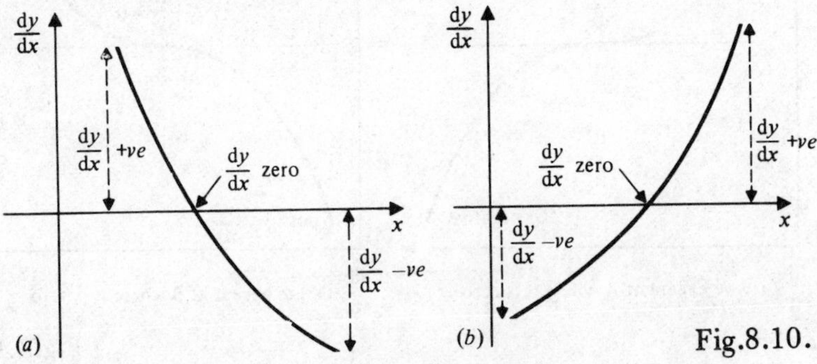

Fig.8.10.

In Fig.8.10(a) $\frac{dy}{dx}$ is decreasing, and therefore has a negative gradient or differential. In Fig.8.10(b) $\frac{dy}{dx}$ is increasing, and therefore has a positive gradient or differential. How do we write the differential of $\frac{dy}{dx}$?

In shorthand: $\frac{d}{dx}$ of $\frac{dy}{dx}$ or $\frac{d(dy)}{dx(dx)}$ or $\frac{d^2y}{dx^2}$

Note: $\frac{d}{dx}$ of $\frac{dy}{dx}$ is pronounced 'dee-by-dee-x of dee-y by dee-x';

$\frac{d(dy)}{dx(dx)}$ is pronounced the same;

$\frac{d^2y}{dx^2}$ is pronounced 'dee-two-y by dee-x-squared'.

Thus for a MAXIMUM point $\frac{d^2y}{dx^2}$ is NEGATIVE at that point

and for a MINIMUM point $\frac{d^2y}{dx^2}$ is POSITIVE at that point.

What happens if $\frac{d^2y}{dx^2}$ is neither positive nor negative, i.e. $\frac{d^2y}{dx^2}$ is zero?

In this case $\frac{dy}{dx}$ does not change from positive to negative or vice versa. Hence the graph can be as shown in Fig.8.11.

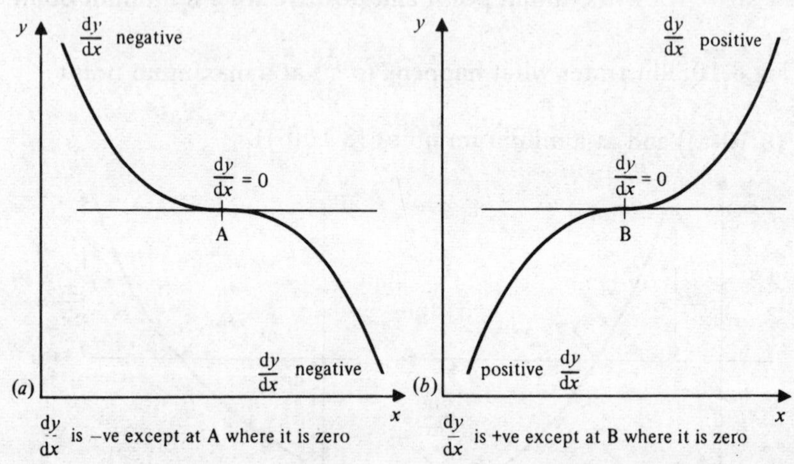

Fig.8.11.

We call this a <u>point of inflexion.</u>

So that we have the following table of tests for all these points called STATIONARY POINTS

y = f(x)	Maximum point	Minimum point	Point of Inflexion
$\frac{dy}{dx}$	Zero	Zero	Zero
$\frac{d^2y}{dx^2}$	−ve	+ve	Zero

Note: Many text-books use the method of taking values of x on either side of the turning points and examining whether the curve is increasing or decreasing at these points. This method can be very difficult in some cases, e.g. curves involving trigonometric functions, and in other cases can lead to serious errors. An infallible method, even if it involves a little extra work (and it is very often the shortest method) is by far the most satisfactory.

Example 1. If $y = x^2 + x - 6$ find the point on the curve at which the gradient is zero.
Sketch the curve.

$$y = x^2 + x - 6 \qquad \ldots\ldots [1]$$

$$\therefore \frac{dy}{dx} = 2x + 1 \qquad \ldots\ldots [2]$$

The gradient of the curve is zero when $\frac{dy}{dx} = 0$
i.e. $2x + 1 = 0$
$\therefore x = -\frac{1}{2}$
When $x = -\frac{1}{2}$, $y = (-\frac{1}{2})^2 + (-\frac{1}{2}) - 6$. from [1]
$= +\frac{1}{4} - \frac{1}{2} - 6$
$= -6\frac{1}{4}$.
$\therefore$ The point $(-\frac{1}{2}, -6\frac{1}{4})$ is the point of zero gradient.

To test whether it is a maximum or minimum point, we find the sign of $\frac{d^2y}{dx^2}$ at the point where $x = -\frac{1}{2}$

From [2] $\frac{d^2y}{dx^2} = 2$. This is **positive** (whatever the value of x).

Therefore $(-\frac{1}{2}, -6\frac{1}{4})$ is a **minimum** point on the graph.

To sketch the curve, first find:

(i) where the curve cuts the x axis;
(ii) where the curve cuts the y axis.

(i) is where $y = 0$
i.e. $0 = x^2 + x - 6$
$0 = (x + 3)(x - 2)$
$\therefore$ $x = -3$ or $+2$

(ii) is where $x = 0$
i.e. $y = 0^2 + 0 - 6$
$\therefore$ $y = -6$

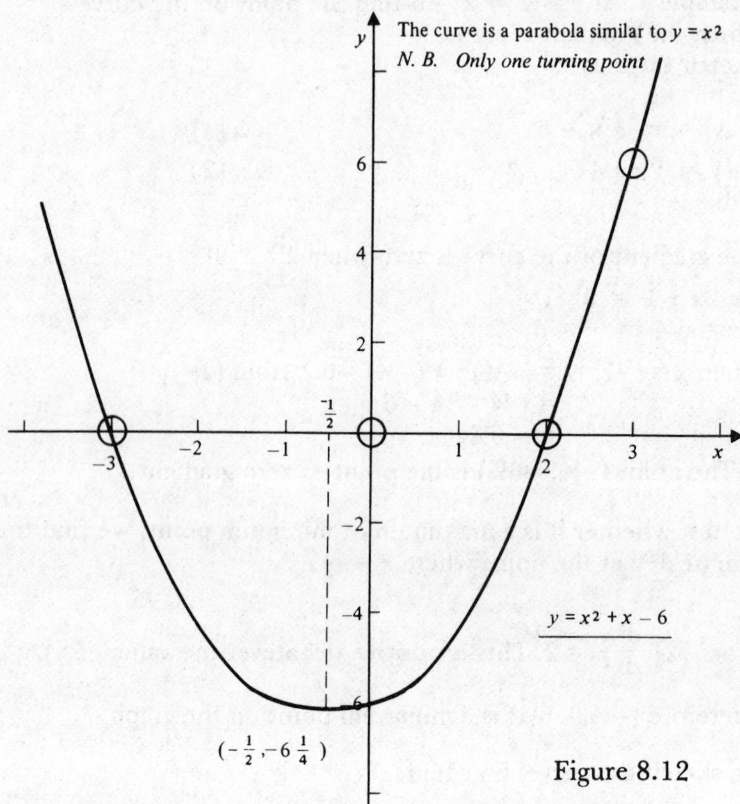

Figure 8.12

Example 2. Find the maximum and minimum values of $y = x^3 - 6x^2 + 9x + 6$ and sketch the curve.

$$y = x^3 - 6x^2 + 9x + 6 \quad \text{.... (1)}$$

$$\therefore \frac{dy}{dx} = 3x^2 - 12x + 9 \quad \text{..... (2)}$$

For a turning point, $\frac{dy}{dx} = 0$

$$\therefore \quad 3x^2 - 12x + 9 = 0$$

Divide by 3: $x^2 - 4x + 3 = 0$

$$\therefore \quad (x - 1)(x - 3) = 0$$

$$\therefore \quad x = 1 \text{ or } x = 3$$

Substituting in (1)

When x = 1, y = 1 − 6 + 9 + 6 = 10

when x = 3, y = 27 − 54 + 27 + 6 = 6

∴ Turning points occur at (1, 10) and (3, 6).

To determine which of these is maximum and which is minimum we must look at the sign of $\frac{d^2y}{dx^2}$ at these points.

From (2) $\frac{d^2y}{dx^2} = 6x - 12$

When $x = 1$ $\frac{d^2y}{dx^2}$ is negative $(= -6)$ $\therefore$ $x = 1$, $y = 10$ is a maximum point

When $x = 3$ $\frac{d^2y}{dx^2}$ is positive $(= +6)$ $\therefore$ $x = 3$, $y = 6$ is a minimum point

Hence the **maximum value** of the function is **10**, and the **minimum value** of the function is **6**.

From (1), when $x = 0$, $y = 6$

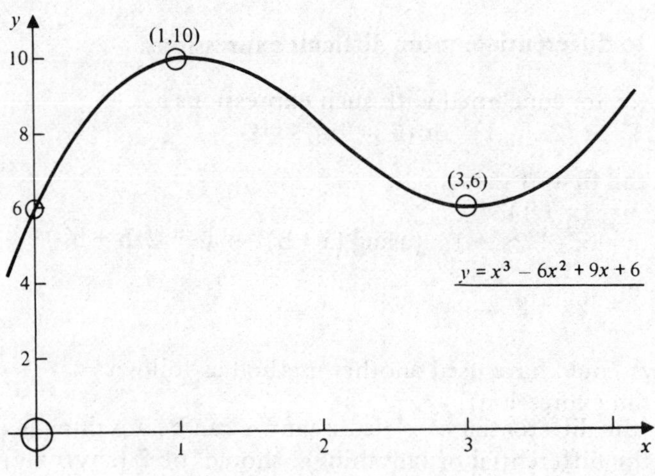

Fig. 8.13

Exercise 26. Examples on Maxima and Minima.

In the following examples find the maximum and/or minimum values of the given functions and the corresponding values of x. (You must discriminate between the maximum and minimum values by considering the sign of $\frac{d^2y}{dx^2}$ at the turning points.)

1. $y = 4x - x^2$
2. $y = x^2 + x + 1$
3. $y = x^2 - 3x + 1$
4. $y = 3x - x^3$
5. $y = x^2 (3 - x)$
6. $y = (x + 3)(7 - x)$

7. The margin of profit in the £ obtained by the sale of a certain article is given by

$$M = 120 - \frac{N}{10} \quad \text{where N is the number sold.}$$

If I is the total income obtained by selling N articles, show that:

$$I = 120N - \frac{N^2}{10}$$

and find the number of articles which must be sold to give the greatest income. (You must give a convincing proof that it is the greatest and not the least income.)

Find also the value of the greatest income.

A FEW TRICKS

How to differentiate more difficult expressions.

Here we are concerned with such expressions as:
$(x + 1)^2$ or $(2x - 1)^3$ or $(5 - 3x)^2$, etc.

Take the first of these.

$$\text{Let } y = (x + 1)^2$$
$$= x^2 + 2x + 1 \quad (\text{using } (a + b)^2 = a^2 + 2ab + b^2)$$
$$\frac{dy}{dx} = 2x + 2$$

But we could have used another method as follows:
$y = (\text{an expression})^2$
Since the differential of x^2 is $2x$ (and x can be anything!) then the differential of $(\text{anything})^2$ should be 2.(anything) i.e. the differential of $(x + 1)^2$ should be $2(x + 1)$ i.e. $2x + 2$.
correct.

This seems to give us a method.

Let us try the second example.

$$\text{Let } y = (2x - 1)^3 = (2x)^3 - 3(2x)^2.1 + 3.2x.1^2 - 1^3$$
$$[\text{using } (a + b)^3 = a^3 + 3a^2b + 3ab^2 + b^3]$$
$$\therefore \quad y = 8x^3 - 12x^2 + 6x - 1$$
$$\frac{dy}{dx} = 24x^2 - 24x + 6 \qquad \text{.... (1)}$$

This is the long way.

By the other method:

$$y = (2x - 1)^3 = (\text{something})^3 \text{ where } (2x - 1) = (\text{something})$$

$$\frac{dy}{dx} = 3(\text{something})^2$$

$$= 3(2x - 1)^2$$

$$= 3(4x^2 - 4x + 1) \text{ using } (a + b)^2 = a^2 + 2ab + b^2$$

$$= 12x^2 - 12x + 3 \qquad \ldots\ldots (2)$$

which does not check with (1). WHY NOT?

The answer is, we have not been differentiating with respect to x, but with respect to the (something), so that we have not quite finished. We must differentiate the (something) w.r.t. x and multiply the answer obtained so far by this.

(Remember w.r.t. means with respect to.)

Now $\frac{d}{dx}(2x - 1) = 2$ .... (3)

and if we multiply (2) by this we obtain

$$\frac{dy}{dx} = 2(12x^2 - 12x + 3)$$

$$= 24x^2 - 24x + 6 \text{ which checks with (1)}$$

We note that the first example gave us the correct answer because the differential of the expression inside the bracket happened to be 1.

Now let us try the third example, by working it both ways.

FIRST METHOD

$$\text{Let } y = (5 - 3x)^2$$

$$= 25 - 30x + 9x^2$$

$$\frac{dy}{dx} = \mathbf{-30 + 18x}$$

SECOND METHOD

$$\text{Let } y = (5 - 3x)^2$$

$$\frac{dy}{dx} = 2(5 - 3x) \times (\text{the differential of what is inside the bracket})$$

$$= 2(5 - 3x) \times (-3)$$

$$= -6(5 - 3x)$$

$$= \mathbf{-30 + 18x}$$

We call this the **differential of a function of a function.** and expressed in symbols :

$$\frac{dy}{dx} = \frac{dy}{dz} \cdot \frac{dz}{dx}$$

where z represents the contents of a bracket or similar function.

Example. Find the differential coefficient of $\sqrt{(3x+1)}$

Let $y = \sqrt{(3x+1)} = (3x+1)^{1/2}$

$$\frac{dy}{dx} = \tfrac{1}{2}(3x+1)^{-1/2} \times \text{(differential of } 3x+1)$$

$$= \tfrac{1}{2}(3x+1)^{-1/2} \,.\, 3$$

$$\frac{dy}{dx} = \frac{3}{2\,.\,\sqrt{3x+1}}$$

This would be difficult to do by any other method.

Exercise 27. Examples of 'function of a function' differentiation. (Questions marked * may be left to a second reading.)

Find the differential coefficients of:

1(a) $(3x-2)^3$ 1(b) $(5-2x)^4$

2(a) $(3-x)^5$ 2(b) $(4+3x)^6$

3(a) $(x^3-2x+1)^2$ 3(b) $(3x^2+5x-1)^3$

4(a) $\sqrt{4x-1}$ 4(b) $\sqrt{1-2x}$

5(a) $\sqrt{ax+b}$ where a and b are constants

5(b) $\sqrt[3]{1-ax}$ $[=(1-ax)^{1/3}]$

*6(a) $\dfrac{1}{1-x}$ $[=(1-x)^{-1}]$ *6(b) $\dfrac{1}{2+3x}$

*7(a) $\dfrac{1}{3x+4}$ *7(b) $\dfrac{1}{3x^4-7}$

*8(a) $\dfrac{1}{x^3-a^3}$ *8(b) $[x-\sqrt{(1-x^2)}\,]^2$

*9 $(x+\dfrac{1}{x})^n$

OTHER TRICKS

Differentiation of a product

We need to know how to differentiate such expressions as:

$(2x+1)^2\ (1-5x)$ or $(2x+1)\sqrt{(x+5)}$

The rule for this is quite simple, namely:

To differentiate a product, multiply the second by the differential of the first and add the first multiplied by the differential of the second.

In symbols: **d(uv) = v du + udv**

where u, v are each functions of some other variable, e.g. x, and du and dv are the differentials of u and v with respect to x.

Example 1. Find the differential of $(3x + 4)(2x + 1)$
Here $u = 3x + 4$ and $du = 3$
$v = 2x + 1$ and $dv = 2$

$$\therefore \text{ the differential of } (3x + 4)(2x + 1) = (2x + 1).3 + (3x + 4).2$$
$$[= vdu + udv]$$
$$= 6x + 3 + 6x + 8$$
$$= \mathbf{12x + 11}$$

Check by multiplying out the brackets and differentiating term by term.

Example 2.

Find $\frac{d}{dx}(2x + 1) . \sqrt{(x + 5)} = \frac{d}{dx}(2x + 1)(x + 5)^{\frac{1}{2}}$

Here $u = (2x + 1)$ $\quad v = (x + 5)^{\frac{1}{2}}$
$du = 2$ $\quad dv = \frac{1}{2}(x + 5)^{-\frac{1}{2}}.1$

$$[d(uv) = vdu + udv]$$
$$d(uv) = (x + 5)^{\frac{1}{2}}. 2 + (2x + 1).\tfrac{1}{2}(x + 5)^{-\frac{1}{2}}.1$$
$$= 2(x + 5)^{\frac{1}{2}} + \tfrac{1}{2}(2x + 1)(x + 5)^{-\frac{1}{2}}$$
$$= 2(x + 5)^{\frac{1}{2}} + \frac{(2x + 1)}{2(x + 5)^{\frac{1}{2}}}$$
$$= \frac{4(x + 5)^{1} + (2x + 1)}{2(x + 5)^{\frac{1}{2}}}$$
$$= \frac{6x + 21}{2(x + 5)^{\frac{1}{2}}}$$
$$= \frac{\mathbf{6x + 21}}{\mathbf{2\sqrt{(x + 5)}}}$$

Differentiation of a quotient. This means one expression divided by another, for example, how do we work $\frac{d}{dx}\left[\frac{(x + 1)}{(x + 2)}\right]$?

We use a similar method to that for the differentiation of a product. It is a little more difficult and is expressed as follows:

differential of $\frac{\mathbf{u}}{\mathbf{v}} = \frac{\mathbf{vdu - udv}}{\mathbf{v^2}}$

where $\quad du = $ differential of top line

and $\quad dv = $ differential of bottom line

Example 1. Find the differential coefficient of $\dfrac{2x+1}{3x+2} = \dfrac{u}{v}$

$u = 2x+1,\ du = 2$

$v = 3x+2,\ dv = 3$

$$d\left(\frac{u}{v}\right) = \frac{vdu - udv}{v^2}$$

$$= \frac{(3x+2).2 - (2x+1).3}{(3x+2)^2}$$

$$= \frac{6x+4-6x-3}{(3x+2)^2}$$

$$= \frac{1}{(3x+2)^2}$$

Example 2. Differentiate

$$\frac{\sqrt{x^2+1}}{1-2x^2} = \frac{u}{v} = \frac{(x^2+1)^{\frac{1}{2}}}{1-2x^2}$$

$u = (x^2+1)^{\frac{1}{2}},\ du = \frac{1}{2}(x^2+1)^{-\frac{1}{2}}.\ 2$

$v = (1-2x^2),\ dv = -4x$

$$d\left(\frac{u}{v}\right) = \frac{v\,du - u\,dv}{v^2}$$

$$= \frac{(1-2x^2).\frac{1}{2}(x^2+1)^{-\frac{1}{2}}.2x - (x^2+1)^{\frac{1}{2}}.(-4x)}{(1-2x^2)^2}$$

$$= \frac{x(1-2x^2)(x^2+1)^{-\frac{1}{2}} + 4x(x^2+1)^{\frac{1}{2}}}{(1-2x^2)^2}$$

Multiplying numerator and denominator by $(x^2+1)^{\frac{1}{2}}$ in order to remove the negative power:

$$d\left(\frac{u}{v}\right) = \frac{x(1-2x^2) + 4x(x^2+1)}{(1-2x^2)^2.(x^2+1)^{\frac{1}{2}}}$$

$$= \frac{x - 2x^3 + 4x^3 + 4x}{(1-2x^2)^2.(x^2+1)^{\frac{1}{2}}} = \frac{5x + 2x^3}{(1-2x^2)^2(x^2+1)^{\frac{1}{2}}}$$

Now we can differentiate sums, differences, products and quotients of quite complicated functions involving powers of x.

You can now differentiate quite easily the following, provided you remember the basic rules:

1. $\frac{d}{dx}(x^n) = nx^{n-1}$

2. $\frac{d(uv)}{dx} = v\frac{du}{dx} + u\frac{dv}{dx}$ where u,v are functions of x.

3. $\frac{d}{dx}\left(\frac{u}{v}\right) = \frac{v\frac{du}{dx} - u\frac{dv}{dx}}{v^2}$

4. $\frac{d}{dx}(\text{something})^n = n(\text{something})^{n-1}$ x (the differential of the something inside the bracket)

Exercise 28. Differentiate the following w.r.t. the variable involved.
(N.B. Set your question down correctly,
e.g. in No.1 Let $y = x^2 + 5x + 1$
$\therefore \frac{dy}{dx} = \ \ldots$ etc.)

1. $x^2 + 5x + 1$

2. $(x^2 + 5x + 1)^3$

3. (a) $(x + 3)^{1/2}$; (b) $(2x + 3)^{1/2}$; (c) $\sqrt{1 - t^2}$

4. (a) $\sqrt[3]{(x + 1)}$ (b) $\sqrt[3]{(2x^2 + 1)}$

5. $(3x + 2)(5x - 1)$ (a) by use of the product rule;
(b) by working the brackets first.

6. $(x^2 + x + 1)(x^2 - x - 1)$

7. $3x.(x + 1)^5$

8. $2x^2 . (4x + 1)^3$

9. $(2x^2 + 7)\ (x + 1)^2$

10. $\sqrt{x}\ (x^2 - 3x + 2)$

11. $\dfrac{x + 1}{x - 1}$

12. $\dfrac{2x^2 + 4}{3x - 2}$

13. $\dfrac{a + x}{a - x}$ (a = a constant)

*14. $\dfrac{(2t^{1/2} + 1)}{2t^{1/2}}$

15. $\dfrac{(x^2 + x - 1)}{(x^2 - x + 1)}$

*16. $\dfrac{2t}{\sqrt{1 - t^2}}$

17. $\dfrac{t^2}{(1 + t)^2}$

*18. $\dfrac{1}{\sqrt{ax + b}}$

Chapter 9
Integration or the reverse process

Having learnt to differentiate successfully, it is a logical step to reverse the process.

When we differentiate a given function we are finding the gradient of the tangent at any point on the graph of the function. Conversely, if we know the gradient of the tangent at every point on a curve, can we find the equation of the curve?

Graphically, we are asking the following:

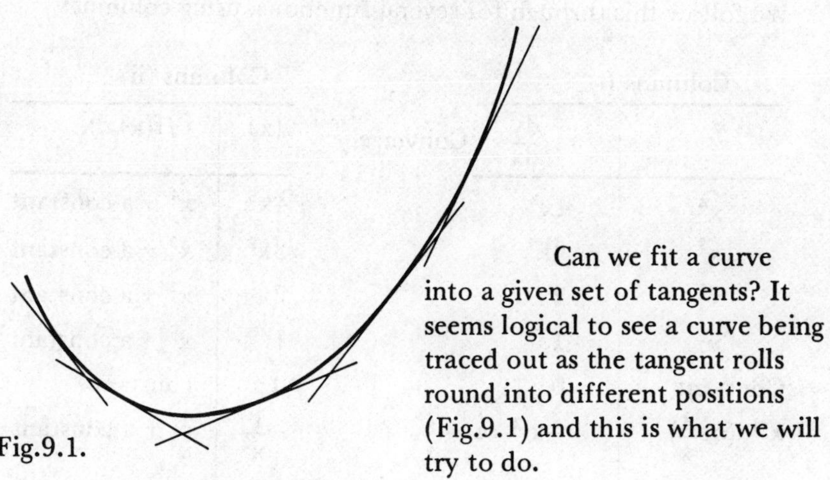

Fig.9.1.

Can we fit a curve into a given set of tangents? It seems logical to see a curve being traced out as the tangent rolls round into different positions (Fig.9.1) and this is what we will try to do.

Thus, differentiating x^3 gives us $3x^2$
so that the reverse, i.e. integrating $3x^2$ with respect to x, gives us x^3

We are asking ourselves: 'If $y = x^3$ and $\frac{dy}{dx} = 3x^2$

then if $\frac{dy}{dx} = 3x^2$

does it follow that $y = x^3$?'

It seems that the easiest method is to check the answer x^3 and see if it gives $\frac{dy}{dx} = 3x^2$, which of course it does.

But is this the only answer? Can you think of any other value for y which when we differentiate it gives $3x^2$? What about $x^3 + 4$ or $x^3 + 10$ or $x^3 - 7$ or $x^3 \pm$ any constant? Yes, the complete answer is x^3 + a constant since the differential of a constant is zero, and we write $\int 3x^2\,dx = x^3$ + a constant and we read it as 'the integral of $3x^2\,dx = x^3$ + a constant' or 'the integral of $3x^2$ with respect to $x = x^3$ + a constant.

Note: The integral sign, $\int$, is the old-fashioned elongated 's', signifying the verb 'sum', which we shall see later is another way of viewing integration.

We follow this through for several functions, using columns:

Columns (i)

y	$\frac{dy}{dx}$
x^4	$4x^3$
x^3	$3x^2$
x^2	$2x$
x	1
Constant	0
x^{-1} (or $\frac{1}{x}$)	$-x^{-2}$ or $-\frac{1}{x^2}$
x^{-2} (or $\frac{1}{x^2}$)	$-2x^{-3}$ or $-\frac{2}{x^2}$

Conversely:

Columns (ii)

f(x)	$\int f(x)\,dx$
$4x^3$	x^4 + a constant
$3x^2$	x^3 + a constant
$2x$	x^2 + a constant
1	x + a constant
0	constant
$-\frac{1}{x^2}$	$\frac{1}{x}$ + a constant
$-\frac{2}{x^3}$	$\frac{1}{x^2}$ + a constant

In general

x^n	$n\,x^{n-1}$		$n\,x^{n-1}$	x^n
$\dfrac{x^{n+1}}{n+1}$	x^n		x^n	$\dfrac{x^{n+1}}{n+1}$

But if we divide the columns of (ii) by the various coefficients we obtain the following:

f(x)	∫ f(x) dx
x^3	$x^4/4$ + constant (dividing both columns by 4)*
x^2	$x^3/3$ + constant (dividing both columns by 3)
x	$x^2/2$ + constant (dividing both columns by 2)
1	$x^1/1$ + a constant (dividing both columns by 1)
0	a constant
$\dfrac{1}{x^2}$	$-\dfrac{1}{x}$ + a constant (changing signs)
$\dfrac{1}{x^3}$	$-\dfrac{1}{2x^2}$ + a constant (changing signs and dividing by 2)

*Note that when we divide a constant by any number it is still a constant.

We can now see that all these are of the following pattern:

$$\int x^n\,dx = \frac{x^{n+1}}{n+1} + \text{constant} \qquad n \neq -1$$

Important Note: We cannot yet integrate $\frac{1}{x}$, i.e. x^{-1}, since in this case $n = -1$. This makes $n + 1 = 0$ and the above formula cannot be applied. We will see how to do this in Chapter 13. (pp 177-180)

In other words: **To integrate a power of x increase the power by 1 and divide by the same number.**

e.g. $\int x^5\,dx = \dfrac{x^{5+1}}{5+1} + \text{constant} = \dfrac{x^6}{6} + c$

Exercise 29. Integrate the following functions of x:
(N.B. write each question down carefully like this:

(i) $\int x^7\,dx = \frac{x^8}{8} + c$

or

(ii) $\int \sqrt[3]{x}\,dx = \int x^{\frac{1}{3}}\,dx = \frac{x^{\frac{1}{3}+1}}{(\frac{1}{3}+1)} + c = \frac{3x^{\frac{4}{3}}}{4} + c$

1. x^6; x^{10}; x^9; x^2; x; 1; 0; $x^{1.4}$; $x^{-1.4}$

2. $\frac{1}{x^3}$, $\frac{1}{x^4}$, $\frac{1}{x^5}$, $\frac{1}{x^6}$;

3. $x^{\frac{1}{2}}$; $\frac{1}{\sqrt{x}}$; $\frac{5}{x^2}$

4. $x^2 + x$; $x^3 - a^3$; $ax^2 + bx + c$ where a, b, c are constants.

5. $3x^2 + 2x - 1$; $5 - x^3 + 2x^2 - x$; $5x^{\frac{1}{2}} + 2x^{\frac{3}{2}}$

(N.B. (i) Check your answers carefully, by differentiating each of them to see that you get back to what you were given.)

(ii) Did you remember the constant of integration each time? This is very important as we shall see later.

ANOTHER WAY OF VIEWING INTEGRATION

In the same way that a differential coefficient, $\frac{dy}{dx}$, can be viewed as:

1. the rate of change of y with respect to x;

or

2. the gradient of the tangent at the point (x,y) to the curve y = f(x), so also, the integral of a function can be viewed in two different ways, namely:

either

1. given the gradient of a curve at every point x, find the equation of the curve, that is, the converse of differentiation (actually a set of curves).

e.g. $\int 3x^2\,dx = x^3 + c$ where c is a constant;

2. As the sum of all such products y.δx as δx approaches zero. We can express this in the form

$$\lim_{\delta x \to 0} \Sigma\, y\delta x = \int y\, dx$$

We read this as: 'the limit as δx approaches nought of sigma y delta x' The symbol Σ is used here for adding up a big number of small bits.

We have mentioned previously that the sign $\int$ is a long S, meaning "find the sum of all such things as."

$\int$dx means 'add up all the little bits of x', which obviously gives a whole x. (Fig. 9.2.)

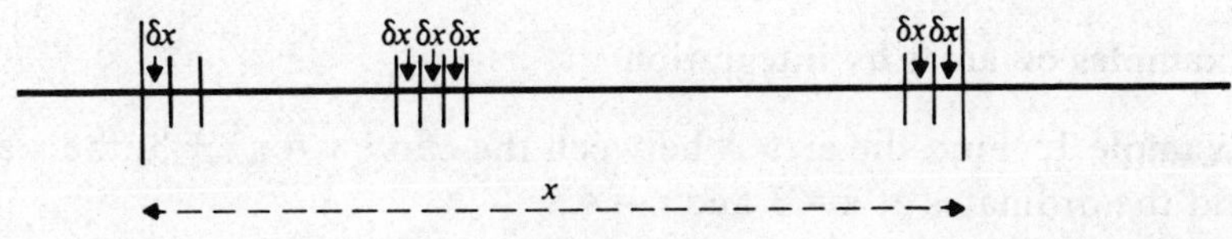

Figure 9.2

AREAS - DEFINITE INTEGRALS

A good example of the second way of viewing an integral is its application to the evaluation of the area between a curve and the x axis, (Fig. 9.3.)

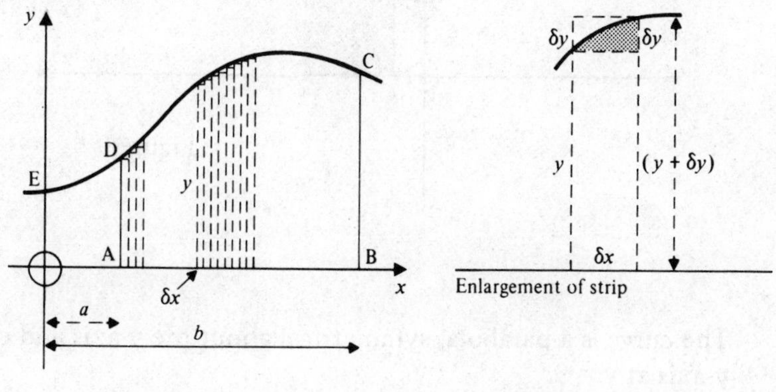

Figure 9.3 (i) Figure 9.3 (ii)

How do we use it?

Take the example of the area ABCD illustrated in Fig. 9.3.
When we need to evaluate the area ABCD the instruction

$$\int_a^b y\,dx \quad \text{means}$$

'find the integral of ydx between the lower limit a and the upper limit b'. In other words, we do not require the area OADE between the origin, 0, and A.
But area ABCD = area OBCE - area OADE. This is saying that the area required is the difference between the integral worked out for the upper limit and the integral worked out for the lower limit.

Some examples will illustrate the method.

Examples on areas by integration

Example 1. Find the area A between the curve $y = x^2 + 3$, the x axis, and the ordinates at $x = 1$ and $x = 4$

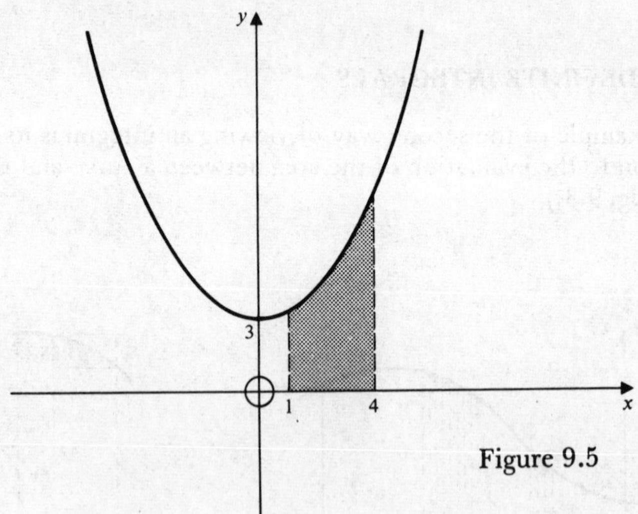

Figure 9.5

The curve is a parabola, symmetrical about the y-axis and cutting the y-axis at y = 3.

To find an area such as ABCD we divide the area into narrow strips of width δx and height y, a few of which are shown in Figure 9.3(i). The area required is the sum of the areas of these strips. Each of these strips can be seen as a rectangle plus a small area just under the curve. (See shaded area in Figure 9.3(ii).)

If we add the areas of the rectangles, we obtain an area approximately equal to the area ABCD, but with a serrated top instead of a smooth curve.

Now imagine the strips becoming narrower until they become merely the thickness of a fine line as in Figure 9.4, in which only a few have been drawn.

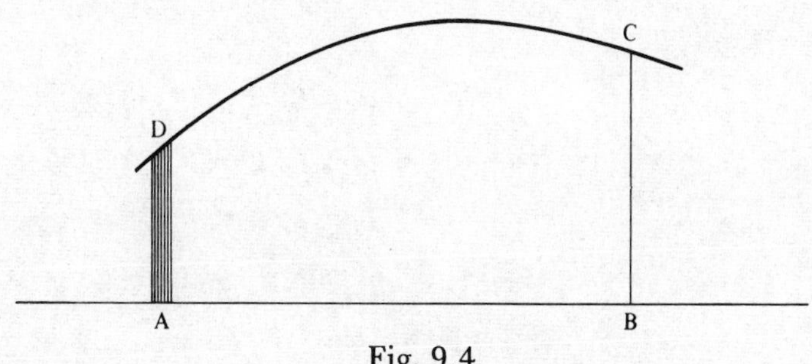

Fig. 9.4

We see that if enough of these lines are drawn they will fill the whole area, and as δx becomes even smaller, and the number of strips becomes correspondingly larger, the serrated edge becomes indistinguishable from the curve itself. In this way we see that the area required is the sum of the areas of a very large number of very narrow rectangles of area $y\,\delta x$ and we say that

the area of ABCD = the limit of the sum of all such areas $y\,\delta x$ as δx approaches zero

or (as explained on page 101), in mathematical shorthand

the area of ABCD $= \lim \Sigma y\,\delta x$ as $\delta x \to 0$

i.e. Area ABCD = = $\int y\,\delta x$ between the limits x = a and x = b

or Area ABCD $= \int_a^b y\,dx$

When we write an integral in this form i.e. between definite limits we call it a **definite integral.**

Acknowledgements
We are are indebted to the following for permission to reproduce copyright material:

John Wiley & Sons, Inc. for table (Appendix 9) from *Reliability Technology* by A. E. Green and A. J. Bourne

$A = \int(x^2 + 3)\,dx$ between the limits x = 1 and x = 4
and we say

$$A = \int_1^4 (x^3 + 3)\,dx.$$ (This is a definite integral.)

$$= \left[\frac{x^4}{4} + 3x + \text{constant}\right]_1^4$$

This means that we substitute, first x = 4 and then x = 1 and subtract the second from the first as follows:

$$A = \left[\frac{4^4}{4} + 3.4 + \text{constant}\right] - \left[\frac{1^4}{4} + (3 \cdot 1) + \text{constant}\right]$$

$$= 64 + 12 + C \qquad - \tfrac{1}{4} - 3 - C$$

(We note that the constant of integration will always cancel out for a definite integral, and it is therefore not necessary to put it in. For an indefinite integral, i.e. without limits,we must include a constant of integration.)

∴ A = 72¾ square units.

Example 2. Find the areas of the two loops enclosed between the curve $y = (x - 1)(x + 2)(x - 3)$ and the x axis.

We note that this is a cubic curve and therefore has two bends.
To find where it cuts the x axis put y = 0.
i.e. $0 = (x - 1)(x + 2)(x - 3)$

$x = +1$ or -2 or $+3$

To find where it cuts the y axis put x = 0
$y = (-1)(+2)(-3) = +6$
A sketch of the curve is therefore as in fig. 9.6,giving the shaded areas required, ABC and CDE.

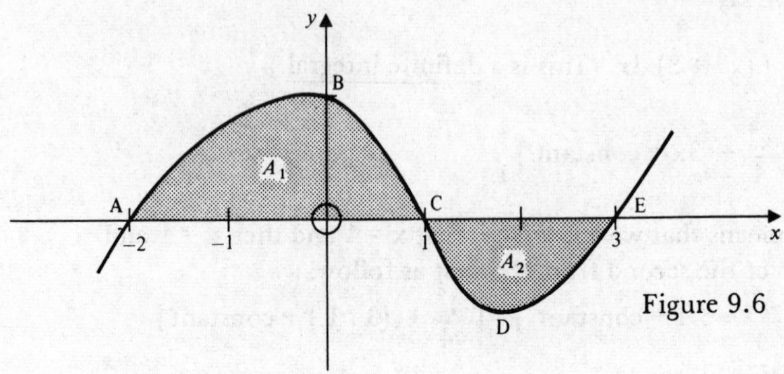

Figure 9.6

So that area ABC, $(A_1) = \int y\,dx$ between limits x = − 2 to + 1.

But $y = (x-1)(x+2)(x-3)$

$= (x-1)(x^2 - x - 6)$ (working out the last two brackets)

$= x^3 - x^2 - 6x - x^2 + x + 6$ (multiplying the second bracket by x and − 1)

$$y = x^3 - 2x^2 - 5x + 6$$

$$A_1 = \int_{-2}^{+1} (x^3 - 2x^2 - 5x + 6)\,dx$$

$$= \left[\frac{x^4}{4} - \frac{2x^3}{3} - \frac{5x^2}{2} + 6x\right]_{-2}^{+1}$$

$$= \left[\frac{1}{4} - \frac{2}{3} - \frac{5}{2} + 6\right] - \left[\frac{(-2)^4}{4} - 2.\frac{(-2)^3}{3} - \frac{5(-2)^2}{2} - 12\right]$$

$$= 3\frac{1}{12} - \left[\frac{16}{4} + \frac{16}{3} - 10 - 12\right]$$

$$= 3\frac{1}{12} - 5\frac{1}{3} + 18$$

= 15¾ square units

Area CDE (A_2) = $\int y\,dx$ between limits x = 1 to 3.

$$A_2 = \left[\frac{x^4}{4} - \frac{2x^3}{3} - \frac{5x^2}{2} + 6x\right]_1^3$$

$$= \left[\frac{3^4}{4} - \frac{2.3^3}{3} - \frac{5.3^2}{2} + 6.3\right] - \left[\frac{1.^4}{4} - \frac{2.1^3}{3} - \frac{5.1^3}{2} + 6.1\right]$$

$$= \left[\frac{81}{4} - 18 - \frac{45}{2} + 18\right] - \left[\frac{1}{4} - \frac{2}{3} - \frac{5}{2} + 6\right]$$

$$= \frac{81}{4} - \frac{45}{2} - \frac{1}{4} + \frac{2}{3} + \frac{5}{2} - 6$$

$$= \frac{80}{4} - \frac{40}{2} + \frac{2}{3} - 6$$

$$= -5\frac{1}{3} \text{ square units.}$$

Can you suggest a reason for the negative sign?
Yes, because the area is below the x axis, and the heights of all the small strips are therefore negative.
But we say area CDE $= 5\frac{1}{3}$ square units

Exercise 30.

1. Find $\int_{-2}^{+3} y\,dx$ for the previous example.

Would you expect this result?

Evaluate the following (in each case make a sketch of the curve);

2. The area between the curve $y = x^2 - x - 2$ and the x axis
3. The area of the trapezium bounded by the line y = 2x + 3 and the ordinates at x = 1 and x = 3.
4. The area between the curve $y = x^2$, the x axis, and the ordinates at x = – 1 and x = + 1.
5. The areas of the loops formed by the curve y = x(x + 1)(x – 2) and the x axis.

The potential at any point in an electric field due to a point charge.

Definition. The potential energy of a unit positive charge placed at any point in an electric field is called the electric potential at that point. It is usually defined as the work done per unit charge, needed to bring a small positive charge from infinity to that point against the electric intensity.
Intensity is the negative potential gradient at that point.
The intensity E at distance x from a charge of q units is $E = \frac{q}{x^2}$ in air and $E = -\frac{dV}{dx}$ where V is the potential energy.

$\therefore$ Potential energy $V = -\int_{\infty}^{r} \frac{q}{x^2}\,dx$ where r is the distance from the charge.

$$= +\left[\frac{q}{x}\right]_{\infty}^{r}$$

$$= \frac{q}{r} - \frac{q}{\infty}$$

$$V = \frac{q}{r} - 0 = \frac{q}{r}$$

giving the potential at any point in an electric field due to a point charge q.
Note: In the S.I. system of units $V = \frac{q}{4\pi\epsilon r}$ where ϵ is the permittivity of free space.

Work done in stretching an elastic string or spring

Hooke's Law

Hooke's Law states that the tension in an elastic spring or string is proportional to the extension.

That is; $T = \frac{\lambda}{l} . x$
Now, the work done in stretching the spring a small distance δx is approximately $T. \delta x$ (force x distance)

T = tension
λ = modulus of elasticity
l = natural length
x = extension

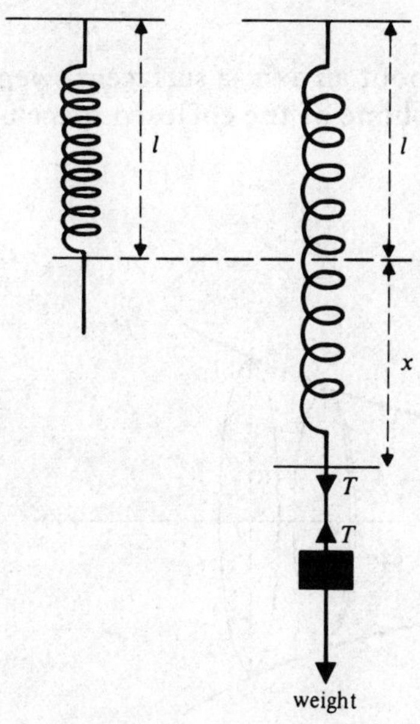

Fig. 9.7.

$\therefore$ total work done $= \int_0^a T\,dx$ where a is the distance stretched from the natural length

$$= \int_0^a \frac{\lambda}{l} \cdot x\,dx \quad (\lambda, l \text{ are constants})$$

$$= \left[\frac{\lambda}{l}\frac{x^2}{2}\right]_0^a$$

$$= \tfrac{1}{2}\frac{\lambda}{l}(a^2 - 0^2)$$

$$= \tfrac{1}{2}\frac{\lambda a^2}{l}$$

This is the potential energy of the stretched string.

Solids of Revolution

If a curve is rotated about an axis, a surface is swept out, and it is possible to find the volume of the enclosed space by integration as follows:

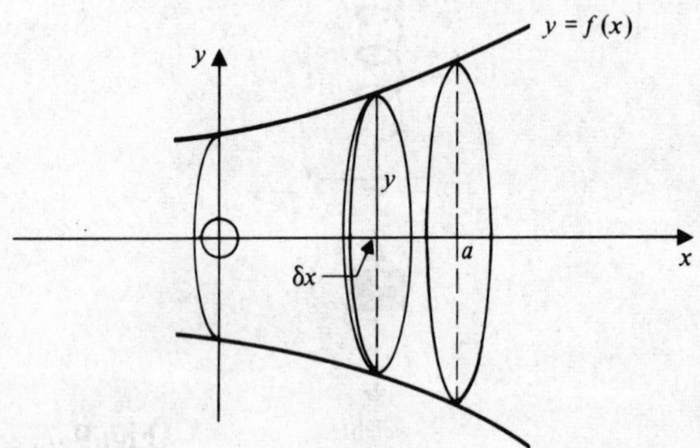

Figure 9.8

Consider any curve, $y = f(x)$. Let this be rotated round the x axis between the limits $x = 0$ and $x = a$. The solid generated is shown in figure 9.8.
Consider a small circular slice of thickness δx and radius y, taken at right angles to the x axis, anywhere within the solid.
Then the volume of the slice $\triangleq \pi y^2 \delta x$, since the slice is approximately a cylinder, radius y and height δx.
$\therefore$ An element of volume, $\delta V \triangleq \pi y^2 \ \delta x$

Summing these elements we get

$$\int dV = \pi \int y^2 \ dx \text{ from } x = 0 \text{ to } x = a$$

as $\delta x \to 0$, the errors due to approximation disappear.

$$\therefore \quad V = \pi \int_{x=0}^{x=a} y^2 \ dx$$

Let us use this fact in a few examples.

Example 1. Prove that the volume of any right cone is $\frac{1}{3}$ X area of base X height.
A right cone is a solid of circular cross-section, with its axis at right angles to the circular base as shown in figure 9.9.

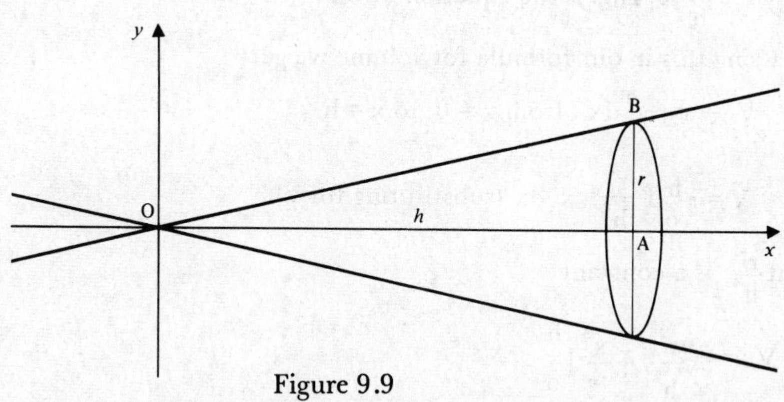

Figure 9.9

To prove $V = \frac{1}{3}\pi r^2 h$, where OA = h, AB = r.
Turning the cone on its side, we can generate the cone by rotating the correct line round the x axis.
We must know the equation of the line. We find this as follows: (Figure 9.10)

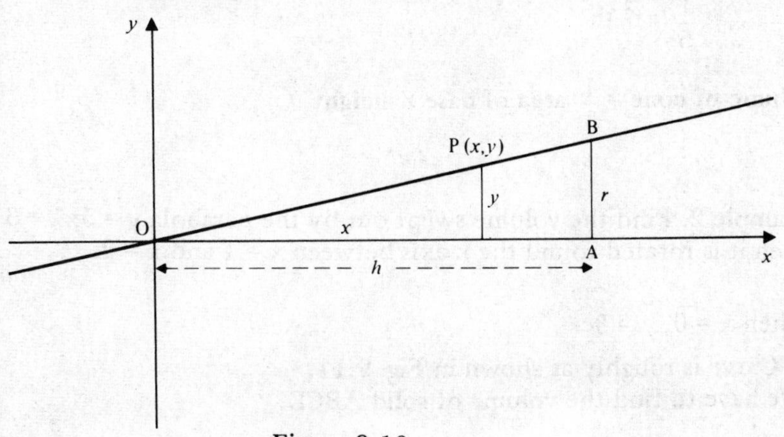

Figure 9.10

Let P be any point on the line with co-ordinates (x,y)
Then the gradient of the line is $\frac{y}{x}$ or $\frac{r}{h}$

$$\therefore \frac{y}{x} = \frac{r}{h}$$

$$\therefore y = \frac{r}{h}.x$$ This is the equation of OB.

∴ Using this in our formula for volume we get:

$$V = \pi \int y^2 dx \quad \text{from } x = 0 \text{ to } x = h.$$

$$V = \pi \int_o^h \frac{r^2}{h^2} . x^2 dx \text{ (substituting for y)}$$

But $\frac{r^2}{h^2}$ is a constant

$$\therefore V = \frac{\pi r^2}{h^2} \left[\frac{x^3}{3}\right]_o^h$$

$$= \frac{\pi r^2}{h^2} \left[\frac{h^3}{3} - 0\right]$$

$$= \frac{\pi r^2 h}{3}$$

$$= \frac{1}{3} (\pi r^2)h$$

Volume of cone = $\frac{1}{3}$ area of base × height

Example 2. Find the volume swept out by the parabola $y = 5x^2 + 3$ when it is rotated round the x axis between x = 1 and x = 2.

When x = 0, y = 3

∴ Curve is roughly as shown in Fig. 9.11.
We have to find the volume of solid ABCD.

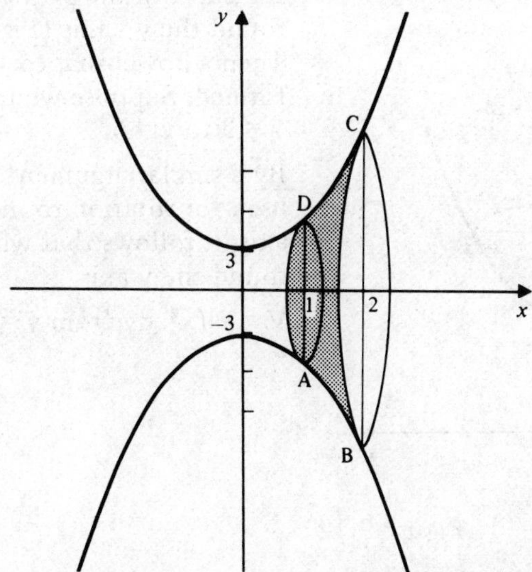

Figure 9.11

$$V = \pi \int y^2 \, dx \quad \text{from } x = 1 \text{ to } x = 2$$

$$= \pi \int_1^2 (5x^2 + 3)^2 \, dx$$

$$= \pi \int_1^2 (25x^4 + 30x^2 + 9) \, dx \quad \text{using } (a + b)^2 = a^2 + 2ab + b^2$$

$$= \pi \left[\frac{25x^5}{5} + \frac{30x^3}{3} + 9x \right]_1^2$$

$$= \pi \left[5x^5 + 10x^3 + 9x \right]_1^2$$

$$= \pi [5.32 + 10.8 + 18] - \pi [5 + 10 + 9]$$

$$= \pi [258 - 24]$$

$= \pi$ [234] **cubic units.**

Example 3. Rotation around the y - axis. Suppose we rotate the curve in the previous example round the y - axis (Fig.9.12). Then a bowel-shaped volume is formed. Suppose we take limits $y = 3$ to $y = 5$.

By a similar argument to that used for rotation round the x axis, it follows that when rotating round the y axis

$V = \pi \int x^2 \; dy$ from $y = 3$ to $y = 5$

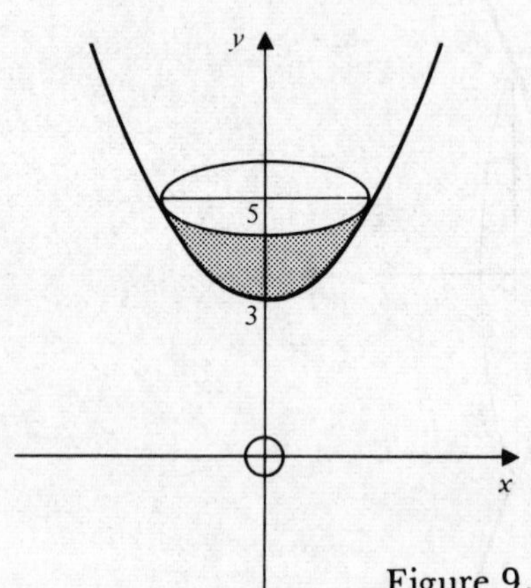

Figure 9.12

$$\text{But} \quad y = 5x^2 + 3$$

$$\therefore \quad y - 3 = 5x^2$$

$$\therefore \quad \frac{y-3}{5} = x^2$$

$$\therefore \quad V = \frac{\pi}{5}\int_3^5 (y-3)\,dy$$

(Note that a constant factor can be taken outside the integral sign).

$$\therefore \; V = \frac{\pi}{5}\left[\frac{y^2}{2} - 3y\right]_3^5$$

$$= \frac{\pi}{5}\left[\frac{25}{2} - 15\right] - \frac{\pi}{5}\left[\frac{9}{2} - 9\right]$$

$$= \frac{\pi}{5}\left[-2\tfrac{1}{2} + 4\tfrac{1}{2}\right]$$

$$= \frac{\pi}{5} \cdot 2$$

$$\therefore \; \mathbf{V} = \frac{2\pi}{5} \; \textbf{cubic units.}$$

Exercise 31. Examples on volumes of solids of revolution.

Find the volumes generated when the areas under the given curves, between the given values of x, are rotated round the x axis. In each case sketch the curve (or straight line) first. Leave answers in terms of π.

1. $y = x$ from $x = 2$ to $x = 4$
2. $2y = x + 3$; $x = 0$ to $x = 8$
3. $y = x^2$; $x = 0$ to $x = 5$
4. $y = x(1 - x)$; $x = 0$ to $x = 1$

Chapter 10

Revision and wider applications

We must now turn aside for the moment from our study of calculus in order to revise and extend our knowledge of trigonometry. But first some revision.

The following are the definitions of the sine, cosine and tangent of an angle less than 90°. In any right-angled triangle ABC (Fig.10.1) if $\angle B = 90°$ then :

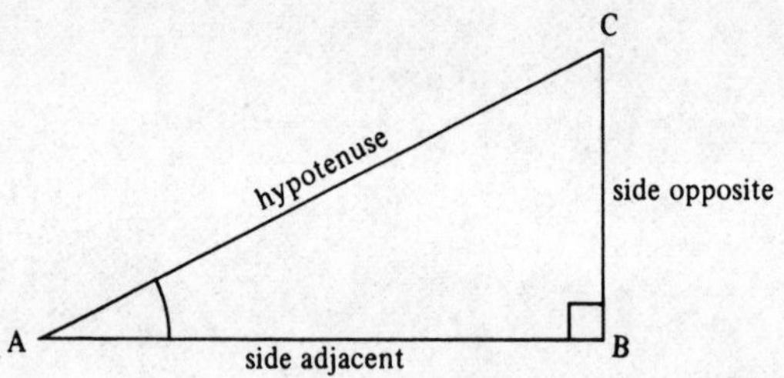

Fig.10.1.

CB is the side opposite $\angle A$

AC is the hypotenuse

AB is the side adjacent to $\angle A$

The definitions are :

$$\sin A = \frac{\text{side opposite}}{\text{hypotenuse}} = \frac{o}{h}$$

$$\cos A = \frac{\text{side adjacent}}{\text{hypotenuse}} = \frac{a}{h}$$

$$\tan A = \frac{\text{side opposite}}{\text{side adjacent}} = \frac{o}{a}$$

Many people find it difficult to remember these.

One jingle which may help is as follows:

(s) o h (c) a h (t) o a
'Silly Old Horses Can Always Have Tons of Apples'

RESUMÉ OF TRIGONOMETRY FORMULAE.

Definitions

$$\sin A = \frac{\text{opposite}}{\text{hypotenuse}} \qquad \text{cosec} = \frac{1}{\sin}$$

$$\cos A = \frac{\text{adjacent}}{\text{hypotenuse}} \qquad \sec = \frac{1}{\cos}$$

$$\tan A = \frac{\text{opposite}}{\text{adjacent}} \qquad \cot = \frac{1}{\tan}$$

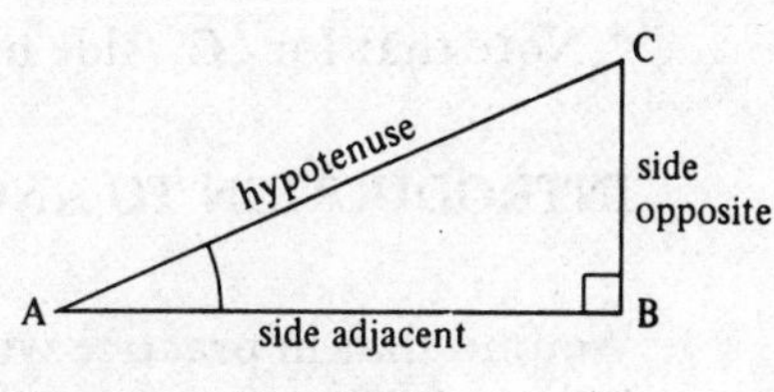

Fig.10.2.

To prove $\frac{\sin A}{\cos A} = \tan A$

$$\left.\begin{aligned} \sin A &= \frac{a}{b} \\ \cos A &= \frac{c}{b} \\ \tan A &= \frac{a}{c} \end{aligned}\right] \therefore \quad \begin{aligned} \frac{\sin A}{\cos A} &= \frac{a}{b} \div \frac{c}{b} \\ &= \frac{a}{\not b_1} \times \frac{\not b^1}{c} \\ &= \frac{a}{c} \\ &= \tan A \end{aligned}$$

$$\therefore \quad \frac{\sin A}{\cos A} = \tan A$$

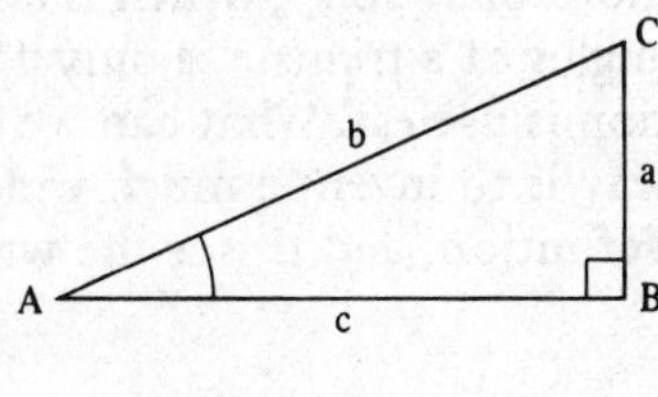

Fig.10.3.

(We label the side opposite $\angle A$ as a, etc.)

To prove $\sin^2 A + \cos^2 A = 1$;

$$\sin^2 A + \cos^2 A = \frac{a^2}{b^2} + \frac{c^2}{b^2}$$

$$= \frac{a^2 + c^2}{b^2}$$

$$= \frac{b^2}{b^2} \quad \text{(Pythagoras' theorem)}$$

$$\sin^2 A + \cos^2 A = 1$$

Also $\sin A = \frac{a}{b} = \cos C$*

$\cos A = \frac{c}{b} = \sin C$

i.e. $\sin A = \cos (90° - A)$
and $\cos A = \sin (90° - A)$

or: **In a right-angled triangle, the sine of one angle equals the cosine of the other.**

* Note that for ∠C, side opposite = AB, side adjacent = BC

INTRODUCTION TO ANGLES OF ANY MAGNITUDE.

We find that in practice we have to deal with angles greater than 90°, in fact angles of any magnitude. Now for an angle of this type, the previous definitions for sine, cosine and tangent do not make sense. How can we have an angle greater than 90° in a right-angled triangle? This would make the sum of two angles more than 180°, which is absurd, since the sum of the three angles of a triangle is only 180°. Therefore the previous definition is useless. What can we do in this situation? The simplest way is to invent a much wider definition to include the previous definition, and this is the way we do it:

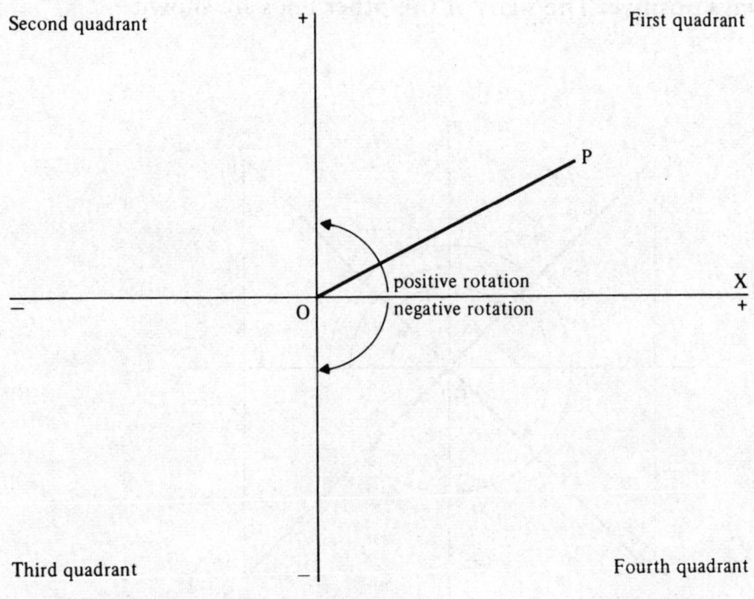

Fig.10.4.

We take axes as usual, and let a positive line OP rotate around the origin O, from OX (Fig.10.4).

Anticlockwise is the **positive** direction.
Clockwise is the **negative** direction.

Distances along the axes are measured positive and negative as shown, in the conventional manner.

Let us take various positions for our rotating radius OP_1, OP_2 OP_3, OP_4 in the various quadrants (Fig.10.5).

For simplicity we have taken symmetrical positions. OP is always positive. The signs of the other lines are shown.

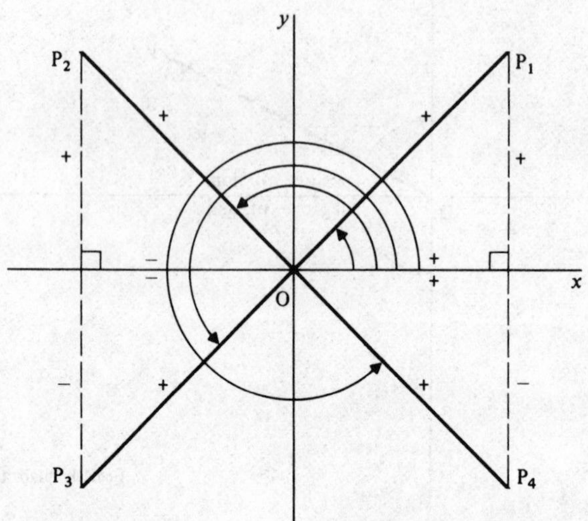

Fig.10.5.

DEFINITION OF TRIGONOMETRIC RATIOS FOR ANGLES OF ANY MAGNITUDE

Consider a positive radius OP, rotating anticlockwise from base-line OX, through $\angle\Theta$ (theta) (Fig.10.6).
Draw PL perpendicular to OX.

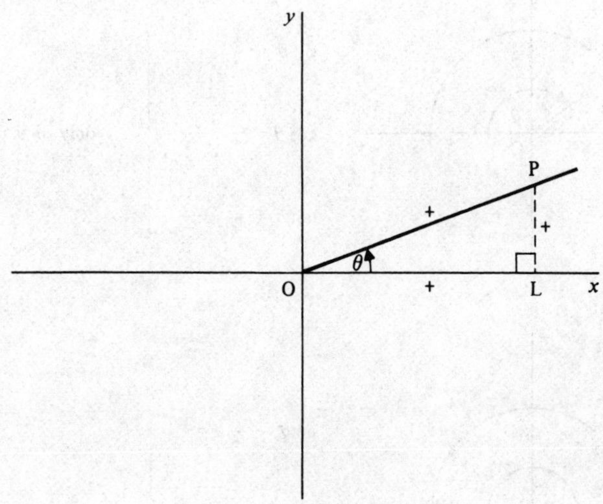

Fig.10.6.

Definitions for any position of P,

sin Θ is defined as $\frac{PL}{OP}$, cos Θ is defined as $\frac{OL}{OP}$

tan Θ is defined as $\frac{PL}{OL}$

Note: **OP is always positive**

First quadrant — Sin, cos, tan, all positive as in the old definition

Second quadrant — From definitions, considering the signs only:

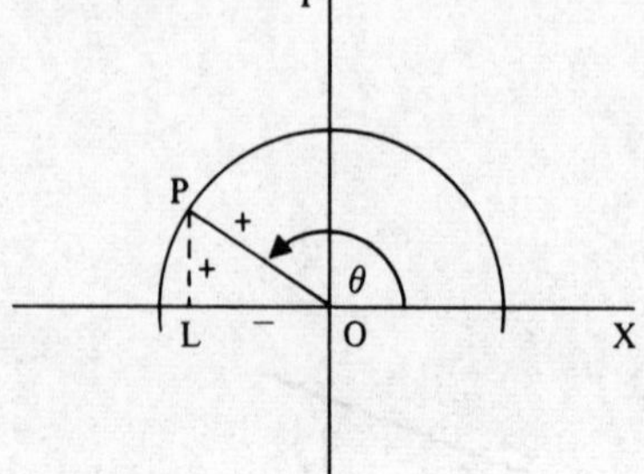

$\sin\theta = \frac{+}{+} = +$

$\cos\theta = \frac{-}{+} = -$

$\tan\theta = \frac{+}{-} = -$

only sin is positive

Third quadrant

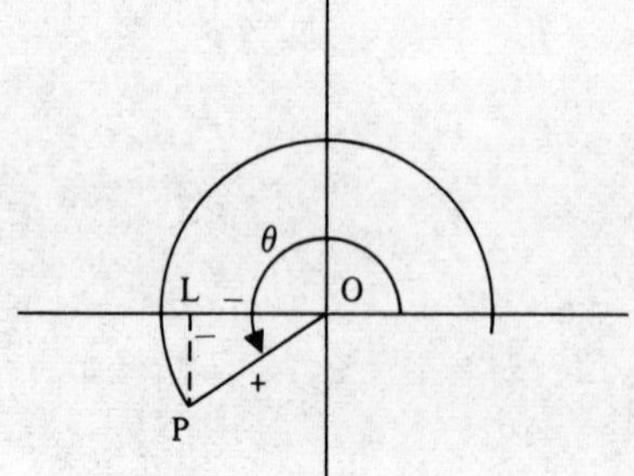

$\sin\theta = \frac{-}{+} = -$

$\cos\theta = \frac{-}{+} = -$

$\tan\theta = \frac{-}{-} = +$

only tan is positive

Fourth quadrant

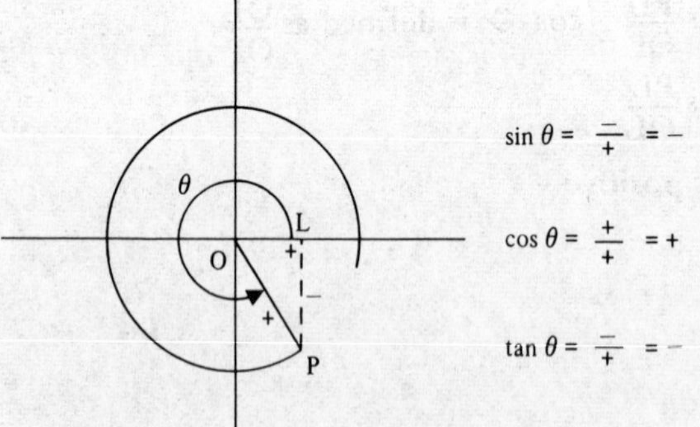

$\sin\theta = \frac{-}{+} = -$

$\cos\theta = \frac{+}{+} = +$

$\tan\theta = \frac{-}{+} = -$

only cos is positive

Fig.10.7.

Briefly

2nd QUADRANT	1st QUADRANT
ONLY	
SIN	ALL
POSITIVE	POSITIVE
ONLY	ONLY
TAN	COS
POSITIVE	POSITIVE
3rd QUADRANT	4th QUADRANT

Abbreviated to:

S	A
T	C

Meaning of $\sin^{-1}$, $\cos^{-1}$, $\tan^{-1}$

$\Theta = \sin^{-1}\frac{4}{5}$ means: 'Θ is the acute angle whose sine is $\frac{4}{5}$' (Fig.10.8)

i.e. $\sin\Theta = \frac{4}{5}$

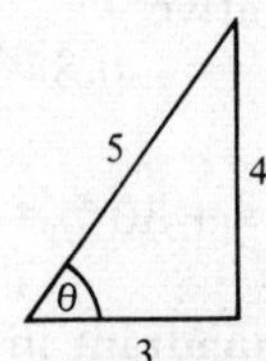

Figure 10.8

Similarly for $\cos^{-1}$. $\tan^{-1}$

$\Theta = \cos^{-1}\frac{3}{5}$ means: 'Θ is the acute angle whose cosine is $\frac{3}{5}$'

Examples. (Angles of any magnitude).

Find the values of the following:

(i)	$\sin 210^{\circ}$	(ii)	$\cos 210^{\circ}$
(iii)	$\tan 210^{\circ}$	(iv)	$\sin 135^{\circ}$
(v)	$\cos 130^{\circ}$	(vi)	$\tan 210^{\circ}$

(i)

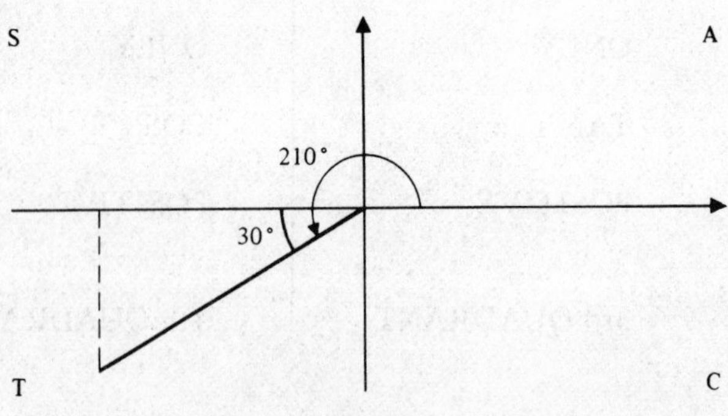

Figure 10.9.

210° is in the third quadrant, in which only tan is positive

$\therefore$ We know $\sin 210^{\circ}$ is negative

We then find the acute angle with the x axis, in this case 30° since $210^{\circ} = 180^{\circ} + 30^{\circ}$.

$\mathbf{\sin 210^{\circ} = -\sin 30^{\circ} = -0.5000}$ **from tables**

N.B. The acute angles used are always taken with the x axis, in order to convert for use of tables.

(ii) $\cos 210^{\circ}$ is also negative
$\cos 210^{\circ} = -\cos 30^{\circ} = -0.8660$

(iii) $\tan 210^{\circ}$ is positive
$\tan 210^{\circ} = \tan (180^{\circ} + 30^{\circ}) = +\tan 30^{\circ} = +0.5774$

(iv) 135° is the second quadrant in which only sin is positive
$\therefore \sin 135^{\circ} = \sin (180^{\circ} - 45^{\circ}) = +\sin 45^{\circ}$ (taking angle with x axis = 45°)

$= +0.7071$

(v) cos 130° (in second quadrant) is negative

$$\therefore \cos 130^{o} = \cos(180^{o} - 50^{o}) = -\cos 50^{o} = \mathbf{-0.6428}$$

(vi) tan 310° (in fourth quadrant) is negative

$$\tan 310^{o} = \tan(360^{o} - 50^{o}) = -\tan 50^{o} = \mathbf{-1.1918}$$

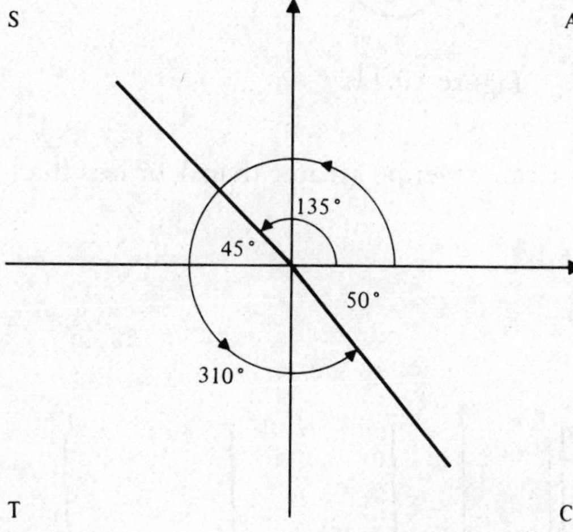

Figure 10.10

Graphs of trigonometrical ratios

y = sin x

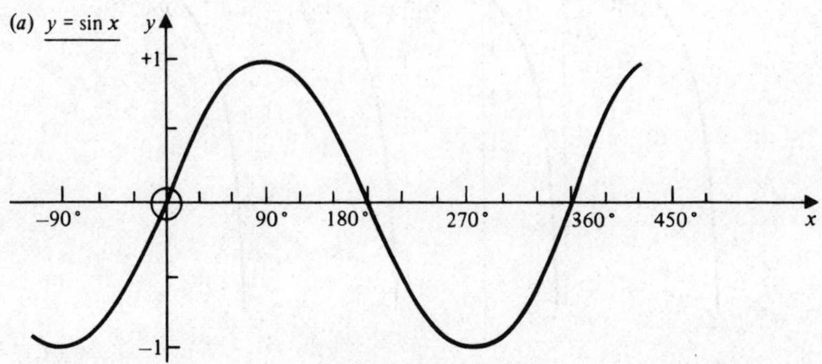

y = cos x

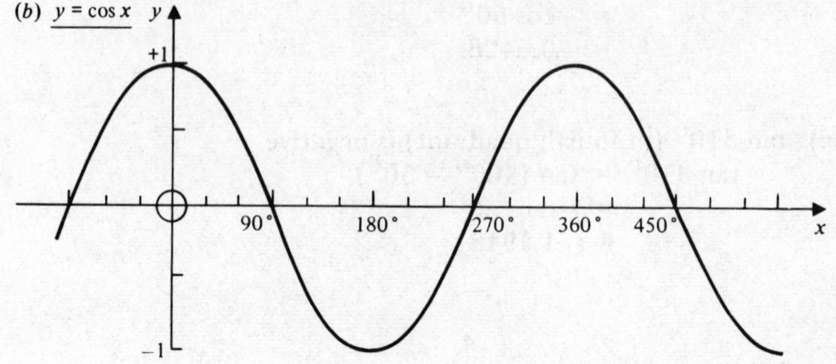

Figure 10.11.

N.B. sin x and cos x can never be greater than 1 or less than − 1

$$-1 \leqslant \begin{matrix} \sin x \\ \cos x \end{matrix} \leqslant +1$$

y = tan x

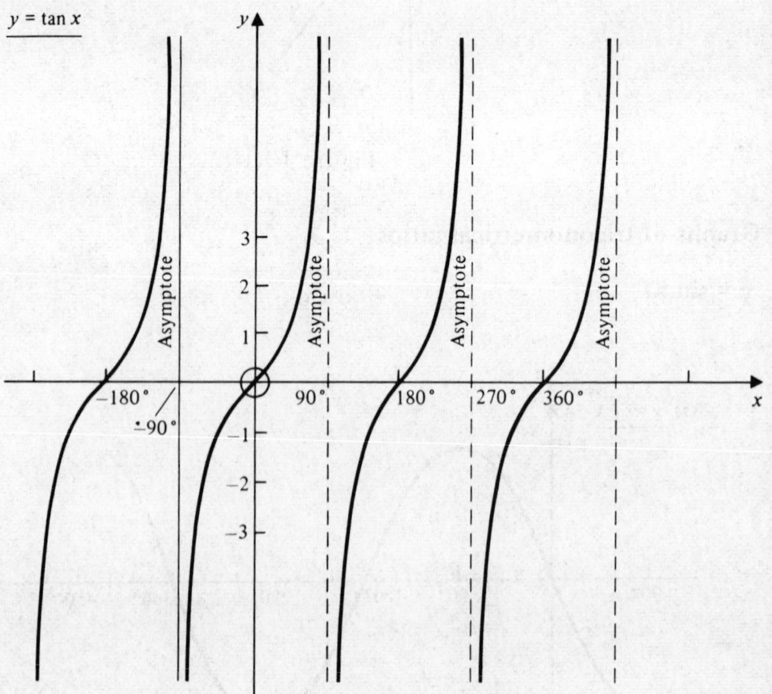

Figure 10.12

SPECIAL TRIANGLES

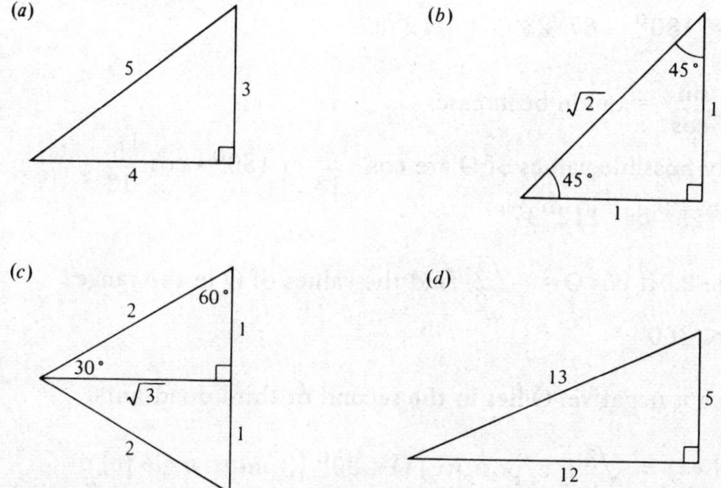

Figure 10.13

a, b and d are verified by Pythagoras' theorem.
c is verified by dividing an equilateral triangle into two congruent triangles and then applying Pythagoras' theorem.

Example 1. If $\sin \Theta = \frac{12}{13}$ calculate all the possible values of $\cos \Theta$, $\tan \Theta$, and of Θ in the range $0 \leqslant \Theta \leqslant 360^o$.

Since $\sin \Theta$ is positive Θ can only lie in the first or second quadrant.
First quadrant. As shown in Fig. 10.14.

$\cos \Theta_1 = \frac{5}{13}$, $\tan \Theta_1 = \frac{12}{5}$

$\Theta_1 = 67^o 23'$

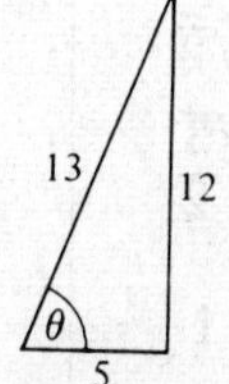

Figure 10.14

Second quadrant. Both cos and tan are negative

$\cos \Theta_2 = -\frac{5}{13} \qquad \tan \Theta_2 = -\frac{12}{5}$

$\Theta_2 = 180^\circ - 67^\circ 23' = 112^\circ 37'$

Check: $\frac{\sin}{\cos}$ = tan in both cases

The only possible values of Θ are $\cos^{-1}\frac{5}{13}$ or $180^\circ - \cos^{-1}\frac{5}{13}$

i.e. $67^\circ 23'$ or $112^\circ 37'$

Example 2. If $\cos \Theta = -\frac{\sqrt{3}}{2}$ find the values of Θ in the range $0 \leqslant \Theta \leqslant 360^\circ$

Since cos is negative, Θ lies in the second or third quadrants.

When $\cos \Theta = \frac{\sqrt{3}}{2}$ (i.e. positive) $\Theta = 30^\circ$ (from triangle (c) of fig.10.13)

When $\cos \Theta = -\frac{\sqrt{3}}{2}$ $\Theta = 150^\circ$ (i.e. $180^\circ - 30^\circ$) in second quadrant

or $\Theta = 210^\circ$ (i.e. $180^\circ + 30^\circ$) in third quadrant.

We can tabulate these special angles as follows:

Angle in degrees	Sine	Cosine	Tangent
0°	0	1	0
30°	$\frac{1}{2}$	$\frac{\sqrt{3}}{2}$	$\frac{1}{\sqrt{3}}$
45°	$\frac{1}{\sqrt{2}}$	$\frac{1}{\sqrt{2}}$	1
60°	$\frac{\sqrt{3}}{2}$	$\frac{1}{2}$	$\frac{\sqrt{3}}{1}$
90°	1	0	∞

These fractions are often easier to handle than the equivalent values given by tables.

CIRCULAR MEASURE OF AN ANGLE

In our study so far we have always measured angles in degrees, using the elementary fact that: 1 complete revolution = 360°
Now we need a more convenient unit in which to measure angles. This is called a **radian.**

Definition. A <u>radian</u> is the angle subtended at the centre of a circle by an arc of the circle of length equal to the radius. (see Fig. 10.15)

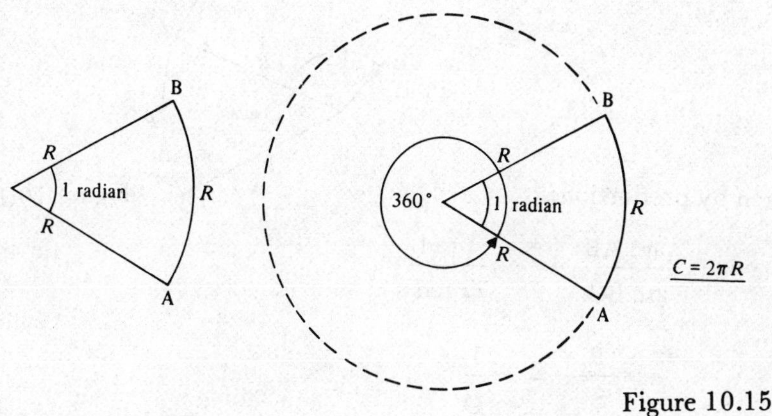

Figure 10.15

By proportion, it follows that:

$$\frac{\text{arc AB}}{\text{whole circumference}} = \frac{1 \text{ radian}}{360^{\circ}}$$

$$\frac{\overset{1}{\cancel{R}}}{2\pi \underset{1}{\cancel{R}}} = \frac{1 \text{ rad}}{360^{\circ}}$$

Cross multiplying: 2π radians = 360°
π radians = 180°

Note: 1 rad $\simeq 57^{\circ}$

Length of an arc of a circle.

There is a very simple connection between the length of the arc and the angle it subtends at the centre of the circle. (see Fig. 10.16)

If Θ = angle in radians subtended at centre by arc BC
S = length of arc BC
R = radius of circle

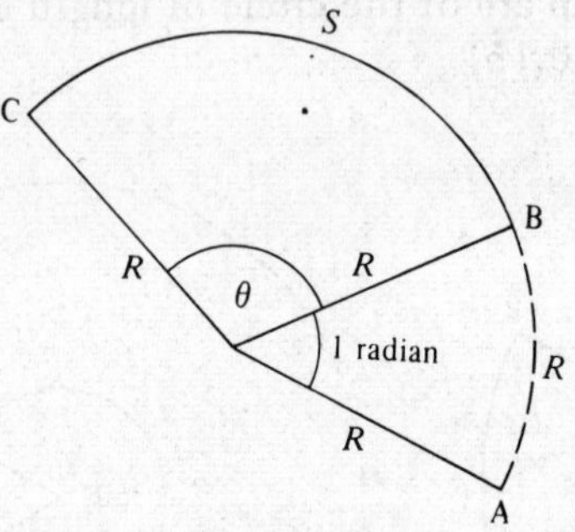

Figure 10.16

then by proportion:

$$\frac{\text{arc AB}}{\text{arc BC}} = \frac{1 \text{ rad}}{\Theta \text{ rad}}$$

$$\frac{R}{S} = \frac{1}{\Theta}$$

By cross multiplication:

$$\mathbf{S = R\Theta} \qquad \text{.......... (1)}$$

Motion of a particle in a circle

Suppose a particle is rotating with angular velocity ω rad/sec at any time t, in a circle of radius R metres. (fig. 10.17.)

Let V metres/sec be the linear velocity of the particle, i.e. the tangential velocity.

Differentiating (1) w.r.t. t:

$$\frac{dS}{dt} = R.\frac{d\Theta}{dt} \qquad \text{since R is constant}$$

But $V = \frac{dS}{dt}$ and $\omega = \frac{d\Theta}{dt}$

V = Rω where ω is in rad/sec.

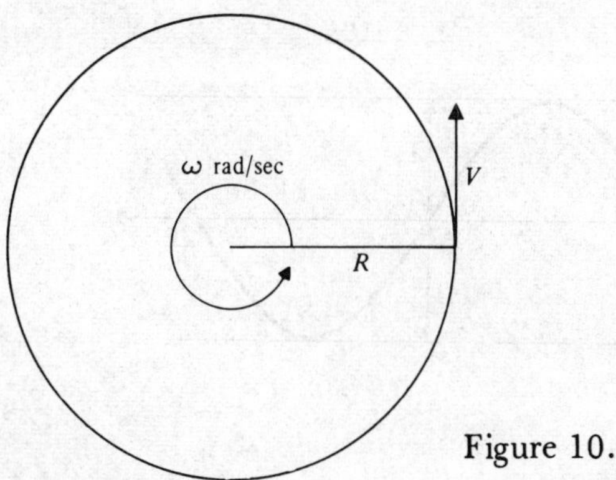

Figure 10.17.

Example. A flywheel is rotating steadily at 200 revs/min. If the radius is 0.5 metres, calculate the speed of a point on the rim in metres per sec.

Rotation = 200 revs/min 1 rev = 2π radians.

$\therefore \quad \omega = \dfrac{200 \times 2\pi}{60}$ rad/sec.

R = 0.5 m

V = Rω

$\therefore \quad V = \dfrac{\frac{1}{2} \times 200 \times 2\pi}{60}$ m/sec

$V = \dfrac{10\pi}{3}$ m/sec

Periodic Motion

The sine and cosine graphs are called *periodic* since the graphs repeat themselves with a period of 2π, i.e. 360°.

i.e. $y = a \sin x$ has a period of 2π

It follows that: $y = a \sin pt$ has a period of $T = \dfrac{2\pi}{p}$

since if t is increased by $\dfrac{2\pi}{p}$

the angle pt is increased by 2π

and $y = a \sin (pt + 2\pi) = a \sin pt$ .... (1)

i.e. y is unchanged.

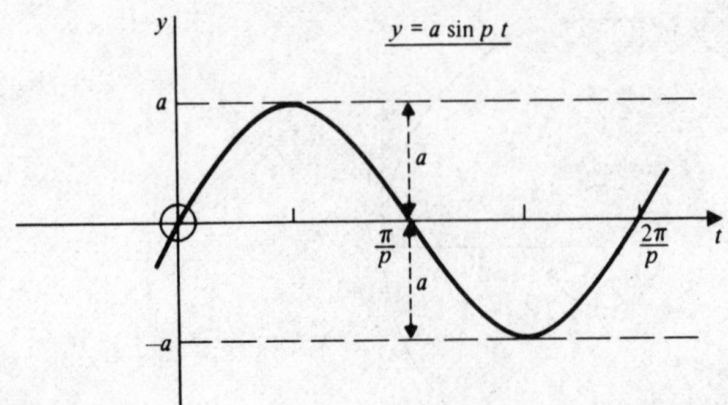

Figure 10.18

Similarly for y = a cos pt .... (2)
a is called the *amplitude*
Since, for both (1) and (2) the greatest value of sin or cos is 1, then the greatest value of y is a.

Example 3. Evaluate, with correct sign, the following:
(i) $\sin(-150^\circ)$: (ii) $\cos(-200^\circ)$; (iii) $\tan\left(-\frac{\pi}{3}\right)$

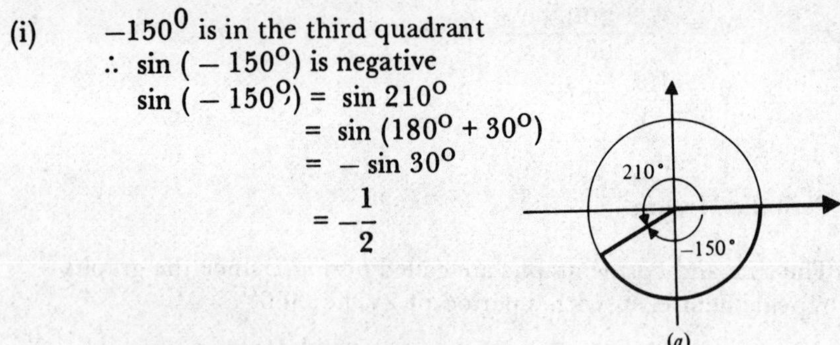

(i) -150° is in the third quadrant
$\therefore$ $\sin(-150^\circ)$ is negative

$$\sin(-150^\circ) = \sin 210^\circ = \sin(180^\circ + 30^\circ) = -\sin 30^\circ = -\frac{1}{2}$$

(*a*)

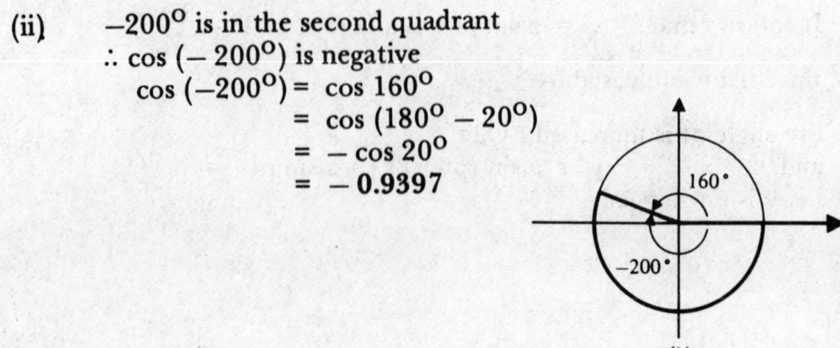

(ii) -200° is in the second quadrant
$\therefore$ $\cos(-200^\circ)$ is negative

$$\cos(-200^\circ) = \cos 160^\circ = \cos(180^\circ - 20^\circ) = -\cos 20^\circ = -0.9397$$

(*b*)

(iii) $-\frac{\pi}{3} = -60^{o}$ is in the fourth quadrant

. tan (-60°) is negative

$\therefore \tan(-\frac{\pi}{3}) = \tan(-60^{o})$

$= -\tan 60^{o}$

$= -\sqrt{3}$

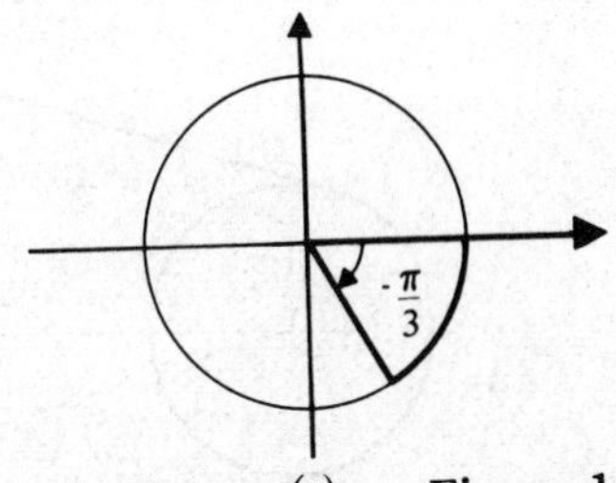

(c) Figure 10.19

Exercise 32.

I. Without using tables, express the following in terms of sin, cos, or tan of angles between 0° and 90°. (If you can use any of the special triangles noted, e.g. $(60^{o}, 30^{o}, 90^{o})$ do so.)

e.g. $\cos 150^{o} = -\cos 30^{o} = -\frac{\sqrt{3}}{2}$

1.	$\sin 210^{o}$	11.	$\cos 120^{o}$	21.	$\tan 120^{o}$
2.	$\sin 330^{o}$	12.	$\cos 300^{o}$	22.	$\tan 180^{o}$
3.	$\sin 30^{o}$	13.	$\cos 60^{o}$	23.	$\tan 225^{o}$
4.	$\sin 225^{o}$	14.	$\cos 135^{o}$	24.	$\tan 315^{o}$
5.	$\sin 325^{o}$	15.	$\cos 110^{o}$	25.	$\tan 150^{o}$
6.	$\sin 160^{o}$	16.	$\cos 250^{o}$	26.	$\tan 260^{o}$
7.	$\sin 100^{o}$	17.	$\cos 170^{o}$	27.	$\tan 322^{o}$
8.	$\sin 180^{o}$	18.	$\cos 350^{o}$	28.	$\tan 134^{o}$
9.	$\sin 190^{o}$	19.	$\cos 95^{o}$	29.	$\tan 171^{o}$
10.	$\sin 260^{o}$	20.	$\cos 255^{o}$	30.	$\tan 356^{o}$

II. Assuming Θ is acute, express the following in terms of sin, cos or tan Θ.
e.g. $\cos(360^{o} - \Theta) = \cos\Theta$

1.	$\sin(180 - \Theta)$	3.	$\cos(90 + \Theta)$	5.	$\tan(270 + \Theta)$
2.	$\sin(180 + \Theta)$	4.	$\cos(90 - \Theta)$	6.	$\tan(270 - \Theta)$

N.B. The answers are still true even when Θ is not acute.

7.

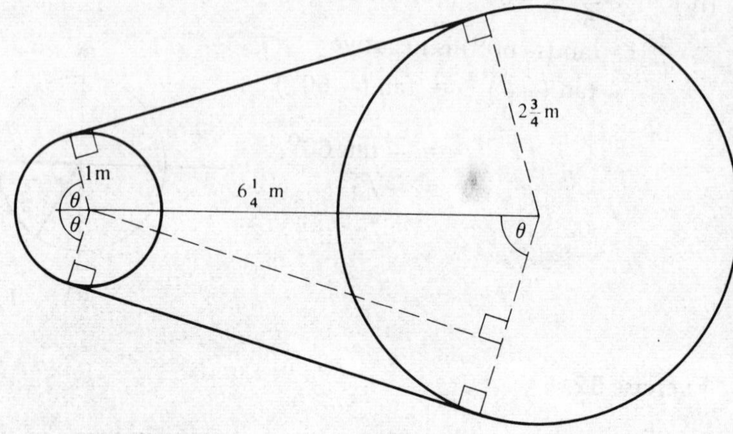

Figure 10.20

Two wheels of radii 2¾ m and 1 m with centres 6¼ m apart are driven by a continuous belt as shown in fig. 10.20. Assuming the belt is tight, find its total length. (Find Θ first in radians and the length of the common tangent.)

8. Write down the period and amplitude of the motion given by y = 10 cos (0.4 t.)

III.

1. A circle is a radius of 4 cm. An arc subtends an angle of 2.5 radians at the centre. What is the length of the arc?
2. A wheel is revolving at 330 rev/min. What is its angular velocity? (Leave in terms of π.)
3. Express 450° in radians. (Leave in terms of π.)

Chapter 11

Differentiation of trigonometric ratios

HOW TO DEAL WITH THE DIFFERENTIATION OF SINES AND COSINES

So far we have differentiated only powers of x or t or some other variable. Now we must learn how to find the gradients of the tangents at points on the following curves:

(i) $y = \sin x$
(ii) $y = \cos x$
where x is an angle expressed in radians.

We often use Greek letters to denote angles, α, β, γ (alpha, beta, gamma) at the beginning of the alphabet to represent known angles or fixed angles, and θ (theta) is often used for a variable angle.

Unless otherwise stated, **angles are always expressed in radians.**

(Remember: π radians = 180°)

Necessary Facts.

1. When x is small and expressed in radians

   $\sin x \triangleq x$

   $\cos x \triangleq 1 - \dfrac{x^2}{2}$ ($\triangleq$ means 'approximately equal to')

2. $\sin (A \pm B) = \sin A \cos B \pm \cos A \sin B$

   $\cos (A \pm B) = \cos A \cos B \mp \sin A \sin B$

(Read $\pm$ as 'plus or minus', and $\mp$ as 'minus or plus')

No proof is given here of fact 1, since a formal proof is better left until later. However, the student may verify these statements by reference to four-figure mathematical tables, in the following way:

Sin x $\triangleq$ x.

First find the tables of 'natural sines' and 'degrees to radians'.

sin 1° is given as 0.0175
1° in radians as 0.0175
Similarly set these down in a table as below:

Angle	sine	radians
1°	0.0175	0.0175
2°	0.0349	0.0349
3°	0.0523	0.0524
4°	0.0698	0.0698
5°	0.0872	0.0873
6°	0.1045	0.1047

correct to 4 places of decimals.

We note that in this range sin x = x (in radians).

$$\cos x \triangleq 1 - \frac{x^2}{2}$$

This is more difficult to verify but at a glance at tables of 'natural cosines' and 'degrees to radians' will show that cos x = 1 for very small angles. (These results can also be verified by a "scientific" calculator.)
The proofs of fact 2 are left to Appendix 3, but it may be useful to point out that:

(a) If we double an angle the sine or cosine is *not* doubled. For example: sin $60^{\circ}(=\frac{\sqrt{3}}{2})$ is not twice sin 30° (= ½)

(b) the sine of two angles added together is *not* equal to the sum of their sines. For example: sin 75° (=0.97) is not equal to sin 45° + sin 30° (= 0.71 + 0.5)

(c) We can verify that:
sin 90° i.e. sin $(30^{\circ} + 60^{\circ})$ = sin 30° cos 60° + cos 30° sin 60°
Using a $(60^{\circ}, 30^{\circ}, 90^{\circ})$ triangle, the sides are 1, 2, $\sqrt{3}$ as shown in Fig. 11.1.

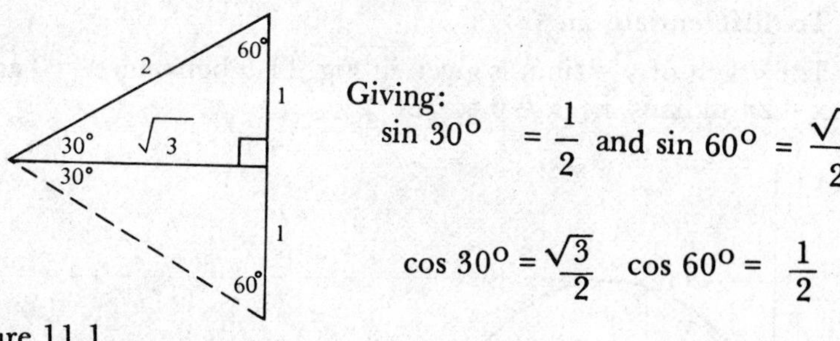

Giving:

$\sin 30^\circ = \frac{1}{2}$ and $\sin 60^\circ = \frac{\sqrt{3}}{2}$

$\cos 30^\circ = \frac{\sqrt{3}}{2}$ $\cos 60^\circ = \frac{1}{2}$

Figure 11.1

$$\therefore \sin 30^\circ \cos 60^\circ + \cos 30^\circ \sin 60^\circ = \frac{1}{2} \times \frac{1}{2} + \frac{\sqrt{3}}{2} \times \frac{\sqrt{3}}{2}$$

$$= \frac{1}{4} + \frac{3}{4} \text{ since } \sqrt{3} \times \sqrt{3} = 3$$

$$= 1$$

$$= \sin 90^\circ \text{ from tables}$$

$$= \sin (30^\circ + 60^\circ)$$

This is one case of
$\sin (A + B) = \sin A \cos B + \cos A \sin B$

As a further example, try the following as an exercise:

By using a $(45^\circ, 45^\circ, 90^\circ)$ triangle, (Fig. 11.2), check that
$\cos (30^\circ + 45^\circ) = \cos 30^\circ \cos 45^\circ - \sin 30^\circ \sin 45^\circ$
$= \cos 75^\circ$ [use tables here.]

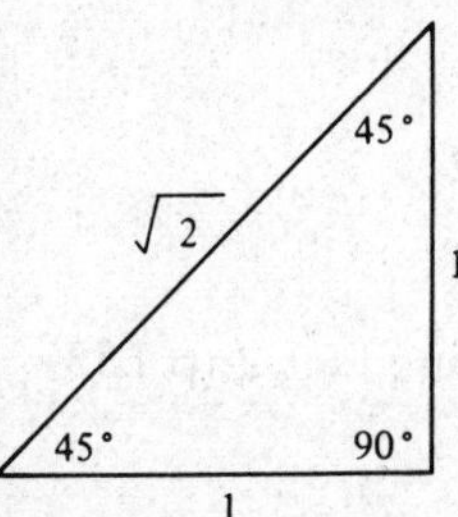

Fig. 11.2

We realise that the verifications quoted are not proofs but perhaps they help us to accept the formulae which mathematicians have proved for us. It is impossible to prove everything in one lifetime. Therefore at some stage we must accept the opinions of the expert.

To differentiate sin x

The graph of y = sin x is given in Fig. 11.3 between x = 0 and x = 2π radians, i.e. x = 0 to 360°

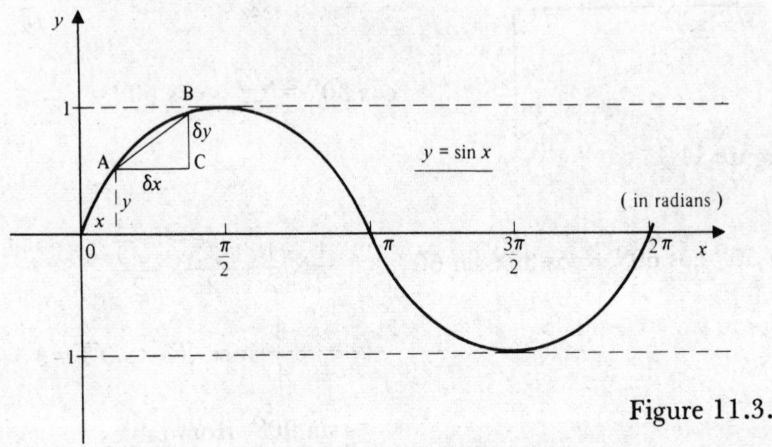

Figure 11.3.

Let y = sin x
Using the usual method for deducing the gradient at a point:
Let A be the point (x, y)
Let B be the point (x $+\delta$x, y + δy)
So that in the small triangle ABC, AC = δx
BC = δy

In the limit:
The gradient of the tangent $= \lim_{\delta x \to 0} \frac{\delta y}{\delta x} = \frac{dy}{dx}$ (by definition)

But y = sin x (given) .... [1]
and y + δy = sin (x + δx) .... [2]
since at any point on the curve the sine of the horizontal reading is equal to the vertical reading.
Subtracting (1) from (2)

$$\begin{aligned}\delta y &= \sin(x+\delta x) - \sin x \\ &= \sin x \cos\delta x + \cos x \sin\delta x - \sin x \\ &= \sin x(\cos\delta x - 1) + \cos x \sin\delta x\end{aligned}$$ using fact 2 (p.133)

$$\therefore \frac{\delta y}{\delta x} = \sin x.\frac{(\cos\delta x - 1)}{\delta x} + \cos x.\frac{\sin\delta x}{\delta x}$$

But since δx is small $\cos\delta x = 1 - \frac{(\delta x)^2}{2}$ by fact 1

and $\sin\delta x = \delta x$

$$\lim \frac{\delta y}{\delta x} = \sin x.0 + \cos x.1$$

$\therefore [\frac{\cos \delta x - 1}{\delta x} = -\frac{\delta x}{2} \to 0 \text{ as } \delta x \to 0]$

$\therefore \frac{dy}{dx} = \cos x$

$$\frac{d}{dx}(\sin x) = \cos x$$

To differentiate cos x

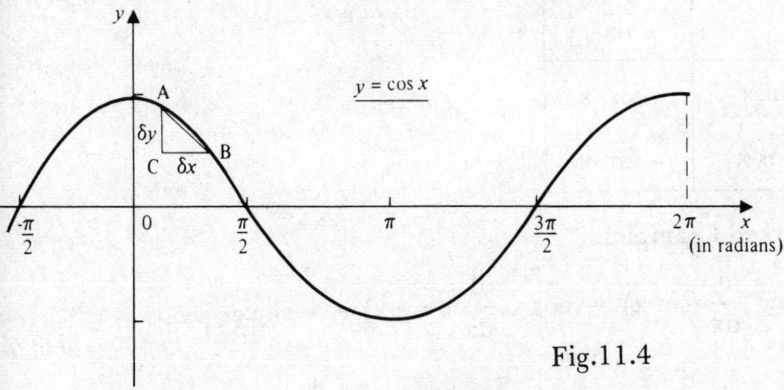

Fig.11.4

The graph is similar to that of y = sin x, with the y - axis moved through a distance of $\frac{\pi}{2}$ to the right.

Let $A = (x, y)$
$B = (x + \delta x, y + \delta y)$

As before, gradient of $AB = \frac{\delta y}{\delta x}$

But $y = \cos x$ . . . [1]

$y + \delta y = \cos (x + \delta x)$ . . . [2]

Subtracting [1] from [2] :

$\delta y = \cos (x + \delta x) - \cos x$

$= \cos x \cos \delta x - \sin x \sin \delta x - \cos x$ (using fact 2)

$= \cos x (\cos \delta x - 1) - \sin x \sin \delta x$ (rearranging)

$$\frac{\delta y}{\delta x} = \cos x \cdot \frac{(\cos \delta x - 1)}{\delta x} - \sin x \cdot \frac{\sin \delta x}{\delta x}$$

As before $\frac{\cos \delta x - 1}{\delta x} \to 0$ and $\frac{\sin \delta x}{\delta x} \to 1$ as $x \to 0$

$$\lim_{\delta x \to 0} \frac{\delta y}{\delta x} = (\cos x) \cdot 0 - (\sin x) \cdot 1$$

$= 0 - \sin x$

$$\frac{dy}{dx} = -\sin\ x$$

$$\frac{d}{dx}(\cos\ x) = -\sin x$$

Note: It is not necessary to remember the above proofs, but the results should be memorised in order to use them quickly.

SUMMARY

y	$\frac{dy}{dx}$
$\sin x$	$\cos x$
$\cos x$	$-\sin x$

Worked Examples.

Using $\frac{d}{dx}(\sin x) = \cos x, \frac{d}{dx}(\cos x) = -\sin x$

Prove: (i) $\frac{d}{dx}(\sin 3x) = 3 \cos 3x$; (ii) $\frac{d}{dx}(\cos 5x) = -5 \sin 5x$

and find. (iii) $\frac{d}{d\Theta}(\sin a\Theta)$ (iv) $\frac{d}{d\Theta}(\sin \Theta \cos \Theta)$;

(v) $\frac{d}{dx}(3x \cos x)$; (vi) $\frac{d}{dx}(\tan x)$;

(vii) $\frac{d}{d\Theta}(\sin^2 \Theta)$.

Solutions.

Example (i)

Let $y = \sin 3x$ Here we treat $3x$ as though in a bracket.
i.e. $y = \sin (3x)$, and differentiate as a simple sine and then 'go inside the bracket', differentiate and multiply by the result.

(c.f. function of a function $\frac{dy}{dx} = \frac{dy}{dz} \times \frac{dz}{dx}$ Chapter 8, p. 91).

$$\frac{dy}{dx} = \cos(3x) \times \text{(differential of } 3x \text{ w.r.t. } x)$$
$$= (\cos 3x) \times 3$$
$$= \mathbf{3 \cos 3x}$$

N.B. We always write the numerical part first in order to save confusion. e.g. cos 3x x 3 could be mistaken for cos 9x.

Example (ii)

Let $y = \cos(5x)$

$$\frac{dy}{dx} = -\sin(5x) \times \text{(differential of } 5x \text{ w.r.t. } x)$$
$$= \mathbf{-5 \sin 5x}$$

Example (iii)

Let $y = \sin(a\Theta)$

$$\frac{dy}{d\Theta} = \cos(a\Theta) \times \text{differential of } (a\Theta) \text{ (a is a constant)}$$
$$= \mathbf{a \cos a\Theta}$$

Example (iv)

Let $y = \sin\Theta \cos\Theta = u \cdot v$ (say) where $u = \sin\Theta$, $\dfrac{du}{d\Theta} = \cos\Theta$

$$\frac{dy}{d\Theta} = v\frac{du}{d\Theta} + u\frac{dv}{d\Theta} \qquad v = \cos\Theta, \frac{dv}{d\Theta} = -\sin\Theta$$

$$= \cos\Theta \cos\Theta + \sin\Theta(-\sin\Theta)$$
$$= \mathbf{\cos^2\Theta - \sin^2\Theta}$$

Example (v)

Let $y = 3x \cos x = uv$ (say) where $u = 3x$, $v = \cos x$

$$\frac{dy}{dx} = v\frac{du}{dx} + u\frac{dv}{dx} \qquad \therefore \quad \frac{du}{dx} = 3, \quad \frac{dv}{dx} = -\sin x$$

$$= (\cos x)3 + 3x(-\sin x)$$
$$= \mathbf{3 \cos x - 3x \sin x}$$

Example (vi)

Let $y = \tan x = \frac{\sin x}{\cos x} = \frac{u}{v}$ (say)

$$\frac{dy}{dx} = \frac{v\frac{du}{dx} - u\frac{dv}{dx}}{v^2}$$

$u = \sin x$
$v = \cos x$
$\frac{du}{dx} = \cos x$
$\frac{dv}{dx} = -\sin x$

$$= \frac{\cos x \cos x - \sin x\,(-\sin x)}{\cos^2 x}$$

$$\frac{dy}{dx} = \frac{\cos^2 x + \sin^2 x}{\cos^2 x}$$

$$= \frac{1}{\cos^2 x}\quad,\ \text{using } \sin^2 x + \cos^2 x = 1$$

$\therefore \frac{d}{dx}(\tan x) = \sec^2 x$ since $\frac{1}{\cos x} = \sec x$ (definition)

We now have the differentials of sin, cos and tan:

y	$\frac{dy}{dx}$
$\sin x$	$\cos x$
$\cos x$	$-\sin x$
$\tan x$	$\sec^2 x$

Example (vii)

Let $y = \sin^2 \Theta$
This is equivalent to $(\sin \Theta)^2$
$\therefore \quad y = (\sin \Theta)^2$
We treat this first as $(\text{something})^2$ and then 'go inside' and differentiate.

$$\frac{dy}{d\Theta} = 2(\sin \Theta) \times \cos \Theta$$

$$= 2 \sin \Theta \cos \Theta$$

Exercise 33.

Using $\frac{d}{dx}(\sin x) = \cos x$

$\frac{d}{dx}(\cos x) = -\sin x$

find the differential coefficients w.r.t. x of :

1. $3 \sin x - 4 \cos x$
2. $\sin 8x$
3. $\frac{1}{6} \cos 3x$
4. $\sin (2x + 5)$
5. $\cos (\frac{\pi}{6} - x)$
6. $3 \sin (3x - 2)$
7. $6 \sin \frac{2}{3} x$
8. $\sin 2\pi nx$ (n = a constant)
9. $\cos^2 x$
10. $4 \sin \frac{1}{2} x$
11. $\sqrt{\sin x}$
12. $\sin x - \frac{1}{6} \sin 3x$

Exercise 34.

Using $\frac{dy}{dx} = \frac{dy}{dz} \cdot \frac{dz}{dx}$, differentiate the following w.r.t. x:

Example:

Find $\frac{dy}{dx}$ if $y = (4 + 5x)^6 = z^6$ (say)

$\frac{dy}{dz} = 6.(4 + 5x)^5$ where $z = 4 + 5x$

$\frac{dz}{dx} = 5$ (i.e. differential of 'what is inside the bracket')

$\therefore \frac{dy}{dx} = 30(4 + 5x)^5$

1. $\sqrt{(1 + 2x)}$
2. $(1 - 3x^2)^4$
3. $\frac{1}{(1 + x^3)^2}$
4. $(a - x)^n$
5. $\sqrt{(ax + b)}$

Evaluate:

6. $\frac{d\sqrt{1 + v^2}}{dv}$
7. $\frac{d(3 - 4l)^6}{dl}$
8. $\frac{d}{dt}\left(\frac{1}{(1 + t^2)^2}\right)$
9. $\frac{d}{dx}\left(\frac{1}{1 + 4x^2}\right)$

Exercise 35. Using

$$d(uv) = u\,dv + v\,du$$

and

$$d\left(\frac{u}{v}\right) = \frac{v\,du - u\,dv}{v^2}$$

find the following differentials w.r.t. x :

1. $\sqrt{x}\sin x$
2. $\sin 2x \cos x$
3. $2x^2 \cos 3x$
4. $\frac{1}{4}x\sqrt{1+x}$
5. $\cos ax \cos bx$
6. $x^2 \sin x$
7. $\dfrac{x}{2x+3}$
8. $\dfrac{3x-1}{x+5}$
9. $\dfrac{3x}{x+3}$
10. $\dfrac{\sin x}{x}$
11. $\dfrac{1+\sin x}{1-\sin x}$
12. $\dfrac{1-x^2}{1+2x}$

SIMPLE HARMONIC MOTION

No study of elementary mathematics is complete without some mention of simple harmonic motion. This type of vibration or oscillation occurs so frequently in nature and everyday science, that it is necessary to know the basic principles.

Examples of Simple Harmonic Motion (S.H.M.)

1. We are all aware of the vibrations of piano wires causing waves which reach our ear registering a musical note. This is motion of the type to be discussed, and gives it its name—simple harmonic motion. Also, the vibration of air in pipes is simple harmonic.

2. Oscillations of a pendulum if kept within 5° of the vertical can be considered to be simple harmonic.

3. The motion of a weight oscillating up and down on the end of a spring is damped harmonic. Owing to air resistance, the oscillations gradually die out and the weight rests at its equilibrium position.

4. The rise and fall of tides is simple harmonic taken over short periods.

5. When a vector rotates with constant angular velocity, the feet of the perpendiculars drawn to the real and imaginary axes, both move with S.H.M. (Real and imaginary numbers and axes will be discussed in Chapter 17.)

Suppose a crank OP of length a rotates with uniform angular velocity ω rad/sec about a fixed point 0. Let PN, PQ be the perpendiculars from P to A'OA and B'OB as in Fig.11.5.

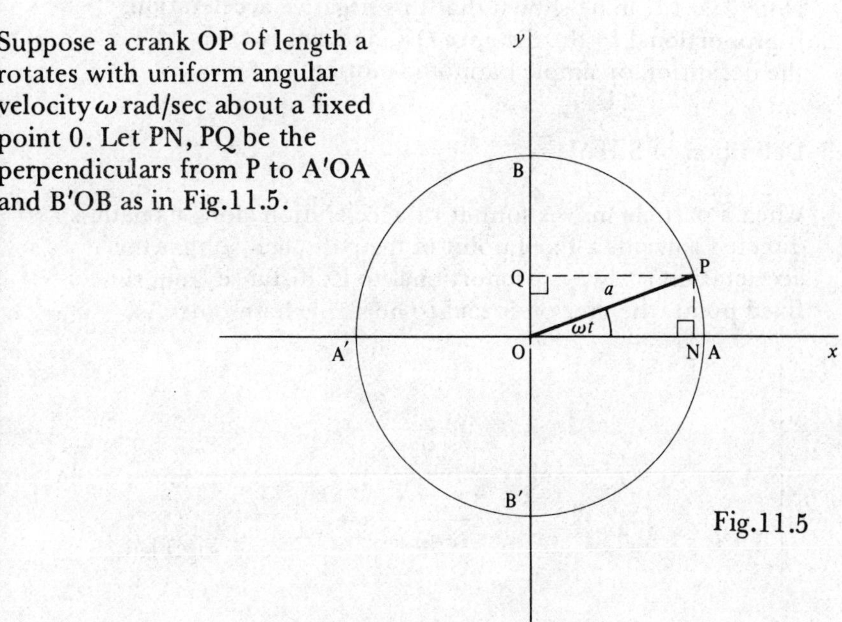

Fig.11.5

Then, after time t secs, angle POA $= \omega t$ radians

$$ON = a \cos\omega t$$
$$OQ = a \sin\omega t$$

As P executes one complete oscillation starting from A, when $t = 0$,
then N oscillates from A to A' and back again
Q oscillates from O to B, B to B' and B' to O.
Both N and Q perform simple harmonic oscillations.

Note 1: As N travels from A to A', we observe that the velocity is zero at A, increases steadily as it moves towards O, where it is maximum, and then gradually decreases as it moves from O to A', where the velocity is zero again and the process is reversed back to A.

(Q moves in a similar way, but starts from O with maximum velocity, ωt, gradually decreasing to zero at B.)

Note 2: Considering the motion of N, as it moves from A to O it is **accelerating** in the direction AO, i.e. in a **negative direction** taking OA as axis of x.

Note 3: It can be shown that this **negative acceleration** is **proportional to the distance ON**, and this is taken as the definition of simple harmonic motion.

Definition of S.H.M.

When a particle moves so that its acceleration along its path is directed **towards a fixed point** in the path, and so that the acceleration is always **proportional to its distance from this fixed point**, the motion is said to be simple harmonic.

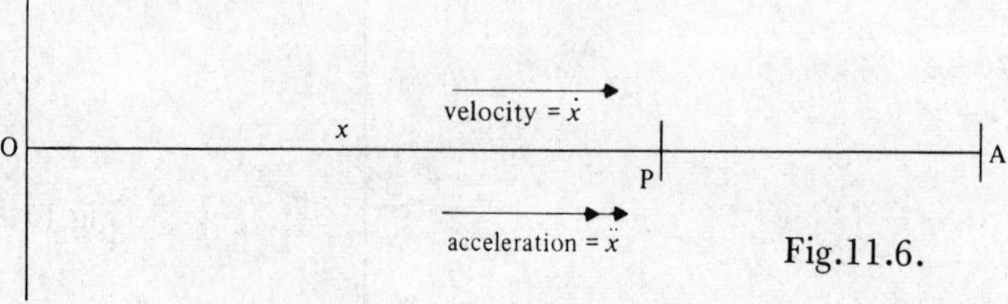

Fig.11.6.

Let P be a point on the path of a particle moving with S.H.M. about a fixed point O.

Let distance OP at time t = x

Then velocity of P at time t = $\frac{dx}{dt}$ or $\dot{x}$

and acceleration of P at time t = $\frac{d^2x}{dt^2}$ or $\ddot{x}$

(measured in direction of x increasing, i.e. away from O)

(The 'dot' notation is only used for differentials w.r.t. time).

Then if P moves with S.H.M., from the definition, the acceleration towards 0 is proportional to the distance from 0

i.e. $-\ddot{x}$ = constant $\times$ x.

(We take this constant as ω^2, since the constant has a physical meaning, i.e. the angular velocity of the 'time-keeper' moving in a circle and keeping time with P.)

$\therefore\ \ddot{x} = -\omega^2 x$

$\therefore\ \ddot{x} + \omega^2 x = 0$ ... [1]

This is the *fundamental equation of S.H.M.* and any particle which moves in this way, so that the second differential of the variable plus (a positive constant) x (the variable) is equal to zero, must move with S.H.M. and the basic theory which follows can be used to solve any problems concerned with its motion.

<u>Note</u>: We shall consider the case of motion in a straight line, but it must be pointed out that any motion which can be represented by an equation such as [1] is S.H.M.

1. x may be the distance of point P moving on a curve, measured along the curve from a fixed point on it.

2. x may be an angle made by a line fixed in a body, oscillating about a fixed axis through O in the body (Fig.11.7). For example, a heavy body oscillating through small angles about a horizontal axis, performs S.H.M.

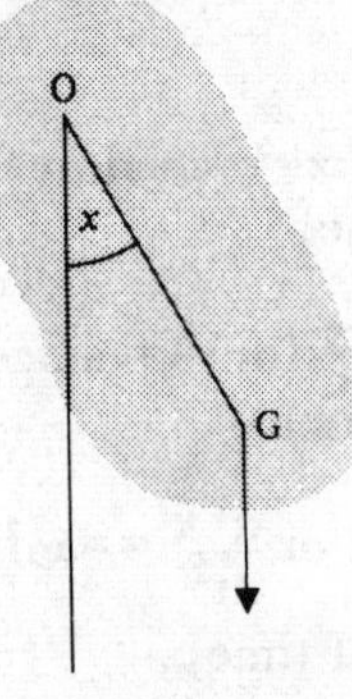

Fig.11.7.

Solution of the simple harmonic equation

$$\frac{d^2x}{dt^2} = -\omega^2 x$$

(This is a differential equation whose solution directly has to be assumed at this stage. See Appendix 4.)

The solution in general is $x = a\sin(\omega t + \epsilon)$
where a is the amplitude of the motion, i.e. the maximum displacement of the particle from the fixed point O.

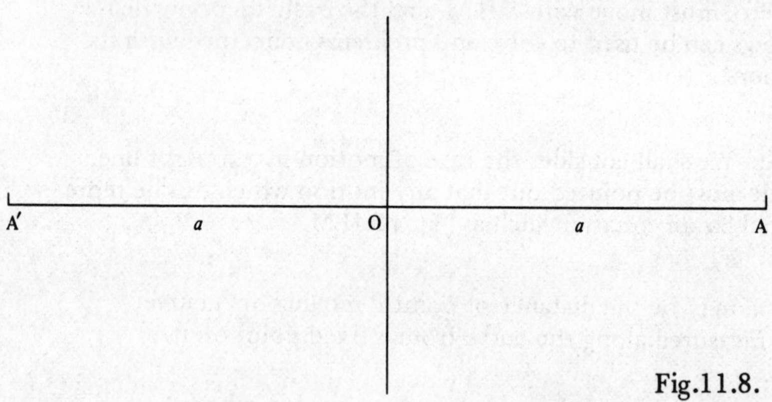

Fig.11.8.

The constant ϵ merely depends on where t is measured from. We shall assume t is measured from when the particle passes through the point O

i.e. $x = 0$ when $t = 0$ and $\epsilon = 0$ from the general solution.

This gives the simple solution $x = a\sin\omega t$ .... [1]
(giving distance in terms of time)

Differentiate w.r.t. t : $\dot{x}$ or $\frac{dx}{dt}$ (or v) = $a\omega\cos\omega t$ .... [2]
(giving velocity in terms of time)

Differentiate again w.r.t. t : $\ddot{x}$ or $\frac{d^2x}{dt^2} = -a\omega^2\sin\omega t$ .... [3]
(giving acceleration in terms of time)

Substitute from [1] in to [3] gives:

$\ddot{x} = -\omega^2 x$ .... [4]

(Fundamental equation of S.H.M. (giving acceleration in terms of distance) thus verifying that the solution [1] is correct.

We now need to find the velocity in terms of distance

But $\quad v = a\omega \cos \omega t$

and $\quad x = a \sin \omega t$

We eliminate t from these equations by squaring each of them

$$v^2 = a^2 \omega^2 \cos^2 \omega t \qquad \therefore \frac{v^2}{a^2 \omega^2} = \cos^2 \omega t \qquad \text{... (i)}$$

$$x^2 = a^2 \sin^2 \omega t \qquad \frac{x^2}{a^2} = \sin^2 \omega t \qquad \text{... (ii)}$$

But $\sin^2 \omega t + \cos^2 \omega t = 1$

$\therefore$ from (i) and (ii)

$$\frac{v^2}{a^2 \omega^2} + \frac{x^2}{a^2} = 1 \qquad \text{Thus eliminating } \omega t.$$

Multiply by $a^2 \omega^2$:

$\therefore v^2 + \omega^2 x^2 = a^2 \omega^2$

$$\therefore \quad v^2 = \omega^2 (a^2 - x^2)$$

$$v = \pm \omega \sqrt{a^2 - x^2} \qquad \text{. . . [5]}$$

The ± values represent the velocities away from and towards 0, i.e. in the directions of x increasing and x decreasing.

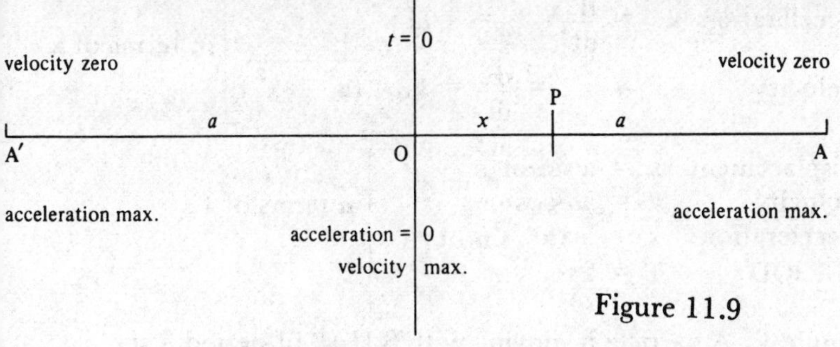

Figure 11.9

These five formulae [1] - [5] enable us to find any variable - distance, time, velocity, acceleration in terms of any other variable.

It only remains to mention the period of oscillation, i.e. the time taken to go from any point on the path through a complete oscillation returning to the original point and travelling in the same direction.

This can be easily seen by studying the 'time-keeper,' i.e. a vector rotating with constant angular velocity ω radians per sec. (fig. 11.10).

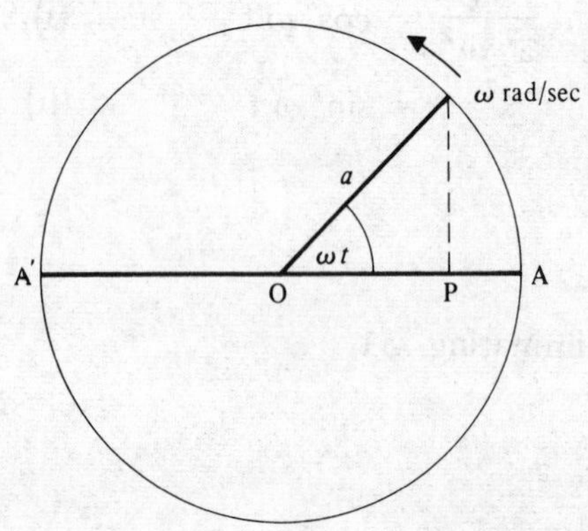

Since there are 2π radians in a complete rotation,
Time of rotation = $\frac{2\pi}{\omega}$ secs.

$\therefore$ $T = \frac{2\pi}{\omega}$ is the period of oscillation of P.

Figure 11.10

SUMMARY OF FORMULAE FOR S.H.M.

In terms of x:

Acceleration $\ddot{x} = \frac{d^2x}{dt^2} = -\omega^2 x$

Velocity $v = \dot{x} = \frac{dx}{dt} = \pm\omega\sqrt{(a^2 - x^2)}$

In terms of t:

Displacement $x = a \sin\omega t$

Velocity $v = a\omega\cos\omega t$

Acceleration $\ddot{x} = -a\omega^2 \sin\omega t$

PERIOD $T = \frac{2\pi}{\omega}$

Example 1. A particle is moving with S.H.M. of period 8 sec. The amplitude of the oscillation is 4 metres. (See Fig. 11.11).

Find:
(i) the maximum velocity;
(ii) the maximum acceleration;
(iii) the velocity when the particle is 2 m from the central position

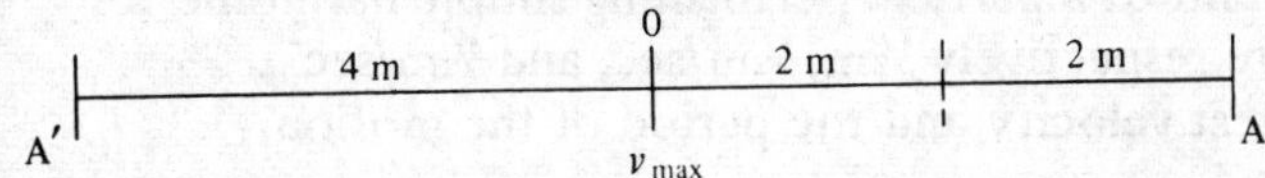

Figure 11.11.

Period $= \frac{2\pi}{\omega} = 8$

giving $\omega = \frac{2\pi}{8} = \frac{\pi}{4}$

Also $a = 4$

(i) Maximum Velocity

$$v = \pm\omega\sqrt{a^2 - x^2}$$

$\therefore$ v is maximum where x is smallest, i.e. $x = 0$

$\therefore v = \pm a\omega$

$$= \pm 4.\frac{\pi}{4}$$

$$= \pm\pi \text{ m/sec} \quad \hat{=} \pm 3.1 \text{ m/sec}$$

(ii) Maximum Acceleration

Acceleration is given by $\ddot{x} = -\omega^2 x$

Hence, acceleration is maximum when x is maximum (and negative. i.e. $x = -a$

Hence maximum acceleration $= \omega^2 a$

$$= \frac{\pi^2}{16}.4 \quad \text{when } x = -4$$

$$\hat{=} 2.5. \text{ m/sec}^2 \quad (\text{taking } \pi^2 \hat{=} 10)$$

(iii) Velocity when x = 2

$$v = \pm\,\omega\sqrt{a^2 - x^2}$$

$$\omega = \frac{\pi}{4}, \quad a = 4, \quad x = 2$$

$$\therefore v = \pm\frac{\pi}{4}\sqrt{16 - 4}$$

$$\omega = \pm\frac{\pi}{4}\sqrt{12}$$

Velocity where $x = 2$, $\hat{=} \pm$ **2.7 m/sec.**

Example 2. If the displacement, velocity and acceleration at a particular instant of a particle performing simple harmonic oscillations are respectively ½m, ½m/sec, and ½m/sec^2, find the greatest velocity and the period of the motion.

when $x = \frac{1}{2}$ m $\quad \ddot{x} = -\frac{1}{2}$ m/sec^2 (since when x is positive $\ddot{x}$ is negative)

using $\ddot{x} = -\omega^2 x$

$$-\tfrac{1}{2} = -\tfrac{1}{2}\omega^2$$

$$\therefore \quad \omega^2 = 1$$

$\therefore \quad \omega = 1$ (ignore negative answer since ω is always taken as positive).

Also when $x = \frac{1}{2}$ m $\quad \dot{x} = \frac{1}{2}$ m/sec

But $\quad \dot{x}^2 = v^2 = \omega^2 (a^2 - x^2)$

$\therefore \quad \frac{1}{4} = \omega^2 (a^2 - \frac{1}{4})$

$\therefore \quad \frac{1}{4} = a^2 - \frac{1}{4}$ since $\omega = 1$

$\therefore \quad a^2 = \frac{1}{2}$

$\therefore \quad a = \frac{1}{\sqrt{2}}$ (a is positive)

$$= \frac{\sqrt{2}}{2}$$

$$\therefore \quad a \triangleq 0.707 \text{ m}$$

$\therefore$ Greatest velocity $= a\omega$

$$= \frac{\sqrt{2}}{2} . 1$$

$$\triangleq 0.707 \text{ m/sec}$$

Also $T = \dfrac{2\pi}{\omega}$

Period $= 2\pi$ secs

Exercise 36.

1. The amplitude of a particle moving with S.H.M. is 5 metres, the acceleration at a distance of 2 metres from the mean position is 4 m/sec^2. Find the velocity when the particle is in its mean position, and also when it is 4 metres from this position.

2. A particle moves in a straight line with S.H.M. The acceleration at a distance of 4 metres from the mean position is 8 m/sec^2. Find the time of one complete oscillation.

3. Repeat No. 2, given the acceleration at a distance of $\frac{3}{4}$ metre is 12 m/sec^2.

4. A point moving with S.H.M. has velocities of 4 m/sec and 3 m/sec at distances of 3 m and 4 m respectively from the centre of oscillation. Find ω, and the amplitude, and hence the maximum acceleration.

5. The maximum velocity of a particle moving with S.H.M. of period π sec is 8 m/sec. Find the amplitude, and the velocity as it passes through a point 3 metres from the central position.

6. Find the maximum velocity and acceleration of a particle moving with S.H.M. of period 2 secs if the amplitude is 3 metres.

CURVATURE OF CURVES (May be left until a second reading)

We must first find the relationship between the curvature of a circle and its radius.

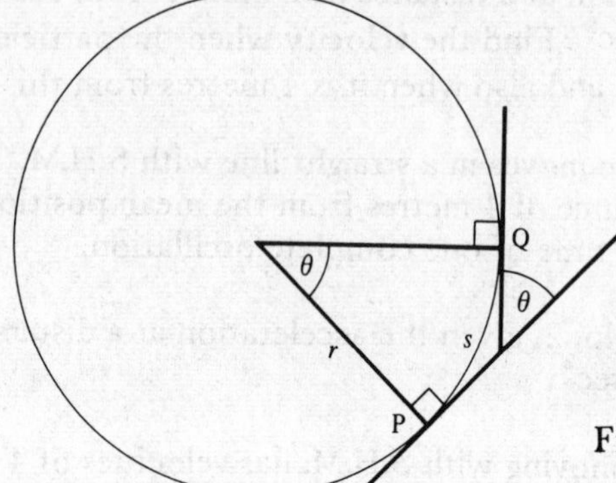

Figure 11.12

Definition. The curvature of a circle is the rate of change of the angle between the tangents with respect to the arc s, as in Fig. 11.12. [θ = angle in radians].

i.e. Curvature at P $= \dfrac{d\Theta}{ds}$

For a circle, radius r, $s = r\Theta$

But r is constant $\therefore\ ds = r\,d\Theta$

$$\therefore \frac{d\Theta}{ds} = \frac{1}{r} \qquad \text{.... (1)}$$

$\therefore$ Curvature $= \dfrac{1}{\text{radius}}$ (i.e. the inverse of the radius)

For a Curve

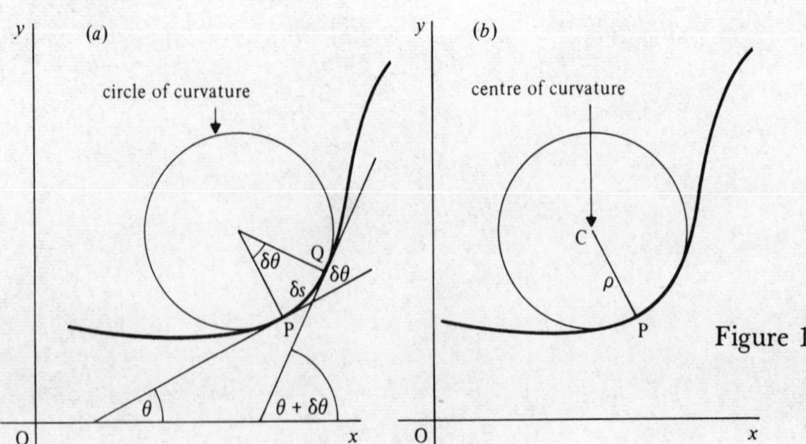

Figure 11

Let P, Q be points close together on the curve (Fig. 11.13).
Let tangents to curve at P and Q make angles Θ and $(\Theta + \delta\Theta)$ with the axis.
Let PQ = δs
Then change in angle between P and Q = $\delta\theta$

$\therefore$ Rate of change $\triangleq \dfrac{\delta\Theta}{\delta s}$ in radians per metre.

$\therefore$ Curvature of curve $= \dfrac{d\Theta}{ds} = \dfrac{1}{\rho}$ where ρ = radius of curvature from (1)

To prove:

$$\frac{1}{\rho} = \frac{d^2y}{dx^2} \Big/ \left[1 + \left(\frac{dy}{dx}\right)^2\right]^{\frac{3}{2}}$$

Proof. With the usual notation,
gradient of curve at any point is given by

$$\frac{dy}{dx} = \tan\theta \; ; \qquad \text{.... (i)}$$

$$\frac{dx}{ds} = \cos\Theta \qquad \text{.... (ii)}$$

(See fig. 11.14)
Differentiating (i) w.r.t. x, we obtain

$$\frac{d^2y}{dx^2} = \sec^2\Theta \cdot \frac{d\Theta}{dx} \qquad \text{.... (iii)}$$

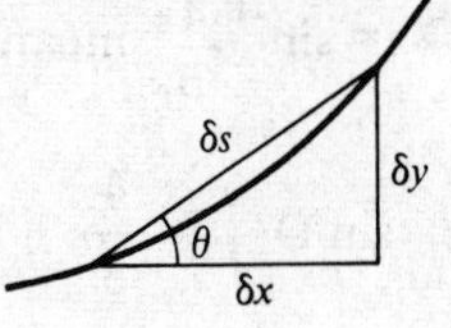

Fig. 11.14

and $\dfrac{d\Theta}{dx} = \dfrac{d\Theta}{ds} \cdot \dfrac{ds}{dx}$

$= \dfrac{1}{\rho} \cdot \dfrac{1}{\cos\Theta} = \dfrac{1}{\rho}\sec\Theta$ from (ii)

$\therefore \dfrac{d^2y}{dx^2} = \sec^2\Theta \cdot \dfrac{1}{\rho} \cdot \sec\Theta$ from (iii)

$= \dfrac{1}{\rho}\sec^3\Theta$

$\therefore \dfrac{1}{\rho} = \dfrac{d^2y}{dx^2} \Big/ \sec^3\Theta$

But $\sec^2\Theta = 1 + \tan^2\Theta$ (Proved by dividing $\sin^2\Theta + \cos^2\Theta = 1$ by $\cos^2\Theta$)

$\therefore \sec^3\Theta = (\sec^2\Theta)^{\frac{3}{2}}$

$$= (1 + \tan^2 \Theta)^{\frac{3}{2}}$$

$$= [1 + (\frac{dy}{dx})^2]^{\frac{3}{2}}$$

$\therefore$

$$\frac{1}{\rho} = \frac{\frac{d^2y}{dx^2}}{[1 + (\frac{dy}{dx})^2]^{\frac{3}{2}}}$$

Note: If $\frac{dy}{dx}$ is small, for example, as in the case of a weighted beam, then $\frac{dy}{dx}$ may be neglected and $\frac{1}{\rho} \simeq \frac{d^2y}{dx^2}$ which is not necessarily small when $\frac{dy}{dx}$ is small.

FURTHER DIFFERENTIATION

In order to be able to complete the solution of some of the differential equations we shall meet, (Chapter 19), we need to know the results of differentiating certain other functions. These are:

$\sin^{-1} x$, $\cos^{-1} x$ and $\tan^{-1} x$.

On page 121, we defined the meaning of these functions. We said:

$\Theta = \sin^{-1} \frac{4}{5}$ means 'Θ is the acute angle whose sine is $\frac{4}{5}$,'

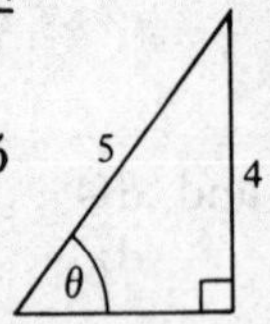

i.e. $\sin \Theta = \frac{4}{5}$

Fig. 11.15

Hence $y = \sin^{-1} x$ means $\sin y = x$ and similarly for $\cos^{-1} x$ and $\tan^{-1} x$

Note: $\sin^{-1} x$ does not mean $(\sin x)^{-1}$

To differentiate $\sin^{-1} x$

Let $y = \sin^{-1} x$ (Then we wish to find $\frac{dy}{dx}$)

$\therefore \sin y = x$

or $x = \sin y$ ... (1)

Now $\dfrac{d}{dy}(\sin y) = \cos y$

$\therefore$ Differentiate (1) w.r.t. y:

$$\frac{dx}{dy} = \cos y$$

$$\therefore \quad \frac{dy}{dx} = \frac{1}{\cos y} \qquad \text{.... (2)}$$

since $\dfrac{dy}{dx} = 1\Big/\dfrac{dx}{dy}$

But we need to know $\dfrac{d}{dx}(\sin^{-1} x)$ in terms of x.

$\therefore$ We eliminate y from (2) by using (1) and the fact that

$$\sin^2 y + \cos^2 y = 1$$

$$\text{i.e. } \cos^2 y = 1 - \sin^2 y = 1 - x^2$$

$$\therefore \cos y = \sqrt{1 - x^2}$$

We take the positive square root here. The reason for this is given later.*

$$\therefore \frac{dy}{dx} = \frac{1}{\sqrt{1 - x^2}}$$

$$\therefore \frac{d}{dx}(\sin^{-1} x) = \frac{1}{\sqrt{1 - x^2}}$$

Exercise. Use a similar method to show that:

$$\frac{d}{dx}(\cos^{-1} x) = -\frac{1}{\sqrt{1 - x^2}}$$

*Why do we choose the positive sign for the square root?

We must look at the graphs of $y = \sin^{-1} x$ (Fig. 11.16(a)) and $y = \cos^{-1} x$ (Fig. 11.16(b)) in order to understand this.

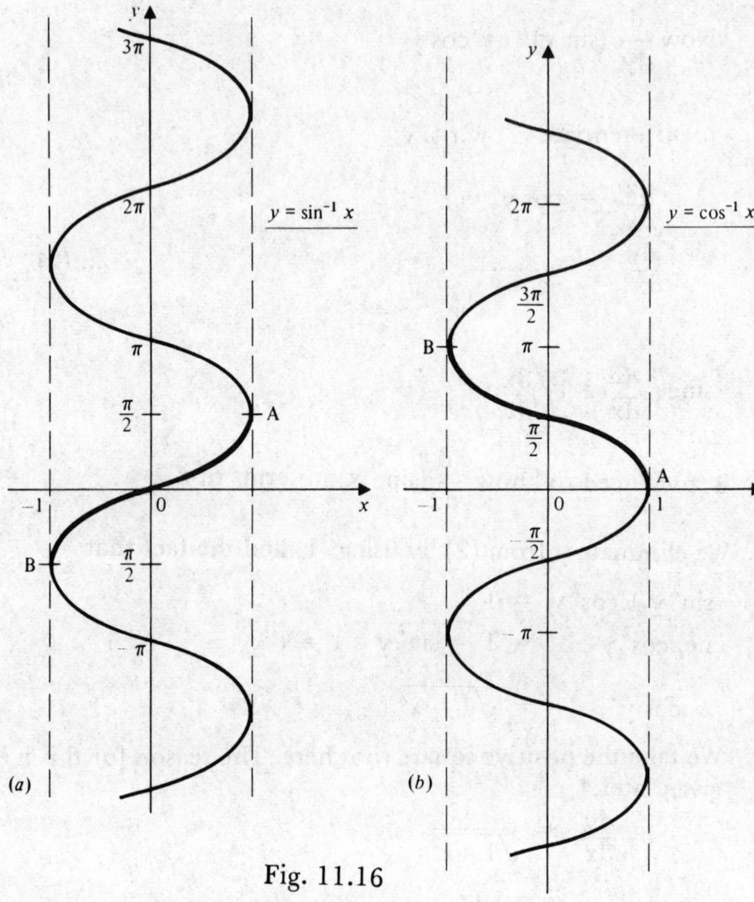

Fig. 11.16

There are two things to notice:

1. The graphs are confined to the region x = −1 to x = +1
2. For any given value of x there are an infinite number of values of y, if the graphs are continued in both directions.

Principal values

The principal value of $\sin^{-1} x$ is defined as that between $\frac{-\pi}{2}$ and $\frac{\pi}{2}$

and corresponds to the thick line AB on the graph (fig. 11.16) It is convention to use this principal value in differentiation and integration, and we see that at any point on this part of the graph the gradient of the tangent is positive. This is the reason why we chose the positive square root of $(1 - x^2)$ in our proof that $\frac{d}{dx}(\sin^{-1} x) = \frac{1}{\sqrt{1 - x^2}}$

The principal value of $\cos^{-1} x$ is that between 0 and π. This is again indicated by the thick line AB on the graph. Can you see why we must take a different range from that for $\sin^{-1} x$? If we took the range $\frac{-\pi}{2}$ to $\frac{\pi}{2}$ then for values of x between 0 and 1 there would be two values of $\cos^{-1} x$, one positive and one negative, which would be very confusing. We see that in the range 0 to π the gradient of the tangent at any point is negative, which agrees with the sign of the result

$$\frac{d}{dx}(\cos^{-1} x) = -\frac{1}{\sqrt{1-x^2}}$$

To differentiate $\tan^{-1} x$

Let $y = \tan^{-1} x$

Then $\tan y = x$

or $x = \tan y \quad \ldots (1)$

$$\therefore \frac{dx}{dy} = \sec^2 y$$

$$\text{and } \frac{dy}{dx} = \frac{1}{\sec^2 y}$$

Here we use $\sec^2 y = 1 + \tan^2 y = 1 + x^2$ (from (1))

(This follows from $\sin^2 y + \cos^2 y = 1$
Dividing by $\cos^2 y$: $\tan^2 y + 1 = \sec^2 y$)

$$\therefore \frac{dy}{dx} = \frac{1}{1+x^2}$$

$$\frac{d}{dx}(\tan^{-1} x) = \frac{1}{1+x^2}$$

The graph of $y = \tan^{-1} x$ is given in Fig. 11.17.

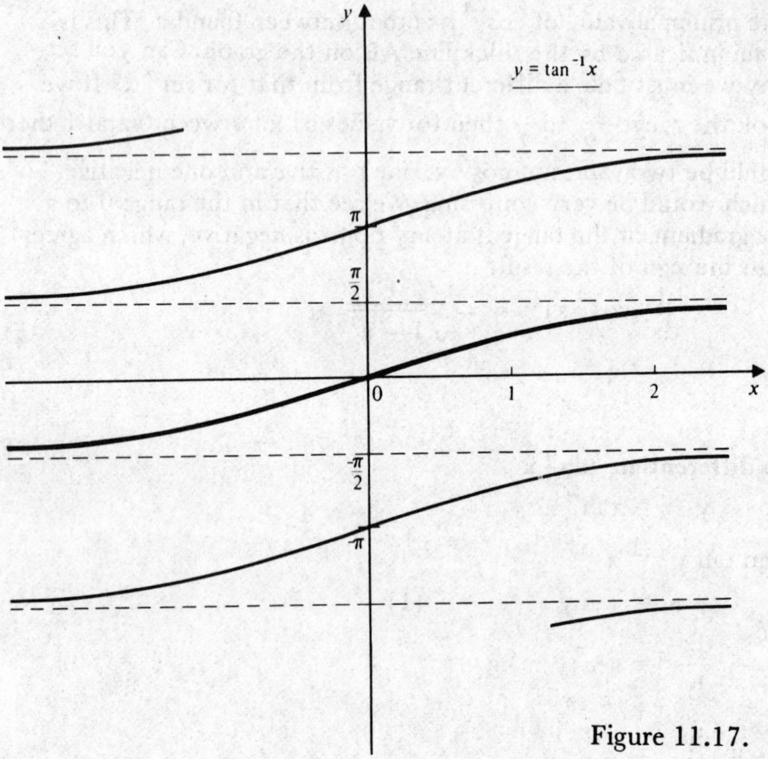

Figure 11.17.

The principal value of $\tan^{-1} x$ is between $\frac{-\pi}{2}$ and $\frac{\pi}{2}$. Here we see again that the gradient of the curve at any point is always positive.

Exercise 37. Differentiate the following functions using the rule for a 'function of a function' :

1. $\sin^{-1}(4x)$	4. $\cos^{-1}(3x)$	7. $\tan^{-1}(3x)$
2. $\sin^{-1}\frac{x}{2}$	5. $\cos^{-1}\frac{x}{3}$	8. $\tan^{-1}\frac{x}{3}$
3. $\sin^{-1}\frac{x}{a}$	6. $\cos^{-1}\frac{x}{a}$	9. $\tan^{-1}\frac{x}{a}$

Note: The answers to Nos 3, 6, 9 are standard differentials.

Exercise 38. Harder examples on maxima and minima.

(You must discriminate between maximum and minimum values).

1. Find the maximum value of the bending moment M of a beam at a point distance x from one end, if $M = \frac{1}{2}w\,(lx - x^2)$ where l = the length of beam, and w = the weight per unit length.

2. In a machine the power W is given by $W = Ei - Ri^2$ where i is the current, E is the E.M.F. and R the resistance. Find the maximum value of W.
   Consider E and R constant.

3. The efficiency of a screw is given by

   $$E = \frac{t(1 - \mu t)}{\mu + t}$$

   where t = the tangent of the angle of pitch and μ = the co-efficient of friction which is constant. For what value of t is E maximum? (μ is the Greek letter mu, pronounced 'mew'.)

4. Find the minimum value of the sum of a positive number and its reciprocal.

5. The cost of a journey works out at £C per hour given by

   $$C = 16 + \frac{v^2}{100}$$

   where v is the speed in km/h. Find what speed gives the least cost for the whole journey.
   Let the length of the journey be d km, and the time taken be t hours.

6. An open metal box with a square base is to be made to hold 4 cubic metres. Find what is the least area of sheet metal which must be used. (Let x metres = edge of square base.)

Chapter 12

The binomial series

Now we need an easy method for expanding in powers of x, expressions such as $(1 + 3x)^{10}$ or $(5 - 2x)^{\frac{1}{2}}$ or $(3x - 2)^{\frac{1}{4}}$.

We start by considering what we already know about some simple cases. We know that:

$$(1 + x)^1 = 1 + x$$
$$(1 + x)^2 = 1 + 2x + x^2$$
$$(1 + x)^3 = 1 + 3x + 3x^2 + x^3$$
$$(1 + x)^4 = 1 + 4x + 6x^2 + 4x^3 + x^4$$

We can check the last two expressions by multiplying the previous lines by $(1 + x)$ and collecting like terms.

Here we can also put in:

$(1 + x)^0 = 1$ (anything to the power nought equals 1)

Taking coefficients only:

$(1+x)^0$ =					1					
$(1+x)^1$ =				1		1				
$(1+x)^2$ =			1		2		1			
$(1+x)^3$ =		1		3		3		1		
$(1+x)^4$ =	1		4		6		4		1	

Note that each coefficient is the sum of the two coefficients immediately above it, as shown.

This suggests coefficients of $(1+x)^5$ = 1 5 10 10 5 1.
We can check this by multiplying $(1+x)^4$ by $(1+x)$ and collecting up. Obviously, this method, although interesting, is not suitable for large powers, negative powers or fractional powers. This pattern of numbers is known as Pascal's triangle.

We have to find a more general formula.
We can check that:

$$(1+x)^3 = 1 + \frac{3}{1}x + \frac{3\cdot 2}{1\cdot 2}x^2 + \frac{3.2.1}{1.2.3}x^3$$

$$(1+x)^4 = 1 + \frac{4}{1}x + \frac{4\cdot 3}{1\cdot 2}x^2 + \frac{4.3.2}{1.2.3}x^3 + \frac{4.3.2.1}{1.2.3.4}x^4$$

$$(1+x)^5 = 1 + \frac{5}{1}x + \frac{5\cdot 4}{1\cdot 2}x^2 + \frac{5.4.3}{1.2.3}x^3 + \frac{5.4.3.2}{1.2.3.4}x^4 + \frac{5.4.3.2.1}{1.2.3.4.5}x^5$$

All these cancel down to the expressions already found.

This pattern suggests that:

$$(1+x)^n = 1 + \frac{nx}{1} + \frac{n(n-1)}{1.2}x^2 + \frac{n(n-1)(n-2)\,x^3}{1.2.3} + \frac{n(n-1)(n-2)(n-3)}{1.2.3.4}x^4 + \ldots\ldots$$

Note 1: The coefficient of any particular power of x in the series has the same number of factors in the numerator and denominator as the power of x, e.g.

$$\text{coefficient of } x^4 = \frac{n(n-1)(n-2)(n-3)}{1\cdot 2\cdot 3\cdot 4} \quad \begin{matrix}\text{4 factors}\\ \text{4 factors}\end{matrix}$$

Note 2: The factors of the numerator decrease by 1: the factors of the denominator increase by 1.

Note 3: We abbreviate $1\cdot 2$ to 2! and read 'two factorial'
$1\cdot 2\cdot 3$ to 3! and read 'three factorial'
$1\cdot 2\cdot 3\cdot 4$ to 4! and read 'four factorial' etc.

Thus: $(1 + x)^n = 1 + \frac{nx}{1!} + \frac{n(n-1)}{2!}x^2 + \frac{n(n-1)(n-2)}{3!}x^3 + \ldots$

This formula was discovered by Sir Isaac Newton and is called The Binomial Series.

Note 1: If n is a positive integer the series ends.

Note 2: If n is fractional or negative the series is unending and in this case x must be numerically less than 1.

Proof of these can be found in any text-book of Higher Algebra.

Example 1. Write down the first four terms of the expansion of $(1 + x)^{10}$

Here $n = 10$

$$(1 + x)^{10} = 1 + \frac{10}{1}x + \frac{10\cdot 9}{1\cdot 2}x^2 + \frac{10\cdot 9\cdot 8\cdot}{1\cdot 2\cdot 3}x^3 + \ldots.$$

(N.B. Don't cancel at this stage. Leave the coefficients clear for checking.)

$$\therefore\ (1 + x)^{10} = 1 + 10x + \frac{\overset{5}{\cancel{10}}\cdot 9}{1\cdot\underset{1}{\cancel{2}}}x^2 + \frac{10\cdot\overset{3}{\cancel{9}}\cdot\overset{4}{\cancel{8}}}{1\cdot\underset{1}{\cancel{2}}\cdot\underset{1}{\cancel{3}}}x^3 + \ldots.$$

$$= \mathbf{1 + 10x + 45x^2 + 120x^3 + \ldots.}$$

Example 2. Give the first four terms of $(1 - 2x)^5$
Here 'x' in the standard formula is replaced by $(-2x)$ and $n = 5$

$$(1 - 2x)^5 = [1 + (-2x)]^5$$

$$= 1 + \frac{5}{1}(-2x) + \frac{5\cdot 4}{1\cdot 2}(-2x)^2 + \frac{5\cdot 4\cdot 3}{1\cdot 2\cdot 3}(-2x)^3 \ \ldots.$$

$$= 1 - 10x + \frac{5\cdot 4\cdot\overset{1}{\cancel{2}}\cdot\cdot 2}{1\cdot\underset{1}{\cancel{2}}}x^2 - \frac{5\cdot 4\cdot\cancel{3}\cdot 2\cdot\cancel{2}\cdot 2}{1\cdot\cancel{2}\cdot\cancel{3}}x^3 + \ldots.$$

$$= \mathbf{1 - 10x + 40x^2 - 80x^3 + \ldots.}$$

(Note the alternating signs.)

Example 3.

(i) Expand $\sqrt{1+x}$ as far as the term in x^3 ; and

(ii) Find an approximation for $\sqrt{1.01}$ correct to 4 d.p. (decimal places).

(i) $\sqrt{1+x} = (1+x)^{1/2}$

$$= 1 + \frac{1}{2}x + \frac{(\frac{1}{2})(-\frac{1}{2})}{1.2}x^2 + \frac{(\frac{1}{2})(-\frac{1}{2})(-\frac{3}{2})}{1.2.3}x^3 \quad \ldots.$$

$$= 1 + \frac{1}{2}x - \frac{1}{2}.\frac{1}{2}\frac{1}{1.2}x^2 + \frac{1}{2}.\frac{1}{2}.\frac{\overset{1}{\cancel{3}}}{2}.\frac{1}{1.2.\underset{1}{\cancel{3}}}x^3$$

$$= 1 + \frac{1}{2}x - \frac{1}{8}x^2 + \frac{1}{16}x^3 \quad \ldots.$$

(ii) $\sqrt{1.01} = \sqrt{1+0.01}$

Put $x = 0.01$ in the above expansion:

$$\sqrt{1.01} = 1 + \frac{1}{2}(0.01) - \frac{1}{8}(0.01)^2 + \frac{1}{16}(0.01)^3$$

$$= 1 + 0.005 - 0.0000125 + 0.00000006$$

$$= 1 + 0.0049875$$

$$= 1.0050$$

$$(0.01)^2 = 0.0001$$

$$\frac{1}{8}(0.01)^2 = 0.0000125$$

$$(0.01)^3 = 0.000001$$

$$\frac{1}{16}(0.01)^3 = 0.00000006$$

We see from the last example that provided x is sufficiently small, $\sqrt{1+x}$ equals approximately $1 + \frac{1}{2}x$.

Exercise 39. Use the binomial expansion to give the first four terms of the following:

1. $(1 + x)^6$
2. $(1 - x)^6$
3. $(1 + x)^8$
4. $(1 - x)^8$
5. $(1 + 2x)^4$
6. $(1 - \frac{3}{2}x)^4$
7. $(3 + x)^5 = 3^5 (1 + \frac{x}{3})^5$
8. $(1 - x)^{\frac{1}{2}}$
9. $(1 + x)^{-\frac{1}{2}}$
10. $(1 - x)^{-3}$

x numerically less than 1, i.e. $|x| < 1$ (Read: 'mod x is less than 1'). In other words x lies between -1 and $+1$.

11. Show that if x is numerically less than 1

$\frac{1}{\sqrt{1 - x}}$ is approximately equal to $1 + \frac{1}{2}x + \frac{1.3}{2.4}x^2 + \frac{1.3.5}{2.4.6}x^3$

12. Write down (without simplifying) the following :

(i) the fourth term of $(1 + 2x)^7$;
(ii) the fifth term of $(1 - x)^{-2}$;
(iii) the fourth term of $\sqrt{(4 - x)}$.

Chapter 13

The law of natural growth

Most of us are aware of the fact that some things increase at an increasing rate. We are continually being reminded for instance that world population is increasing at an increasing rate, or more impressively, that man's available travel speed during the last 100 years or so, since the invention of the steam locomotive, has grown from about 13 mph to 18,000 mph with space travel (Fig.13.1).

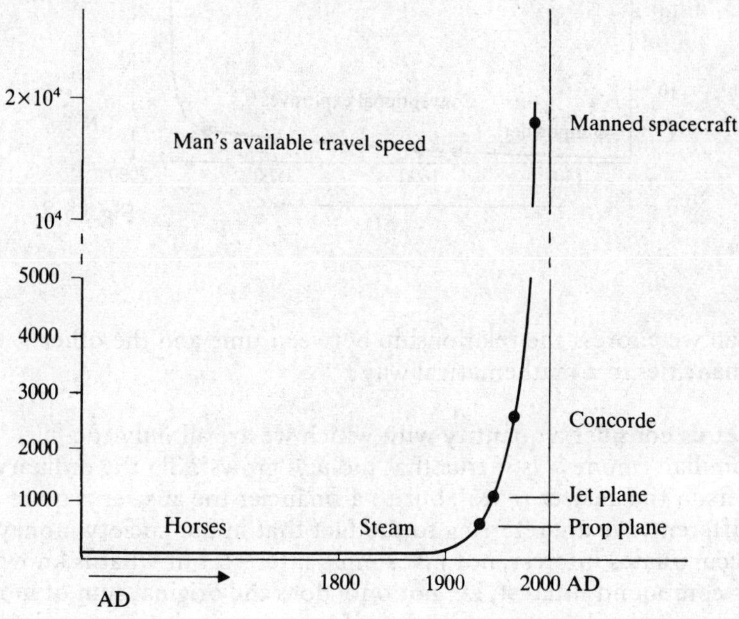

Fig.13.1

The growth in explosive power available to men shows a similar pattern (Fig.13.2), as does the number of books published.

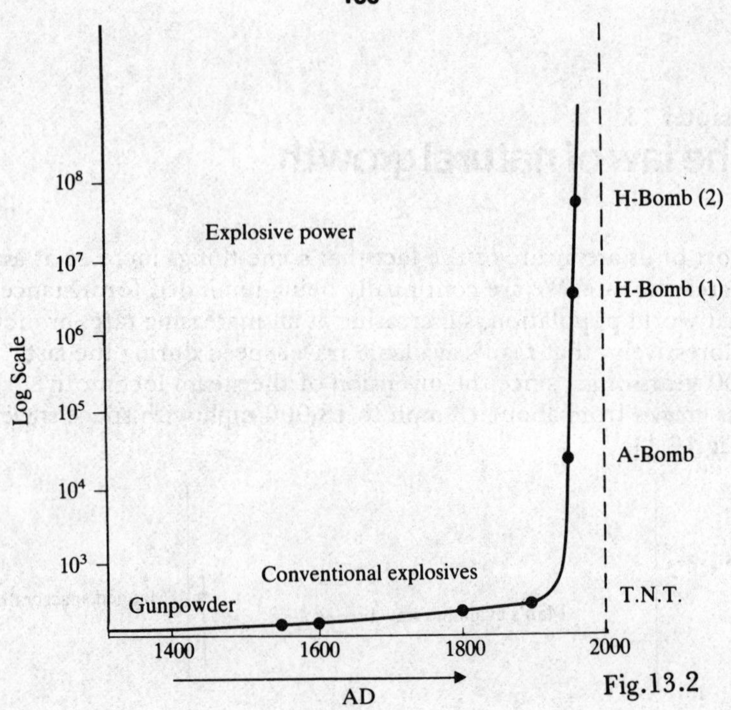

Fig.13.2

Can we express the relationship between time and the other quantities in a mathematical way?

Let us consider a quantity with which we are all only too familiar - money. Is it true that money 'grows'? To the ordinary person the answer is 'no', but to a financier the answer is quite different. We are referring to the fact that in our society money accumulates interest, not just simple interest, but what is known as compound interest, i.e. not only does the original sum of money gain interest, but the interest itself accumulates interest, and the interest on the interest accumulates more interest, and so on. Let us see how this works by taking an example.

Bank rate at the moment is 8 per cent (say). If we invest a £100 unit, at simple interest*, reckoned yearly this would gain £8 interest each year steadily and the graph of the growth of our money would look like Fig.13.3. In other words, a straight line graph with a gradient of £8 per year.

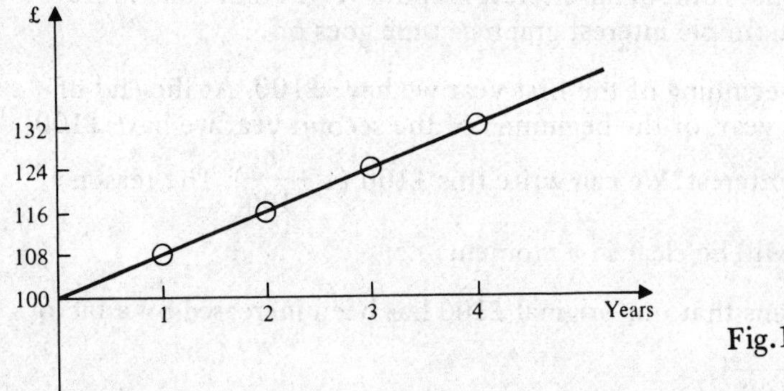

Fig.13.3

(*The term 'simple interest' implies that at the end of each year the interest is drawn out of the bank, and kept somewhere without interest.)

On the other hand, if the interest is left to accumulate in the bank account, a different picture arises.

We started with £100 at the beginning.

We gained £8 during the first year making a total of £108.

This £108 then accumulates interest at 8 per cent, that is the extra £8 also gains some interest, so that the interest during the second year is a bit more than £8, in fact £8.64, and during the third year this extra bit also accumulates interest. And so on. This is called compound interest.

The graph looks like Fig.13.4.

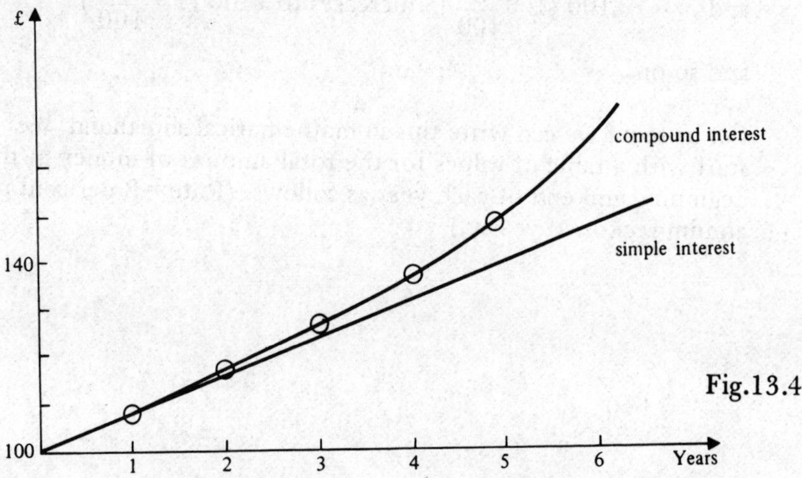

Fig.13.4

So that the compound interest graph diverges more and more from the simple interest graph as time goes on.

At the beginning of the first year we have £100. At the end of the first year, or the beginning of the second year we have £100 plus £8 interest. We can write this £100 $(1 + \frac{8}{100})$. The reason for this will be clear in a moment.

This means that our original £100 has been increased by a factor of $(1 + \frac{8}{100})$.

If we had started with £50 it would have increased to £50 plus £4 interest i.e. £50 $(1 + \frac{4}{50})$. In other words, it has increased by the same factor.

This will happen whatever amount we start with and whatever year we are dealing with. The multiplying factor is the same.

Hence, £200 increases to £200$(1 + \frac{8}{100})$

£x increases to £ $x(1 + \frac{8}{100})$

and also £100 $(1 + \frac{8}{100})$ increases to £100 $(1 + \frac{8}{100})(1 + \frac{8}{100})$

$= £100\ (1 + \frac{8}{100})^2$

and £100 $(1 + \frac{8}{100})^2$ increases to £100 $(1 + \frac{8}{100})^3$

and so on.

Let us see if we can write this in mathematical shorthand. We start with a table of values for the total amount of money at the beginning and end of each year as follows. (Rate = 8 per cent per annum reckoned yearly.)

Yearly

Year	Beginning £	End £	
1	100	100 + 8	$= 100\,(1 + \frac{8}{100})$ i.e.
2	$100\,(1 + \frac{8}{100})$	$100\,(1 + \frac{8}{100})^2$	a <u>multiplying</u> <u>factor</u> of
3	$100\,(1 + \frac{8}{100})^2$	$100\,(1 + \frac{8}{100})^3$	$(1 + \frac{8}{100})$ each year.

and so on.

This is when the interest is reckoned yearly.

But the interest can be reckoned half-yearly, quarterly, monthly, or even day by day.

Take the second case of half-yearly interest. Our 8 per cent per year would now be split into two 4 per cent interests every half-year. So that during the second half year interest is gained on the previous half year's 4 per cent interest.

Making a table of this we see the following:

Half yearly.

	½ Year	Beginning £	End £
Year 1	1st	100	$100\,(1 + \frac{8}{200})$ *
	2nd	$100\,(1 + \frac{8}{200})$	$100\,(1 + \frac{8}{200})^2$
Year 2	1st	$100\,(1 + \frac{8}{200})^2$	$100\,(1 + \frac{8}{200})^3$
	2nd	$100\,(1 + \frac{8}{200})^3$	$100\,(1 + \frac{8}{200})^4$

and so on.

* We leave it in this form for comparison with the 8 per cent per annum figure.

If interest is reckoned monthly: i.e. at $\frac{8}{12}$ per cent interest each month:

Monthly

	Month	Beginning £	End £
	1st	100	$100\ (1 + \frac{8}{1200})$
	2nd	$100\ (1 + \frac{8}{1200})$	$100\ (1 + \frac{8}{1200})^2$
Year 1	3rd	$100\ (1 + \frac{8}{1200})^2$	$100\ (1 + \frac{8}{1200})^3$
	12th		$100\ (1 + \frac{8}{1200})^{12}$

Noting this last amount, we are justified in saying that if the interest of 8 per cent is reckoned n times per year,

The amount at the end of year = $100\ (1 + \frac{8}{100\,n})^n$

If the interest is x per cent per annum reckoned n times per year, we have an interest at the end of 1 year of

£ $(1 + \frac{x}{100\,n})^n$ on every £1 invested.

This type of expression of the type
$(1 + \frac{a}{n})^n$ where a is a constant ($= \frac{x}{100}$, here)

is a recurring pattern in technology.

What happens if the growth is continuous? That is, the growth takes place steadily instead of in distinct steps, as in our examples. We are asking, what happens when the growth is reckoned second by second? In our language we are asking what happens when n gets very large. Yes, you have guessed it. What happens when $n \to \infty$?

Definition

The limit of this function $(1 + \frac{x}{n})^n$ as $n \to \infty$ is called e^x

In this form it looks rather formidable, but let us see what we can do with it. Using the standard binominal expansion

i.e. $(1 + x)^n = 1 + nx + \frac{n(n-1)}{2!}x^2 + \;\; \ldots.$

Replacing x by $(\frac{x}{n})$ we get

$$(1 + \frac{x}{n})^n = 1 + n\cdot(\frac{x}{n}) + \frac{n(n-1)}{2!}(\frac{x}{n})^2 + \frac{n(n-1)(n-2)}{3!}(\frac{x}{n})^3 + \ldots$$

Rearranging the n's in the denominator:

$$(1 + \frac{x}{n})^n = 1 + \frac{n}{n}x + \frac{\frac{n}{n}(\frac{n-1}{n})}{2!}x^2 + \frac{\frac{n}{n}(\frac{n-1}{n})(\frac{n-2}{n})}{3!}x^3 \;\; \ldots.$$

$$= 1 + x + \frac{1(1-\frac{1}{n})}{2!}x^2 + \frac{1(1-\frac{1}{n})(1-\frac{2}{n})}{3!}x^3 + \;\; \ldots.$$

Now let $n \to \infty$. Then $\frac{1}{n} \to 0$.

$$\therefore \text{Lim } (1 + \frac{x}{n})^n = 1 + x + \frac{1\cdot1}{2!}x^2 + \frac{1\cdot1\cdot1}{3!}x^3 + \;\; \ldots.$$

$$\therefore e^x = 1 + x + \frac{x^2}{2!} + \frac{x^3}{3!} + \frac{x^4}{4!} + \;\; \ldots.$$

This is an infinite series, i.e. a series containing an infinite number of terms (it has no ending).

What is the value of e?

We can deduce this by putting x = 1

$\therefore e = 1 + 1 + \frac{1}{2!} + \frac{1}{3!} + \frac{1}{4!} + \ldots$ (the first three terms total 2.5)

$$= 2.5 + \frac{1}{6} + \frac{1}{24} + \frac{1}{120} + \frac{1}{720} + \ldots$$

This can be evaluated to any number of decimal places and gives

e = 2.71828 to 5 d.p.

This constant e is very important, as it has some very special characteristics.

DIFFERENTIATION OF e^x

First method

$$e^x = 1 + x + \frac{x^2}{2!} + \frac{x^3}{3!} + \frac{x^4}{4!} + \ldots..$$

Differentiating term by term:

$$\therefore \frac{d}{dx}(e^x) = 0 + 1 + \frac{2x}{2.1} + \frac{3x^2}{3.2.1} + \frac{4x^3}{4.3.2.1} + \ldots..$$

$$= 1 + x + \frac{x^2}{2.1} + \frac{x^3}{3.2.1} + \ldots.$$

$$\therefore \frac{d}{dx}(e^x) = e^x$$

N.B. e^x is the only function which has the gradient at every point on its graph equal to the value of the function at that point.

Second method from first principles

$$\text{Let } y = e^x \qquad \ldots (1)$$

$$\therefore \quad y + \delta y = e^{x + \delta x}$$

$$= e^x . e^{\delta x} \qquad \text{(rule of indices for multiplication)}$$

$$= e^x \left[1 + \delta x + \frac{(\delta x)^2}{2!} + \frac{(\delta x)^3}{3!} + \ldots..\right] \qquad \ldots (2)$$

$\therefore$ Subtracting (1) from (2)

$$\delta y = e^x \left[1 + \delta x + \frac{(\delta x)^2}{2!} + \frac{(\delta x)^3}{3!} + \ldots..\right] - e^x$$

$$= e^x \left[\delta x + \frac{(\delta x)^2}{2!} + \frac{(\delta x)^3}{3!} + \ldots..\right]$$

$$\therefore \quad \frac{\delta y}{\delta x} = e^x \left[1 + \frac{\delta x}{2!} + \frac{(\delta x)^2}{3!} + \ldots..\right]$$

$$\therefore \quad \lim_{\delta x \to 0} \frac{\delta y}{\delta x} = e^x . 1 \qquad \text{since all other terms approach 0.}$$

$$\therefore \quad \frac{dy}{dx} = e^x$$

$$\therefore \quad \frac{d}{dx}[e^x] = e^x$$

Examples. Differentiate the following:

(i) e^{2x} ; (ii) e^{ax} ; (iii) e^{-x} ; (iv) e^{-x^2} (v) $e^{(3x+2)}$

(i) Let $y = e^{2x}$

$$\therefore \frac{dy}{dx} = e^{2x} \times \text{(differential of } 2x)$$
$$= 2e^{2x}$$

(ii) Let $y = e^{ax}$

$$\frac{dy}{dx} = a.e^{ax}$$

(iii) Let $y = e^{-x}$

$$\therefore \frac{dy}{dx} = e^{-x} \times \text{(differential of } -x)$$
$$= -e^{-x}$$

(iv) Let $y = e^{-x^2}$

$$\therefore \frac{dy}{dx} = e^{-x^2} \times \text{(differential of } -x^2)$$
$$= -2x\, e^{-x^2}$$

(v) Let $y = e^{(3x+2)}$

$$\therefore \frac{dy}{dx} = e^{(3x+2)} \times [\text{differential of } (3x+2)]$$
$$= 3e^{(3x+2)}$$

Exercise 40. Differentiate the following functions of x :

1. e^{-x}
2. e^{3x}
3. $e^{(4x-1)}$
4. $e^{(ax+b)}$
5. $3e^{2x}$
6. $\frac{1}{4}e^{(4x+2)}$
7. $e^{-\frac{x}{2}}$
8. e^{2x^2}
9. $3x^2 e^x$ (Use $d(uv) = v\,du + u\,dv$)
10. $e^x + e^{-x}$
11. xe^{ax} (use $d(uv) = v\,du + u\,dv$)
12. $e^{\sin x}$
13. $\dfrac{e^x - e^{-x}}{e^x + e^{-x}}$ (use $d(uv) = \dfrac{v\,du - u\,dv}{v^2}$)

    (Remember: $e^x \,.\, e^x = e^{2x}$)
14. $\dfrac{x^2 + 2x}{e^x}$

Integrate the following functions of x using $\int e^{ax}\,dx = \dfrac{e^{ax}}{a} + c$:

15. e^{-x}
16. e^{3x}
17. $e^{(4x-1)}$
18. $e^{(ax+b)}$
19. $3e^{2x}$
20. $\frac{1}{4}e^{(4x+2)}$
21. $e^{-\frac{x}{2}}$
22. $e^{x} + e^{-x}$
23. xe^{2x^2} (c.f. No. 8)

Theory of logarithms, including logs to base e

At this stage it is convenient to revise common logarithms, i.e. logarithms to base 10, in preparation for studying natural or Naperian logarithms, i.e. logs to base e.

Revision

Logarithms arise naturally from our laws of indices, which in symbols, as we already know, are as follows:

(i) $a^m \times a^n = a^{m+n}$

(ii) $a^m \div a^n = a^{m-n}$

(iii) $(a^m)^n = a^{mn}$

(iv) $\sqrt[n]{a^m} = a^{\frac{m}{n}}$

OR in words:

(i) When multiplying powers of the same number or letter add the indices.

(ii) When dividing powers of the same number or letter subtract the indices.

(iii) When raising one power to another power multiply the indices.

(iv) When taking a square root of a power of a letter or number, divide the power by 2, and similarly for other roots.

We know that

$$1000 = 10^3$$

$$100 = 10^2$$

$$10 = 10^1$$

$$1 = 10^0$$

$$\frac{1}{10} = 10^{-1}$$

$$\frac{1}{100} = 10^{-2}$$

and so on.

These indices are the logarithms of the corresponding numbers, e.g. 3 is the $\log_{10} 1000$.

That is:

$\log_{10} 1000 = 3$ (Read: 'log of 1000 base 10 equals 3')

$\log_{10} 100 = 2$

$\log_{10} 10 = 1$

$\log_{10} 1 = 0$

It follows that:

(i) the log of a number between 1 and 10 lies between 0 and 1
(ii) the log of a number between 10 and 100 lies between 1 and 2.
(iii) the log of a number between 100 and 1000 lies between 2 and 3.

and so on.

These facts enable us to use one set of logarithm tables, i.e. from 1 to 10, to find the logarithm of any number, by adjusting the whole number part of the logarithm. The decimal part always remains the same for any given set of figures regardless of the position of the decimal point.

Example. From tables,

$\log_{10} 3.0 = 0.4771$

$\therefore \log_{10} 30 = 1.4771$

and $\log_{10} 300 = 2.4771$

$\log_{10} 3000 = 3.4771$

Note that the whole number part of the log is increased by 1 every time the number is multiplied by 10.

Reversing the process, and moving the decimal point the other way:

log 0.3. = log (3×10^{-1}) = $\bar{1}.4771$ (Read $\bar{1}$ as 'bar one')
log 0.03 = log (3×10^{-2}) = $\bar{2}.4771$ (Read $\bar{2}$ as 'bar two')
etc.

These 'bar' numbers are negative whole numbers. The negative is written over the top of the number instead of in front, as we must keep the decimal part of the log positive, and this method conveys the fact that the negative sign applies only to the number on which it stands. These 'bar' numbers are added and subtracted in the normal way as with negative numbers.

To change from powers to logarithmic form and vice-versa.

Since 1000 = 10^3 ← log we say $\log_{10} 1000 = 3$
(1000 ↓ number; 10 ↓ base)

Similarly if (a number) = (a base)^{power}

we say $\log_{\text{base}}(\text{number}) = \text{power}$

i.e.

i.e. if $x = a^n$
then $\log_a x = n$

These two things are saying the same thing.

It is possible to construct tables of logarithms to any base. Three sets of tables are in general use.

Common logarithms are logarithms to base 10, and are used mainly for straight-forward calculations.

Natural or Naperian logarithms have a base e and are used mainly in theoretical work, since the differential coefficient of $\log_e x$ is simple. (see below)

In communication problems in electronics it is useful to use logarithms to base 2. The reasons for this are too lengthy to explain here.

RULES OF LOGARITHMS

Logarithms are indices. Hence the rules are as follows, for logs to any base:

1. **To MULTIPLY two numbers using logarithms ADD their logarithms.**
2. **To DIVIDE two numbers using logarithms SUBTRACT their logarithms.**
3. **To SQUARE a number MULTIPLY the logarithm by TWO and similarly for cubing, etc.**
4. **To find the SQUARE ROOT of a number DIVIDE the logarithm by 2, and similarly for a cube root, etc.**
5. **Then use antilogarithm tables to convert back to numbers.**

In symbols:

1. $\log(AB) = \log A + \log B$
2. $\log(A/B) = \log A - \log B$
3. $\log A^n = n \log A$
4. $\log \sqrt[n]{A} = \frac{1}{n} \log A$

Natural or Napierian Logarithms

These are also called hyperbolic logarithms, and are logs to base e

Let $y = e^x$

Then $\log_e y = x$ by definition

To find the differential coefficient of $\log_e x$

Let $y = \log_e x$ ... (1)

$\therefore x = e^y$ ... (2)

Differentiate w.r.t. y :

$$\therefore \frac{dx}{dy} = e^y$$

$$\therefore \frac{dy}{dx} = \frac{1}{e^y} \quad \text{inverting both sides}$$

$$\therefore \frac{dy}{dx} = \frac{1}{x} \quad \text{since } x = e^y \text{ from (2)}$$

$$\therefore \frac{d}{dx}(\log_e x) = \frac{1}{x}$$

and also $\int \frac{1}{x} dx = \log_e x + \text{constant}$

Example 1. Differentiate:

(i) $\log_e(3x+2)$ (ii) $\log_e(2-x^2)$

(iii) $\log_e\dfrac{(3+x)}{(3-x)}$ (iv) $\log_e(1+x^2)$

(i) Let $y = \log_e(3x+2)$

$$\therefore \frac{dy}{dx} = \frac{1}{3x+2} \cdot \text{[differential of } (3x+2)]$$

$$= \frac{3}{3x+2}$$

(ii) Let $y = \log_e(2-x^2)$

$$\therefore \frac{dy}{dx} = \frac{1}{2-x^2} \quad \text{[differential of } (2-x^2)]$$

$$= \frac{-2x}{2-x^2}$$

(iii) Let $y = \log_e\dfrac{3+x}{3-x}$

$$= \log_e(3+x) - \log_e(3-x)$$

$$\therefore \frac{dy}{dx} = \frac{1}{(3+x)}.1 - \frac{1}{(3-x)}.(-1)$$

$$= \frac{1}{3+x} + \frac{1}{3-x}$$

$$= \frac{3-x+3+x}{(3+x)(3-x)}$$

$$= \frac{6}{(9-x^2)}$$

(iv) Let $y = \log_e(1+x^2)$

$$\therefore \frac{dy}{dx} = \frac{1}{(1+x^2)} \cdot \quad \text{(differential of } (1+x^2))$$

$$= \frac{2x}{(1+x^2)}$$

Example 2. Find the integrals of :

(i) $\frac{1}{3x+2}$: (ii) $\frac{3}{1-x}$: (iii) $\frac{6}{4-3x}$

with respect to x

(i) $\int \frac{1}{3x+2}\,dx = \log_e(3x+2)$ (divided by the differential of what is inside the bracket.)

(This is the converse of Example 1, Part (i))

$\therefore \int \frac{1}{3x+2}\,dx = \frac{1}{3}\log_e(3x+2) + \text{constant}$

Check: By differentiating the R.H.S., the 3's cancel out giving the quantity under the $\int$ sign.

(ii) $\int \frac{3}{1-x}\,dx = 3\int \frac{1}{1-x}dx$

$= 3\log_e(1-x) \div$ [differential of $(1-x)$] + constant

$= 3\log_e(1-x) \div (-1) + \text{constant}$

$= -3\log(1-x) + \text{constant}$

(iii) $\int \frac{6}{4-3x}\,dx = 6\log_e(4-3x) \div (-3) + \text{constant}$

$= -2\log(4-3x) + \text{constant}$

Always check integrals by differentiation of the answer.

Note 1: We can integrate fractions of this type by inspection, only if the expression in the denominator is of the first power in x.
We cannot reverse the process used in Example 1, part (iii) without some practice with partial fractions (See Chapter 18).

Note 2: Some harder integrals of this type can be done by inspection, provided the integral is of a special type (see Example 1, part (iv) and reverse the process).

These integrals are of the type

$$\int \frac{\text{differential of denominator}}{\text{denominator}}.\,dx$$

For example: $\int \frac{6x - 2}{3x^2 - 2x + 1} \, dx$

$$= \log_e(3x^2 - 2x + 1) + \text{constant}$$

Check: Differentiating gives $\frac{1}{(3x^2 - 2x + 1)}$ multiplied by

[differential of $3x^2 - 2x + 1$]

$$= \frac{6x - 2}{3x^2 - 2x + 1}$$

GRAPHS OF e^x, e^{-x}, $\log_e x$

The graph of $y = e^x$ is a steadily increasing function.
If we interchange x and y in the equation $y = e^x$

we get $x = e^y$

or $\log_e x = y$

It can be shown that the graphs of $y = e^x$
and [$y = \log_e x$ (i.e. $x = e^y$)]
are reflections of each other in the line $y = x$ (Fig. 13.5), since this effects the interchange of x and y.

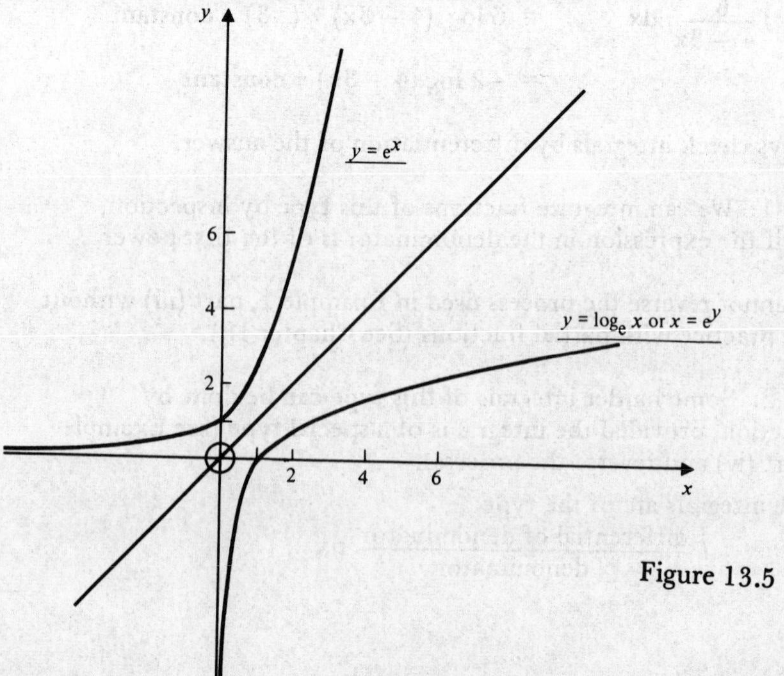

Figure 13.5

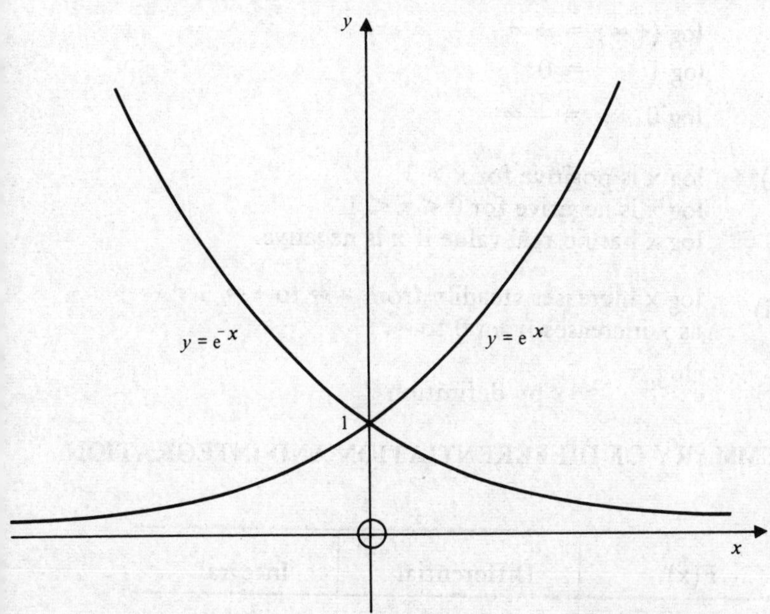

Figure 13.6

Also, since e^{-x} may be derived from e^x by changing the signs of x, the graph of e^{-x} is the reflection of the graph of e^x in the y axis (Fig. 13.6).

Properties of e^x

The following properties of e^x are worth noting.
The graph of e^x helps to memorise them.

1. $e^\infty = \infty \qquad e^0 = 1 \qquad e^{-\infty} = 0$

2. $e^x > 1$ for all positive values of x

   $e^x < 1$ for all negative values of x

3. **e^x is always positive for all values of x** and steadily increases from 0 to $+\infty$ as x increases from $-\infty$ to $+\infty$.

4. The equation $y = e^x$ for a given value of y has only one solution. This solution is $\mathbf{x = \log_e y}$.

Properties of $\log_e x$

(i) $\log(+\infty) = +\infty$

$\log 1 = 0$

$\log 0 = -\infty$

(ii) log x is positive for $x > 1$

log x is negative for $0 < x < 1$

log x has no real value if x is negative.

(iii) log x increases steadily from $-\infty$ to $+\infty$ as x increases from 0 to ∞.

(iv) $e^{\log_e x} = x$ by definition

SUMMARY OF DIFFERENTIATION AND INTEGRATION

F(x)	Differential	Integral
e^{kx}	$k\,e^{kx}$	$\dfrac{e^{kx}}{k}$
$\log_e(ax + b)$	$\dfrac{a}{ax + b}$	
$\dfrac{1}{ax + b}$	$-\dfrac{a}{(ax + b)^2}$	$\dfrac{1}{a}\log_e(ax + b)$

Now we can make a more complete table of differentials and integrals as follows:

f(x)	d f(x)
x^n	$n\,x^{n-1}$
sin x	cos x
cos x	− sin x
tan x	$\sec^2 x$
e^x	e^x
e^{ax}	ae^{ax}
$\log_e x$	$\frac{1}{x}$
sin ax	a cos ax
cos ax	− a sin ax
tan ax	$a\sec^2 ax$
uv	u dv + v du
$\frac{u}{v}$	$\frac{v\,du - u\,dv}{v^2}$

$$\left[\ \frac{dy}{dx} = \frac{dy}{dz} \times \frac{dz}{dx}\ \right]$$

f(x)	∫f(x) dx	
x^n	$\frac{x^{n+1}}{n+1}$	$n \neq -1$
$\frac{1}{x}$	$\log_e x$	
sin x	− cos x	
cos x	sin x	
e^x	e^x	
e^{ax}	$\frac{1}{a}e^{ax}$	
sin ax	$-\frac{1}{a}\cos ax$	
cos ax	$\frac{1}{a}\sin ax$	

Exercise 41. Differentiate the following :

1. $\log_e(3x)$
2. $\log_e(4x - 1)$
3. $2 \log_e(x^2)$
4. $\log_e(ax + b)$
5. $x^3 \log_e x$ (use the product rule)
6. $\log_e(\sin x)$
7. $\log_e(\cos x)$
8. $\log_e \frac{a + x}{a - x}$
   (use $\log\frac{A}{B} = \log A - \log B$)
9. $\log_e(e^x + e^{-x})$
10. $x \log_e 2x$
    (use the product rule)
11. $\log_e(\sqrt{\sin x})$
    (use $\log A^{½} = ½ \log A$)
12. $\sin ax \log_e bx$
    (use the product rule)
13. $\log_e ax \log_e bx$

Integrate the following:

14. (i) $\int \frac{dx}{1 + x}$ (ii) $\int \frac{dx}{1 - x}$

15. (i) $\int \frac{3\,dx}{2 + 3x}$ (ii) $\int \frac{3\,dx}{2 - 3x}$

16. (i) $\int \frac{dx}{1 - 4x}$ (ii) $\int \frac{dx}{3 + 2x}$

17. (i) $\int \frac{2x\,dx}{1 + x^2}$ (ii) $\int \frac{6x^2}{2 + 2x^3}\,dx$

18. (i) $\int \frac{2x - 3}{x^2 - 3x}\,dx$ (ii) $\int \frac{\sin x}{\cos x}\,dx$

Evaluate the following definite integrals.

(Remember - the log tables involved are logs to base e, not common logarithms.)

19. $\int_1^2 \frac{1}{1 + x}\,dx$

20. $-\int_2^3 \frac{3}{x - 1}\,dx$

21. $\int_0^{1.5} \frac{x}{1 + x^2}\,dx$

22. $\int_{1.5}^{2.5} \frac{2}{1 + 3x}\,dx$

23. $\int_{1}^{2} (e^{x} + e^{-x})\, dx$

25. $\int_{-\frac{1}{2}}^{1} e^{(2x+1)}\, dx$

24. $\int_{-0.25}^{0.25} \frac{1}{4} e^{3x}\, dx$

THE EXPONENTIAL FUNCTION AND THE LAW OF NATURAL GROWTH

We now have to consider the use of all this theory. Has it any uses and if so, what? What is the law of natural growth?

We state it first in words and then translate it into the familiar symbols.

The Law of Natural Growth states that a quantity obeys the law if the rate of increase (or decrease) of the quantity is always proportional to the quantity itself.

This law is very important as it occurs frequently in mechanics, physics and engineering sciences and biology.

In mathematical terms:

Let the quantity be y, which is a function of x (say)

Then the rate of increase of y w.r.t. x is $\frac{dy}{dx}$

This is proportional to y itself.

$$\frac{dy}{dx} = ky \qquad \text{where k is a constant}$$

This is a differential equation which we have to solve.
Can we solve it by integrating both sides w.r.t. x?
This would give $y = \int ky\, dx$ + constant.
But we don't know what y is in terms of x. (This is what we want to know). So it is impossible to integrate the right-hand side directly.

Note: Do not confuse the equation $\frac{dy}{dx} = ky$

with the equation $\frac{dy}{dx} = kx$

The latter is easily integrated, and gives

$$y = \int kx\, dx + \text{constant}$$

$$y = \frac{kx^2}{2} + \text{constant}$$

Let us try again to integrate $\frac{dy}{dx} = ky$

We can write this $\frac{dx}{dy} = \frac{1}{ky}$ inverting both sides

Now we can integrate with respect to y

$$\therefore \quad x = \int \frac{1}{ky}\,dy + \text{constant}$$

$$= \frac{1}{k}\log_e y + \text{constant} \quad \text{... (1)}$$

Suppose that y is some value (say C) when x = 0

Substituting: $$0 = \frac{1}{k}\log C + \text{constant}$$

$$\therefore \text{the constant} = -\frac{1}{k}\log C \quad \text{...(2)}$$

Substituting in (1) $$x = \frac{1}{k}(\log y - \log C)$$

$$= \frac{1}{k}\log\frac{y}{C}$$

$$\therefore \quad kx = \log_e\frac{y}{C}$$

$$\therefore \quad e^{kx} = \frac{y}{C} \quad \text{(by definition of logs)}$$

$$Ce^{kx} = y \text{ - an exponential function}$$

Summary

The solution of the equation $\frac{dy}{dx} = ky$

is $y = Ce^{kx}$

where C is a constant depending on initial conditions.

Conversely, every exponential function obeys the law of natural growth,

i.e. if $y = Ce^{kx}$ where C and k are constants

Differentiate w.r.t. x:

$$\frac{dy}{dx} = C\,ke^{kx}$$

$$\therefore \quad \frac{dy}{dx} = ky$$

That is, the rate of increase of y is proportional to y itself.

Examples in Science

Expansion of a metal rod

The law states that the rate of increase of the length of a metal rod with respect to temperature is proportional to the length of the rod at that temperature.

Let l = length of rod at temperature T^o

Then $\frac{dl}{dT} = kl$ where k is a constant depending on the type of metal used.

From preceding theory:

$l = l_o e^{kT}$ where l_o = original length when $T = 0$.

N.B. This increase is so small that in practice the terms of the exponential series after the first two terms are usually ignored giving:

$$l = l_o(1 + kT)$$

Newton's law of cooling

This states that the rate of cooling of a hot body is proportional to the temperature difference between the body and its surroundings.

Since the temperature is falling the gradient of the temperature-time graph is negative.

i.e. $\frac{dT}{dt} = -kT$ where T is the temperature difference at time t

$\therefore \quad$ **$T = T_o e^{-kt}$ where T_o is the temperature difference when $t = 0$**

Tension in a belt round a rough pulley

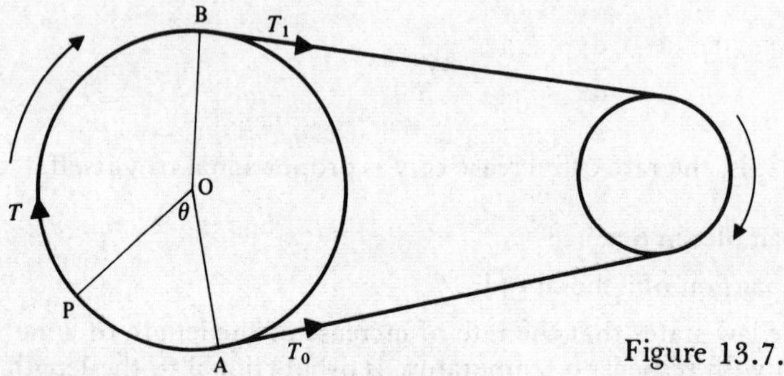

Figure 13.7.

If a belt is in contact with a rough pulley (Fig. 13.7) along an arc AB and is about to slip in the direction shown, then friction acts in the opposite direction, so that T_1 is greater than T_o.

It can be shown that if T is the tension at any point P on AB

$$T = T_o e^{\mu\Theta} \quad \text{where } \mu = \text{ coefficient of friction}$$

$$\text{and } \Theta = \angle AOP$$

Decay of current in an inductive circuit

The current i amperes in a circuit of resistance R ohms and inductance L henrys satisfies the equation:

$$L\frac{di}{dt} + Ri = E$$

where E volts is the E.M.F. applied to the circuit.

If the E.M.F. is cut off, i.e. E = 0, we get

$$L\frac{di}{dt} + Ri = 0$$

$$\therefore \quad \frac{di}{dt} = -\frac{R}{L}.i.$$

$$\therefore \quad i = i_o e^{-\frac{R}{L}.t}$$

where i_o = current at the time when the E.M.F. was cut off.

The population explosion

If it is assumed that the rate of increase of the population is proportional to the population at any given time, then we have:

$$\frac{dP}{dt} = kP$$ where k is a known constant and P is the population at time t.

If we take the rate of increase of P, i.e. the excess of births over deaths, as (say) 5 per 1000 per year, then

$$\frac{dP}{dt} = 0.005\,P \qquad \text{... (1)}$$

This is of the same form as our standard form

$\frac{dy}{dx} = ky$ whose solution is $y = Ce^{kx}$

Suppose the population was roughly 53½ million in 1970, i.e. when t = 0 (say) The solution of equation (1) is

$$P = C\,e^{0.005t} \qquad \text{...(2)}$$

But when $t = 0$, $P = 53\tfrac{1}{2}$ million

Substituting in (2) :

$\therefore$ 53½ million $= Ce^{0}$

But $e^{0} = 1$

$\therefore \quad C = 53\tfrac{1}{2}$ million

$\therefore \quad P = 53\tfrac{1}{2}\,e^{0.005t}$ in millions

To find the population in the year 2000, say i.e. when t = 30

$$\begin{aligned} P &= 53\tfrac{1}{2}\,e^{0.005 \times 30} \\ &= 53\tfrac{1}{2}\,e^{0.15} \\ &= 53\tfrac{1}{2} \times 1.1618 \quad \text{from } e^{x} \text{ tables} \\ &\triangleq 62.2 \text{ million} \end{aligned}$$

Damped Vibrations.

Many vibrations are vibrations with a diminishing amplitude (see Simple Harmonic Motion p. 142). For example, if a weighted spring oscillates up and down, the oscillations gradually die away due to air and other resistances.

A simple damped vibration is of the form $y = e^{-t} \sin t$ where t is positive

We know that the graph of $y = \sin x$ is a wave lying between $y = +1$ and $y = -1$

It follows that the graph of $y = e^{-t} \sin t$ lies between the graphs of $y = e^{-t}$ and $y = -e^{-t}$, touching each in turn.

Maxima and minima occur when

$$\frac{dy}{dt} = 0$$

i.e. when $\frac{dy}{dt} = e^{-t} (\cos t) + \sin t\,(-e^{-t}) = 0$

$$0 = e^{-t}(\cos t - \sin t)$$

But e^{-t} cannot be zero $\therefore$ Maxima and minima occur when

$$\cos t = \sin t$$

i.e. when

$$\tan t = 1$$

$$t = \frac{\pi}{4}, \frac{5\pi}{4}, \frac{9\pi}{4}, \text{ etc. for maxima and minima.}$$

Also $y = 0$ when $\sin t = 0$

i.e. the curve crosses the x axis when $t = 0, \pi, 2\pi, 3\pi$, etc.

The graph is therefore as shown in Fig.13.8.

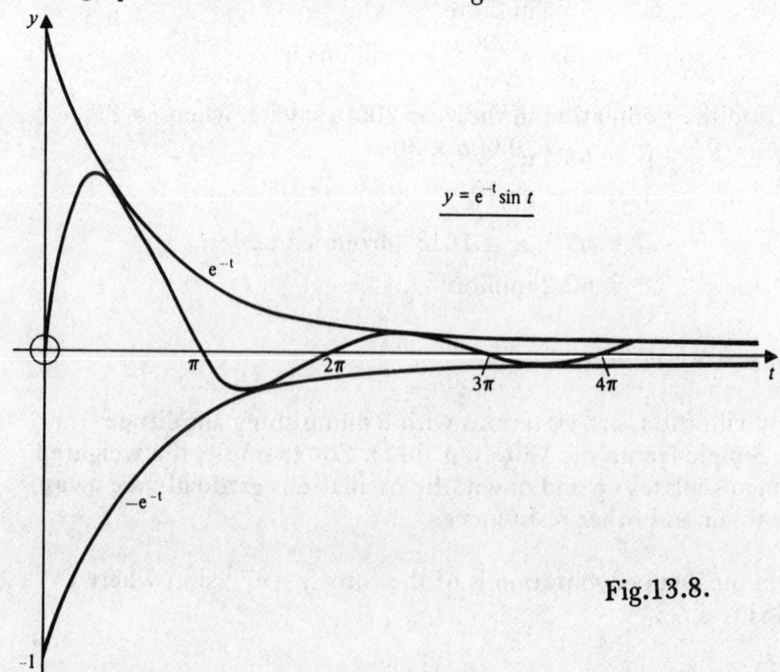

Fig.13.8.

Exercise 42.

1. If a population of flies under certain conditions satisfies the law that

$$\frac{dP}{dt} = 0.35\ P$$ where P is the population at time t days :

(i) estimate the probable population at the end of 10 days if initially it is 200;

(ii) find the number of days it will take to double the colony correct to 1 place of decimals.

2. The rate at which a radio-active substance decays is proportional to the number of atoms N present at any time t. If the constant of proportionality is λ (the decay constant) and initially there are N_0 atoms present, express

(i) N as a function of t;

(ii) find also the time taken for half of the initial amount to decay, i.e. the half-life of the substance.

Chapter 14

Graphs and their use in experimental work

Many students view graphs with apprehension, perhaps due to a very formal approach in early years. Yet graphs are a normal part of everyday life. One very rarely opens a newspaper without being presented with a graph illustrating what is happening to such things as unemployment, the birth rate, profits, etc. We need graphs to give us a quick picture of trends, to find out whether a certain item is increasing, decreasing or levelling off. No set of figures could do this.

In the same way, the scientist and technologist and many others need to study the relationship between different variables to see if there is any connection, and if so, what connection, so that they are able to predict what will happen when changes are made. For example, how will a small increase in productivity per machine affect the profits, bearing in mind extra bonuses paid, and a bigger sales drive required to sell the extra goods?

In our study of different types of graph, there is only one graph which is easily drawn - the straight line. In the same way, if we are given a set of points on graph paper, the only one which is easily identified, even allowing for experimental errors, is the straight line. This then, is our first task, i.e. to find the law which governs the set of points which seem to fall into a straight line, always bearing in mind the relationship between any graph and its equation, that is:

1. **the (x,y) values at every point ON the graph satisfy the equation** of the graph

2. **the (x,y) values at every point NOT ON the graph DO NOT satisfy the equation** of the graph.

In other words, the graph is made up of points all of which have something in common, i.e. the law of the graph. This is what we call the equation of the graph.

Example. To take a very easy case, a motor cyclist passes a certain point on a motorway at 09.00 hours and travelling at a constant speed of 60 km/h. Draw a graph illustrating his distance from the given point and find out how far he will have travelled at 09.25, 10.15, 10.35, and 10.55. Also find at what time he reaches a point A, 35 km. along the road.

GRAPH OF MOTOR-CYCLIST'S JOURNEY.

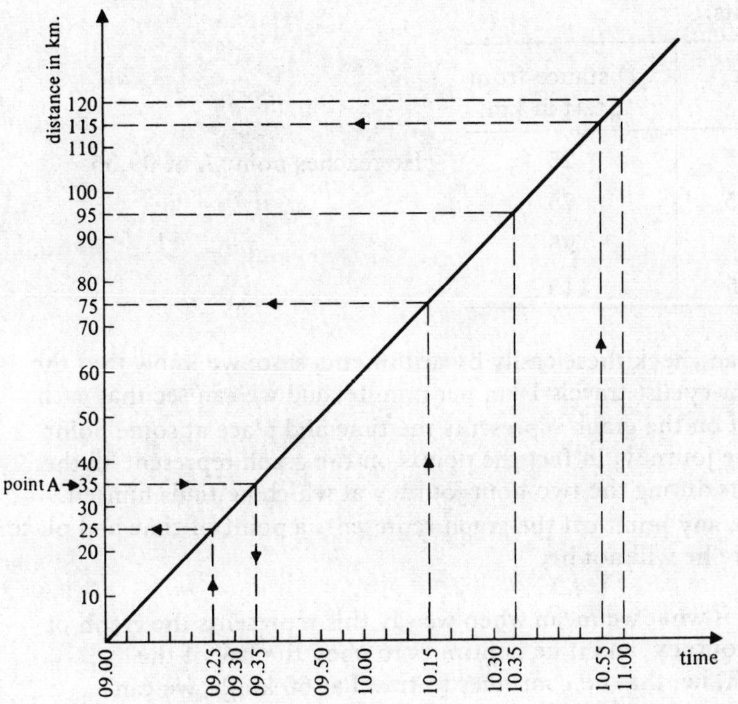

Fig.14.1

We know that the distance increases steadily with time, so that we have a straight-line graph. (Fig. 14.1) We also know that to draw a straight line we only need two points. Let us choose:

Time	Distance from Start in km.
09.00	0
11.00	120

Putting these on a graph, with a time scale chosen to show 5-minute intervals we obtain the graph as above. Reading off results:

Time	Distance from Start in km.
09.25	25
10.15	75
10.35	95
10.55	115

He reaches point A at 09.35

We can check these easily by arithmetic, since we know that the motor-cyclist travels 1 km per minute, and we can see that each point on the graph represents the time and place at some point of the journey. In fact the points on the graph represent all the points during the two-hour journey at which he finds himself. Also, any point off the graph represents a point of time and place where he will not be.

This is what we mean when we say this represents the graph of the journey, and if he continues to obey the law of the graph, i.e. that he continues to travel at 60 km/h, we can predict where he will be at any time, without doing any arithmetic.

This is an obvious case, but the same principles apply to more complicated graphs.

THE STRAIGHT-LINE LAW.

We have already seen that the straight line has a special kind of equation (see Chapter 8) and is of the form

$$y = mx + c$$

where m = gradient

c = intercept on the y axis passing through $x = 0$

and we can easily draw such a graph when the equation is known, by calculating two points on the line, and using a third point as a check.

Now we need to do the reverse process i.e. given a set of points on a graph to find out its equation. This equation is often required for use in predicting other results in combination with other equations. We proceed as below.

Example. The effort E and load W in a certain simple machine are connected by the following table:

E	270	295	320	345	370	395
W	1000	1100	1200	1300	1400	1500

E and W both measured in grams.

(i) Draw the graph showing load, W, horizontally and find the law connecting E and W; and

(ii) Find E when W = 50, assuming the law holds for this load.

Graph showing effort against load in a machine.

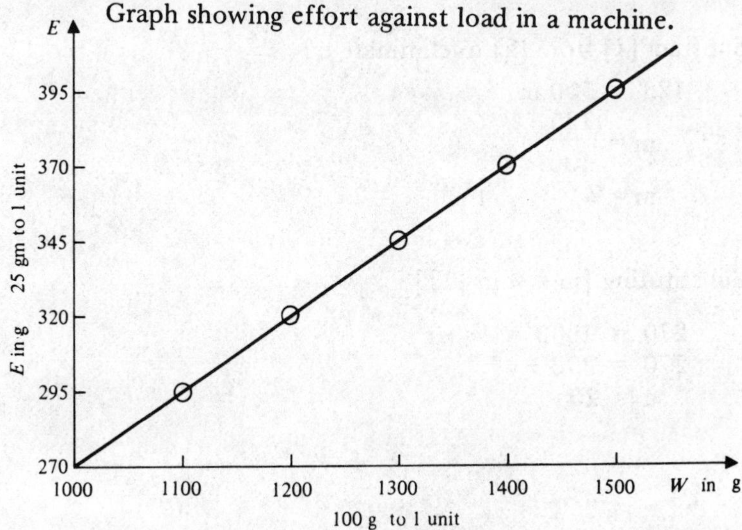

Fig.14.2.

The graph is a straight line, and is therefore of the form

E (vertically) = m x W (horizontally) + c
where m and c are constants.

Now, it could be assumed that the easiest method of finding m and c is merely to read off the gradient and the intercept on the vertical axis. But the intercept must be the *intercept on the vertical axis through the origin* and in this case (and most cases) it does not appear on the graph.

The following method is always successful (providing of course the arithmetic is sound!).

Take two points on the line, well separated, and having convenient readings horizontally. (The vertical readings which follow have to take care of themselves). Suppose we take the first and last readings in our table which are obviously on the line.

When E = 270, W = 1000
E = 395, W = 1500
But E = mW + c

∴ Substituting the above values in turn:

270 = 1000m + c ... [1]
and 395 = 1500m + c ... [2]

Subtract [1] from [2] to eliminate c :

$$125 = 500\,m$$
$$\therefore \quad m = \frac{125}{500}$$
$$m = \tfrac{1}{4}$$

Substituting [m = ¼ in [1]]

$$270 = 1000 \times \tfrac{1}{4} + c$$
$$\therefore \quad 270 = 250 + c$$
$$\therefore \quad c = 20$$

Check: In [2], 395 = 1500.¼ + 20 = 375 + 20   Correct

(i) The law of the straight line is E = ¼W + 20

(ii) When W = 50
E = ¼ x 50 + 20
∴ E = 32½

This method is usually easier to complete than other methods.

N.B. A further check of m and c can be made by using another good reading on the graph.

Exercise 43.

1. The velocity v cm/sec of a body after t secs is found by a series of experiments to be given by the following table:

t	2.5	4	6	9	10
v	33.5	38	44	53	56

If v and t are connected by a law v = u + ft, find u and f.

2. The volume V of a gas was measured in an experiment with increasing temperatures, t, as shown in the following table:

t	10	20	30	40	50	60	70
V	94.9	98.3	101.7	105.1	109.0	111.9	115.3

(i) Show by drawing a graph of V against t, that one of these readings was not sound, and say which it is.

(ii) Find the equation connecting V and t in the form
V = at + b where a and b are constants.

(iii) What is the temperature when V = 100 ?

3. The resistance R ohms of a length of copper wire at different temperatures $t^{o}C$ was found experimentally to be as follows:

$t^{o}C$	0	40	75	105	160	200
R ohms	39.8	46.4	52.0	56.6	65.4	71.8

Plot R vertically against t horizontally, and see if they suggest a law of the linear form $R = at + b$ where a and b are constants. Draw the probable line among the points, and find the values of a and b. Hence find t when $R = 48$ and R when $t = 90$.

Hints:

1. Since all of the given values are experimental all of them may be slightly inaccurate. In other words none of the given pairs of values need be on the required straight line, which should be drawn evenly among them. i.e. with as many points above the line as below.

2. When evaluating a and b make sure that the values of R and t used are taken from points actually on the line since none of the given values may be accurate enough to use.

TO FIND THE LAW CONNECTING THE VARIABLES IN PRACTICAL CASES

In experimental work, the task of fitting an equation to a curve may be very tedious and time consuming. If one obtains, by experiment a set of points which seem to form a reasonable curve, how is one to find out what type of equation will fit this? Could it be part of a parabola, a cubic, an exponential curve, or even part of a sine wave? How can we decide this? The only set of points which is easily recognised is that which gives a straight line.

Hence, if we can so to speak 'straighten out the curve' into a straight line we are well on the way to solving our problem. This is essentially a trial and error method, but some knowledge of the methods available is useful.

First we consider a basic list of equations whose graphs can be reduced to a straight line. There are many more 'tricks' which may be used, beyond the scope of this book.

Types of laws which can be reduced to straight-line graphs

(i) The law $y = ax^n$ where a and n are constants.

(ii) The exponential law $y = ae^{cx}$ where a and c are constants.

(iii) Algebraic types

(a) $y = a + \frac{b}{x}$

and $y = \frac{b}{x}$

(b) $y = \frac{b}{x^2}$

and similarly for higher powers of x.

(c) $y = a + b\sqrt{x}$

$y = a + \frac{b}{\sqrt{x}}$

(d) $y = \frac{a}{1 + bx}$

(e) $xy + ax + by = 0$

(f) $y = \frac{ax}{1 + bx}$

(g) $y = ax + bx^2$

(In (a) to (g) above, a and b represent constants.)

Types (i) and (ii) involve using logs.
Note that type (i) passes through the origin.

(i) $y = ax^n$

Take logs of both sides (base 10)

$\log y = \log a + n \log x$

Let $\left.\begin{array}{l}\log y = Y\\ \log x = X\\ \log a = A\end{array}\right]$ and we get

$$Y = A + nX$$

Thus if we plot Y against X, i.e. log y against log x, we should get a straight line, where n is the gradient and A is the intercept on the Y axis through (0,0). By the usual method, we can find A and n and thus a.

Hence we obtain $y = ax^n$

(ii) **The exponential law** $y = ae^{cx}$

The log form is $\log y = \log a + cx \log e$ (logs to base 10)

Put $\left.\begin{array}{l}\log y = Y\\ \log a = A\\ c \log e = C\end{array}\right]$

$$\therefore \quad Y = A + Cx$$

This is a straight line if we plot Y against x (i.e. log y against x), where C is the gradient and A is the intercept on the Y axis through (0,0).

Note: The work involved in the above two cases is reduced if logarithmic graph paper is used, i.e. special graph paper which converts either both or one variable directly to logs without use of tables.

(iii) **Algebraic types not involving logs**

(a) $y = a + \frac{b}{x}$

Put $\frac{1}{x} = X$, and we get

$$y = a' + bX$$

$\therefore$ Plotting y against X, i.e. $\frac{1}{x}$, reduces the curve to a straight line, gradient b and intercept a on the y axis through (0,0).

(b) $y = a + \frac{b}{x^2}$

Put $X = \frac{1}{x^2}$

$\therefore \quad y = a + bX$ reducing to a straight line by plotting y against $\frac{1}{x^2}$

The gradient is b, and a is the intercept on the y axis through (0,0).

(c) $y = a + b\sqrt{x}$ and $y = a + \frac{b}{\sqrt{x}}$

Put $X = \sqrt{x}$ Put $X = \frac{1}{\sqrt{x}}$

Plot y against $\sqrt{x}$ Plot y against $\frac{1}{\sqrt{x}}$

The gradient is b, and a is the intercept on the y axis through (0,0).

Similarly for any power of x, positive, negative or fractional.

(d) $y = \frac{a}{1 + bx}$

Cross multiply:

$y + bxy = a$

$\therefore y = -bxy + a$

Plotting y against (xy) gives a straight line.
The gradient is $-b$, and a is the intercept on the y axis through (0,0).

(e) $xy + ax + by = 0$

Divide by xy:

$1 + \frac{a}{y} + \frac{b}{x} = 0$

$\therefore \frac{1}{y} = -\frac{b}{a}.\frac{1}{x} - \frac{1}{a}$

Plotting $\frac{1}{y}$ against $\frac{1}{x}$ gives a straight line.

The gradient is $-\frac{b}{a}$ and $-\frac{1}{a}$ is the intercept on the $\frac{1}{y}$ axis through (0,0).

(f) $y = \dfrac{ax}{1 + bx}$

Cross multiply:

$y + bxy = ax$

Divide by y:

$1 + bx = a.\dfrac{x}{y}$

$\therefore \dfrac{1}{a} + \dfrac{b}{a}x = \dfrac{x}{y}$

Plotting $\dfrac{x}{y}$ against x gives a linear graph. The gradient is $\dfrac{b}{a}$ and $\dfrac{1}{a}$ is the intercept on the $\dfrac{x}{y}$ axis through (0,0).

(g) $y = ax + bx^2$ (a parabola through the origin)

Divide by x:

$\dfrac{y}{x} = a + bx$

Plotting $\dfrac{y}{x}$ against x gives a straight line. The gradient is b, and a is the intercept on the $\dfrac{y}{x}$ axis through (0,0).

In all these cases there are only two constants at most in the relationship, and reduction to a straight line will yield these two constants and no more.

If the relationship to be verified contains more than two constants, one of them must be found by some other means, e.g. by moving the origin or finding an intercept on the y axis directly from the graph.

WARNING: Having obtained the probable law of the curve, **it is extremely dangerous to extrapolate**, i.e. continue the curve and predict values outside the range. Conditions beyond the observed values may fundamentally change the tendency of the curve.

THE USE OF LOGARITHMIC GRAPH PAPER

There are several types of graph paper which help to eliminate the tedious work involved in plotting the logarithms of the variable or variables in experimental work. These different types are needed to fit the many different ranges of the variables involved. The main types are:

1. Semi-logarithmic graph paper, often called 'log-linear' graph paper.
2. Logarithmic graph paper, usually called 'log-log' graph paper.

The logarithmic scale.

The logarithms to base 10 of the integers between 1 and 10 are as follows:

Number	1	2	3	4	5	6	7	8	9	10
$\log_{10}$	0	0.301	0.477	0.602	0.699	0.778	0.845	0.903	0.954	1

For numbers between 10 and 100 :

Number	10	20	30	40	50	60	70	80	90	100
$\log_{10}$	1	1.301	1.477	1.602	1.699	1.778	1.845	1.903	1.954	2

Lengths are marked off along an axis corresponding to the logarithms (see figure 14.3). This gives the logarithms of numbers without further use of tables. The intervals are further subdivided to give intermediate values. This logarithmic scale is the same as that used on the slide rule.

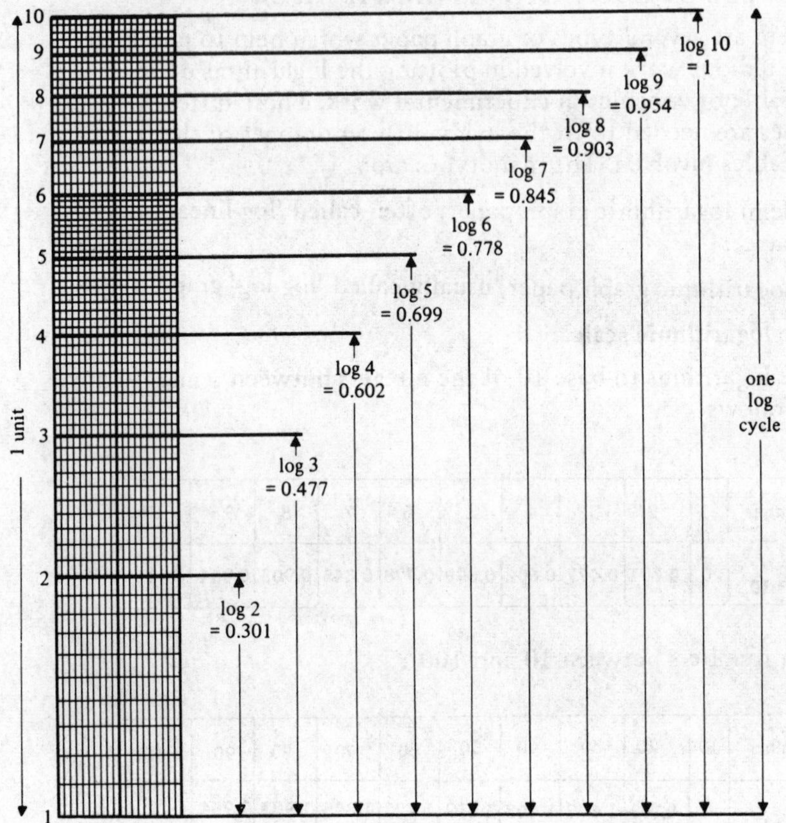

Figure 14.3.

The unit used is called one 'log cycle' and may be extended to several cycles to represent the logarithms of numbers between 10 and 100, 100 and 1000, and so on. Printed log paper is available with as many as five log cycles for plotting a range of values from 1 to 10^5, or 0.1 to 10^4, or any similar range.

Semi-logarithmic graph paper is usually printed with a logarithmic scale vertically, and a uniform (i.e. linear) scale horizontally, but of course these may be reversed if necessary by rotating the paper.

Logarithmic graph paper is printed with logarithmic scales on both axes.

The use of each of these types is illustrated by the following examples.

Example 1. In an experiment on a certain woollen material the values of one of its properties, y, were observed for various values of another property x, as follows:

x	4	8	12	16	20	24	28	32	36	40	44	48	52
y	1.45	1.8	2.4	3.15	3.9	5.1	6.6	8.4	11.0	14.0	17.5	23.0	29.9

It is thought that these results may obey a relationship of the form $y = ae^{bx}$ where a and b are constants. Verify this, and find the probable values of a and b.

If $y = ae^{bx}$

then $\log_{10} y = \log_{10} a + bx \log_{10} e$ (taking logs of both sides) .... (1)

Let $Y = \log_{10} y$, $A = \log_{10} a$, $B = b \log_{10} e$. .... (2)

Then $Y = A + Bx$ .... (3)

Hence if Y is plotted against x, the graph should be a straight line. Thus we plot Y (= $\log_{10} y$) vertically against x horizontally, which needs a semi-log (or log-linear) graph paper.

Note 1: The range of values of y is 1.45 to 29.9. This means we need two log cycles 1 to 10 and 10 to 10^2.

Note 2: The logarithms of the y values are automatically given by plotting the values of y on the vertical logarithmic scale. (See Fig. 14.4).

The plotted points appear to be in a straight line, allowing for experimental errors, thus verifying that $y = ae^{bx}$ is the form which fits the given values of x and y.

To find the equation of the line we evaluate A and B in equation (3).

To find a and b, we use $\log_{10} a = A$ and $b = B/\log_{10} e$ (from (2))

To find A and B, and hence a and b, we proceed as follows:

P and Q are two points on the line
$Y = A + Bx$

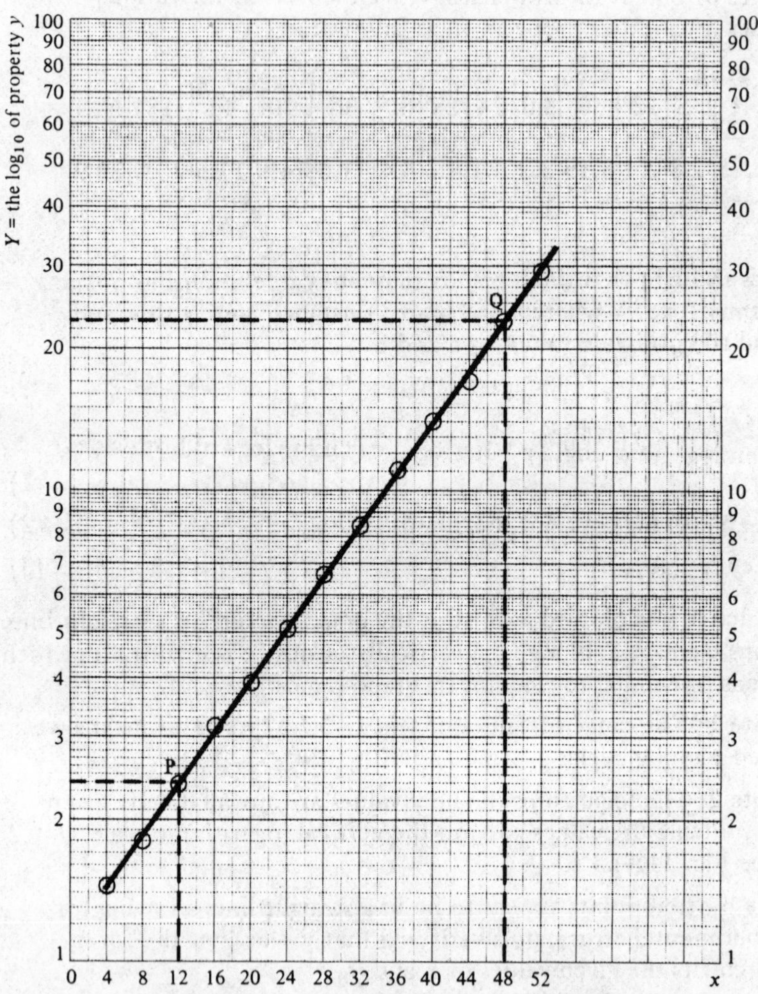
Y = the log10 of property y
100
90
80
70
60
50
40
30
20
10
9
8
7
6
5
4
3
2
1
Q
P
0
4
8
12
16
20
24
28
32
36
40
44
48
52
x

Figure 14.4

At P, when x = 12, Y (= $\log_{10} y$) = log 2.4 (see table of values)

$\therefore \quad \log 2.4 = A + B.12$ .... (4)

At Q, when x = 48. Y = log 23.0

$\therefore \quad \log 23.0 = A + B.48$ .... (5)

Subtract (4) from (5) :

$\log 23.0 - \log 2.4 = 36B$

$$\therefore B = \frac{\log 23.0 - \log 2.4}{36}$$

$\therefore B \triangleq 0.0273$ (by calculator)

$$\text{But } b = B/\log_{10} e \triangleq \frac{0.0273}{0.4343} = 0.063$$

From (5) $A \triangleq \log 23.0 - 48B$

$\therefore A \triangleq 0.0530$

$\therefore a \triangleq$ antilog 0.0530 from (2)

$\therefore a \triangleq 1.13$

and $b \triangleq 0.063$

The law of the curve is $y \triangleq 1.13e^{0.063x}$ .... (6)

Check: Another point on the line is x = 24, y = 5.1

From (6) when x = 24 $\quad y \triangleq 1.13e^{0.063 \times 24}$

$\therefore y \triangleq 5.125$ by calculator

which checks with the observed value of 5.1

Example 2. In an experiment similar to that in Example 1 above, another property of the material, z, was observed for the same values of x as before.

x	4	8	12	16	20	24	28	32	36	40	44	48	52
z	3.6	6.4	9.2	11.9	14.1	17.0	18.5	21.0	23.0	25.5	27.2	29.7	31.9

Verify that these results obey the law $z = kx^n$ and find the probable values of k and n.

If $z = kx^n$

Then $\log_{10} z = \log_{10} k + n \log_{10} x$ .... (1)

Let $Z = \log_{10} z, \quad K = \log_{10} k, X = \log_{10} x$ .... (2)

Then $Z = K + nX$ .... (3)

Hence if Z (= log z) is plotted against X (= log x), a straight line should be obtained.

Here we need logarithmic scales on both axes, i.e. 'log-log' graph paper.

Note 1: The range of values of x is the same as before and therefore needs two log cycles. The range of values of Z is 3.6 to 31.9 and also needs two log cycles.

Note 2: The logarithms of both x and z values are shown automatically by using 'log-log' paper (See Fig. 14.5).

The points lie approximately on the line drawn, thus verifying that the law connecting x and z is of the form $z = kx^n$.

To find n and K and hence k, we proceed as follows:

P and Q are two points on the line $Z = K + nX$

At P, $x = 4$, $z = 3.6$. Hence $X = \log 4$, $Z = \log 3.6$ from (2)

Substituting in (3):

$$\log 3.6 = K + n \log 4 \quad \text{.... (4)}$$

At Q, similarly, $X = \log 52$, $Z = \log 32$

$$\therefore \log 32 = K + n \log 52 \quad \text{... (5)}$$

Subtracting (4) from (5) :

$$\log 32 - \log 3.6 = n (\log 52 - \log 4)$$

$$\therefore \log (32/3.6) = n \log (52/4)$$

$$\therefore n = \log (8.889) \div \log 13$$

$$n = 0.85 \text{ by calculator}$$

Substituting in (5) :

$$\log 32 = K + 0.85 \log 52$$

$$\therefore K = \log 32 - 0.85 \log 52$$

$$\therefore K \simeq 0.0472$$

$$\therefore k = \text{antilog } 0.0472$$

$$k \simeq 1.12$$

Hence the law connecting x and z is given by

$$z = 1.12x^{0.85} \quad \text{.... (6)}$$

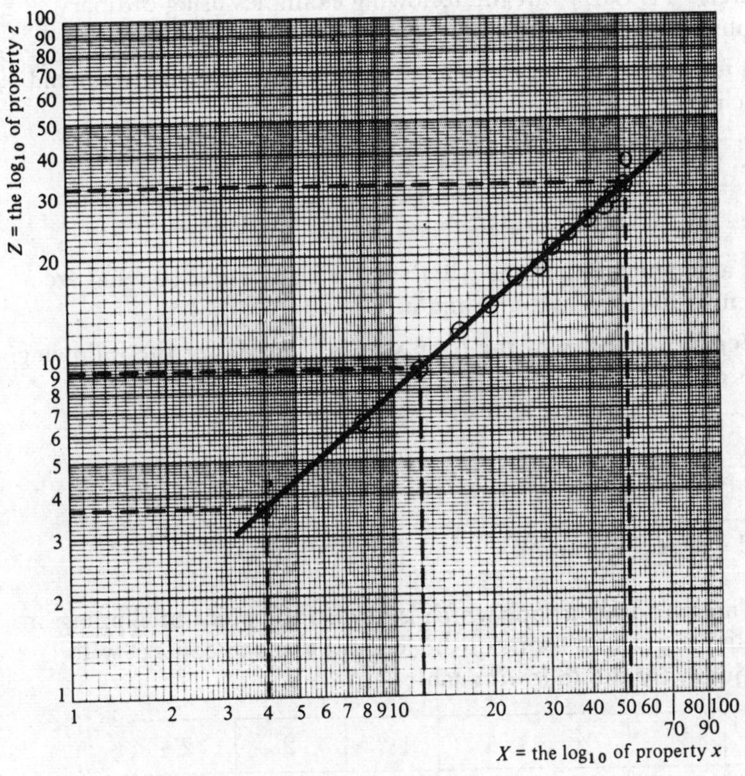

Figure 14.5

Check: When x = 12 $\quad z = 1.12\,(12)^{0.85}$ from (6)

$\therefore\ z = 9.251$ by calculator

which agrees approximately with the observed value of 9.2 in the table.

Exercise 44. Carry out the following examples using ordinary graph paper and logarithmic graph paper.

The following table gives pairs of values of two quantities p and q, which probably follow the law $q = ap^k$

p	0.92	1.81	3.7	5.54	8.65	12.5
q	2.5	4.2	7.6	11	15	21

Plot a graph to determine whether this is so, and if so what are the most likely values of a and k.

2. Verify that a law of the form $y = Ce^{kx}$ holds for the following pairs of values:

x	0	1.0	1.5	2.5	4.0
y	4.2	0.937	0.4427	0.0987	0.0105

Find values for C and k.

3. The tension in a rope which is just on the point of slipping on a pulley is given in terms of the length l turns in contact with the pulley by the following table:

l	¼	¾	1	1¼	2	2½
T	3.17	7.90	12.68	19.9	80.3	201.5

Verify the law $T = T_o e^{2\pi\mu l}$ and find T_o and μ

4. Show that the following values of two observed quantities, x and y, satisfy a law of the form $y = a + bx^2$, and find a and b.

x	1.1	1.8	2.5	2.9	3.6	4.3	4.8	5.4
y	1.91	2.13	2.40	2.65	3.10	3.66	4.09	4.73

5. In an experiment, values for the quantities x and y were found as follows:

x	1	2	4	6	8	9	10
y	0.39	0.667	1.045	1.27	1.43	1.5	1.55

Show that these values are satisfied by a relation of the form

$$y = \frac{ax}{1 + bx} \quad \left(\text{plot } \frac{x}{y} \text{ against } x\right)$$

and find a and b.

Chapter 15

Simultaneous equations

In the main, we have so far only dealt with equations involving one unknown, with the exception of the use of two sets of values for x and y when trying to evaluate m and c in the straight line equation $y = mx + c$ (page 196).

Example. Suppose a straight line is drawn between the points $(-2, 1)$ and $(3, -5)$ (Fig. 15.1). What is the equation?

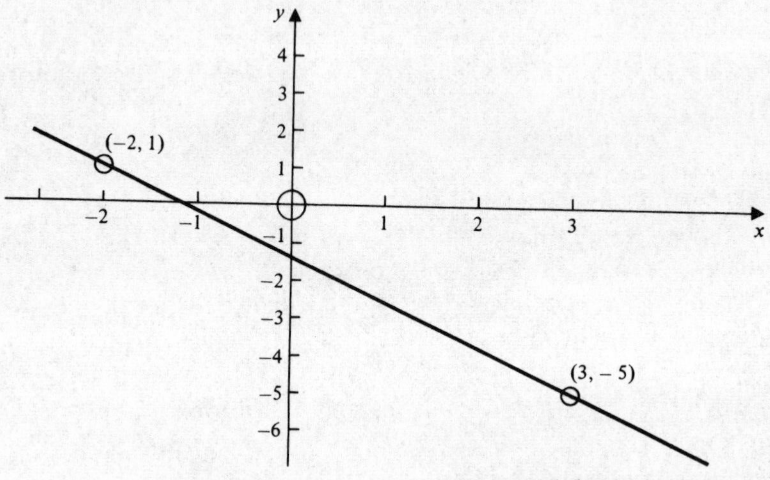

Figure 15.1.

Note that we cannot draw the line unless we know at least two points on it.

Assume the equation of the line is

$y = mx + c$ where m and c are constants (see page 74)

The line passes through the point where

$$x = -2 \text{ when } y = +1$$

$$\therefore +1 = m.(-2) + c$$

$$\text{i.e. } +1 = -2m + c \qquad \ldots (1)$$

Also $x = 3$ when $y = -5$

$$\therefore -5 = m.3 + c$$

$$\text{i.e. } -5 = 3m + c \qquad \ldots (2)$$

Rewriting (1) : $+1 = -2m + c$ .... (1)

Subtracting (1) from (2) (changing the signs on the lower line and adding) :

$$-6 = 5m \quad \text{the c disappearing}$$

$$\therefore \quad m = \frac{-6}{5}$$

Substituting for m in (1) :

$$+1 = (-2)(-\frac{6}{5}) + c$$

$$\therefore +1 = \frac{12}{5} + c$$

$$\therefore c = -1\frac{2}{5}$$

which we see checks with Fig. 15.1, c being the intercept on the y axis through the origin.

We can also check by substituting in (2), giving :

$$-5 = 3\,(-\frac{6}{5}) - \frac{7}{5}$$

$$-5 = -\frac{18}{5} - \frac{7}{5}$$

which is correct.

Therefore the equation of the line is

$$y = -\frac{6}{5}x - \frac{7}{5}$$

$$\text{or} \quad 5y = -6x - 7$$

$$\text{or} \quad 5y + 6x + 7 = 0$$

Thus we see that we need two equations if we have to solve an equation containing two unknowns.

Pairs of equations of this type involving two unknowns, are called *simultaneous equations,* since they are both true at the same time.

We need to make a more detailed study of such equations and the easiest way to deal with them, as they occur very frequently.

THE METHOD OF DEALING WITH TWO EQUATIONS INVOLVING TWO UNKNOWNS

Consider the following problems. Two numbers have a sum of 8 and a difference of 2. What are the numbers? If we merely knew that their sum was 8, there would be an infinite number of solutions, taking into account all the possibilities of the numbers both being fractional or decimal. We see, therefore, that one fact alone is insufficient to determine the numbers, but as soon as we are given the second fact, i.e. their difference is 2, we can sort out mentally that only 3 and 5 fit the facts.

It is obviously impossible to work every problem mentally this way, but we can illustrate the method by using this very simple example.

Example 1. The sum of two numbers is 8 and their difference is 2. Find the numbers. Let the numbers be x and y, x being the larger.

$$\therefore x + y = 8 \qquad \ldots\ (1)$$
$$x - y = 2 \qquad \ldots\ (2)$$

We notice that the signs of y in the two equations are opposite signs. Therefore to eliminate y we must add the equations.
Add (1) and (2) :

$$2x = 10$$
$$\therefore x = 5 \qquad \text{by substituting in (1)}$$
$$\therefore y = 3$$

Check: In (2), 5 – 3 = 2. Correct.

On the other hand, if we wish, we could eliminate x instead. The signs of x are the same signs.

∴ We subtract the equations.

Subtract (2) from (1) : (changing signs on the lower line and adding)

$$2y = 6$$
$$\therefore y = 3$$
$$x = 5 \qquad \text{as before}$$

We have worked this simple example both ways, to illustrate the fact that we approach the problem in the following order:

1. Decide which unknown it is possible to eliminate. If it is not possible immediately, there is a simple method of doing this which is described later.

2. Look at the signs of the terms to be eliminated.
If they are of the **same sign** then we **subtract**;
If they are of the **opposite signs** then we **add**.

Example 2. Solve the following equations :

$$a + 2b = 7 \quad \text{.... (1)}$$
$$3a - 2b = 4 \quad \text{.... (2)}$$

Fact 1: We cannot eliminate the a terms by adding or subtracting, but the b terms are the same except for sign. Therefore we eliminate b.

Fact 2: The terms in b are opposite signs. Therefore we add the equations.

Adding (1) and (2) :

$$4a = 11$$
$$a = \frac{11}{4}$$

Substituting in (1) :

$$\frac{11}{4} + 2b = 7$$
$$\therefore \quad 2b = 7 - \frac{11}{4}$$
$$\therefore \quad 2b = \frac{17}{4}$$
$$\therefore \quad b = \frac{17}{8}$$

Check: From (2) (the equation unused in substitution)

$$3a - 2b = \frac{33}{4} - \frac{17}{4} = \frac{16}{4} = 4. \quad \text{Correct.}$$

Example 3. If neither of the terms are exactly the same in the two equations we deal with the problem quite simply in the following way :

Suppose

$$3a - 2b = -11 \quad \text{.... (1)}$$
$$2a + 6b = +22 \quad \text{.... (2)}$$

1. Decide whether to eliminate a or b. Here we notice that 6b in equation (2) is 3 times 2b in equation (1), which is easier than dealing with the a term;
2. Multiply the whole of equation (1) by 3 (and say so) to make the b terms the same.

Multiply (1) by 3 :

$$9a - 6b = -33 \quad \text{.... (3)}$$
$$\text{and} \quad 2a + 6b = 22 \quad \text{.... (2)}$$

3. We note that the b terms are opposite in sign. Therefore we add (2) and (3) to make them disappear.

Add (3) and (2) :

$$11a = -11$$
$$a = -1$$

We now substitute in one equation and check in the other.
Substitute in (1) :

$$-3 - 2b = -11$$
$$\therefore \quad 8 = 2b$$
$$b = 4$$
$$\text{and } a = -1$$

Check: In (2)

$$2a + 6b = -2 + 24 = +22 \qquad \text{Correct.}$$

Exercise 45. Solve the following pairs of equations, first deciding which unknown can be most easily eliminated, and whether to add or subtract.

1. $a + b = 3$
   $a - b = 1$
2. $a + b = 7$
   $a - b = 4\frac{1}{2}$
3. $2a + b = 3$
   $a + b = 2$
4. $3a + 2b = 5$
   $a + 2b = 7$
5. $2a - 3b = 2$
   $2a + 7b = 5\frac{1}{3}$
6. $3a - 4b = 6$
   $5a + 4b = 2$
7. $3x + y = 4$
   $x + 2y = 1$
8. $3y - z = 11$
   $2y - 3z = 5$

Next we consider the case where neither the coefficients of x nor y can be made equal by a simple multiplication of one equation.

Example 4.

$$7x - 6y = 20 \qquad \text{.... (1)}$$
$$2x - 5y = 9 \qquad \text{.... (2)}$$

Here we see neither the x terms nor the y terms are equal or a simple multiple of one another. Therefore we must make one pair equal. Suppose we decide to make the x terms equal.

We notice that the least common multiple of 7 and 2 is 14.
∴ We multiply the first equation by 2 and the second by 7, i.e. the numbers in reverse order, and we put it down as follows :

$$\begin{array}{rcl|c|rcll} 7x - 6y & = & 20 & \times 2 & 14x - 12y & = & 40 & \text{.... (3)} \\ 2x - 5y & = & 9 & \times 7 & 14x - 35y & = & 63 & \text{.... (4)} \end{array}$$

The x terms are now of the same value and the same sign. Therefore we subtract.

Subtract (4) from (3) :

$$23y = -23$$
$$y = -1$$

Substitute in (1) :

$$7x + 6 = 20$$
$$7x = 14$$
$$x = 2$$
$$y = -1$$

Check: In (2) $\quad 2x - 5y = 4 + 5 = 9 \quad$ Correct.

Reminder:

1. Don't forget to multiply the whole equation by the appropriate number, the R.H.S. as well as the L.H.S.

2. Always find the second unknown by substituting in one of the original equations and checking in the other.

3. Always number your equations for easy reference.

4. If answers involve awkward fractions, check the working again, or eliminate the other variable instead.

Example 5.

$$\frac{1}{x} + \frac{1}{y} = \frac{5}{6} \qquad \text{.... (1)}$$

$$\frac{2}{x} + \frac{3}{y} = 2 \qquad \text{.... (2)}$$

Multiply equation (1) by 2

$$\frac{2}{x} + \frac{2}{y} = \frac{5}{3} \qquad \text{.... (3)}$$

Multiply equation (2) by 1:

$$\frac{2}{x} + \frac{3}{y} = 2 \qquad \text{.... (4)}$$

Subtract (4) from (3)

$$-\frac{1}{y} = -\frac{1}{3}$$

$$\therefore y = 3$$

Substitute in (1)

$$\frac{1}{x} = \frac{5}{6} - \frac{1}{3} = \frac{1}{2}$$

$$\therefore x = 2$$

and $y = 3$

Check: In [2]; $\frac{2}{x} + \frac{3}{y} = \frac{2}{2} + \frac{3}{3} = 2.$ Correct.

Exercise 46.

1. $4x + 3y = 1$
   $5x + 4y = 2$

2. $2x + 5y = 8$
   $3x + 4y = 5$

3. $6s - 5t = 21$
   $5s - 4t = 17\frac{1}{2}$

4. $6a - 5b = 24$
   $9a - 4b = 22$

5. $\frac{5}{x} + \frac{3}{y} = 9$
   $\frac{2}{x} - \frac{5}{y} = 16$

6. $1\frac{1}{2}x + 2y = -5\frac{1}{2}$
   $5x + 6y = -7$

7. $\frac{1}{a} + \frac{1}{b} = 20$
   $\frac{1}{a} - \frac{1}{b} = 4$

8. $\frac{2}{u} + \frac{3}{v} = 7$
   $\frac{1}{u} + \frac{2}{v} = 8$

SIMULTANEOUS EQUATIONS INVOLVING THREE UNKNOWNS

Example. Solve:

$$x + y + z = 6 \quad \ldots [1]$$
$$2x + y - z = 1 \quad \ldots [2]$$
$$3x - 4y + 6z = 13 \quad \ldots [3]$$

In this case we eliminate one of the variables, say z, and obtain two equations involving x and y. We then proceed as before.

[1] is obviously the easiest equation. Therefore, we take [1] and [2] and eliminate z, and [1] with [3] and eliminate z.

We have:

$$x + y + z = 6 \quad \text{... [1]}$$
$$2x + y - z = 1 \quad \text{... [2]}$$

Add to eliminate z: $$3x + 2y = 7 \quad \text{... [4]}$$

Multiply [1] by 6: $$6x + 6y + 6z = 36 \quad \text{... [5]}$$

Multiply [3] by 1: $$3x - 4y + 6z = 13 \quad \text{... [6]}$$

Subtract [6] from [5] : $$3x + 10y = 23 \quad \text{... [7]}$$

Rewriting [4] and [7] : $$3x + 2y = 7 \quad \text{... [4]}$$
$$3x + 10y = 23 \quad \text{... [7]}$$

Subtracting: $$-8y = -16 \quad \text{...}$$
$$y = 2$$

Substituting in [4] : $$3x = 7 - 4$$
$$x = 1$$

Substituting in [1] : $$z = 3$$

$$\therefore \quad x = 1$$
$$y = 2$$
$$z = 3$$

Check: From [2] , 2 + 2 – 3 = 1. From [3] , 3 – 8 + 18 = 13.
Correct.

General Instructions

(i) First decide which of the three unknowns it is easiest to eliminate.

(ii) Eliminate this unknown, by taking the equations two at a time, and obtaining two new independent equations involving only two unknowns.
(Note: It is no use obtaining a third equation, as this will be a combination of the first two, and will yield nothing new.)

(iii) Treat these two equations involving two unknowns in the usual way.

(iv) Always use the original equations for checking.

Chapter 16
Determinants

A determinant is merely a shorthand way (and also a more easily remembered way) of writing quite complicated algebraic expressions.

An example will illustrate the meaning.

Suppose we wish to find the area of a triangle formed by joining three points whose co-ordinates are given.

Let us take a numerical example first.

Example 1. Find the area of the triangle whose vertices are (2, 1), (3, 4) and (5, 2).

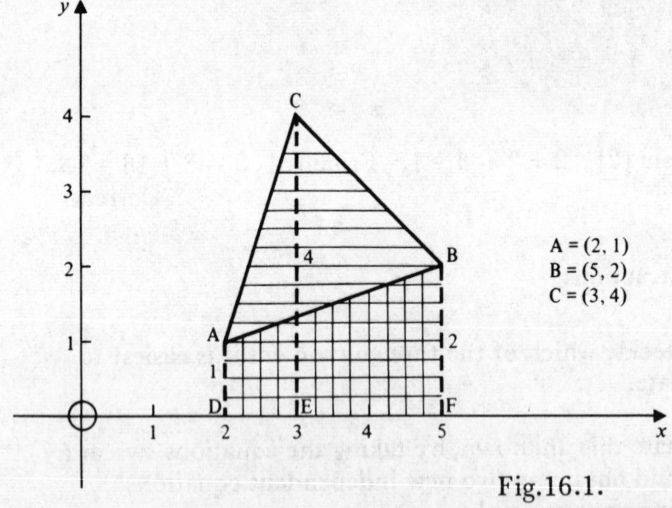

Fig.16.1.

We draw the perpendiculars AD, CE, BF to the x - axis (Fig.16.1). We use the fact that Δ ABC = trapezium ADEC + trapezium CEFB – trapezium ADFB

The area of a trapezium = ½ (sum of || sides) x distance between them.

Area ADEC = ½· 1 (1 + 4) = ½· 5
Area CEFB = ½· 2 (4 + 2) = ½·12
Area ADFB = ½· 3 (1 + 2) = ½· 9

∴ Area of ABC = ½ (5 + 12 − 9)
= ½· 8
= 4 square units.

Example 2. Consider the triangle formed by the vertices $(x_1\ y_1), (x_2, y_2), x_3, y_3)$. (Fig. 16.2).

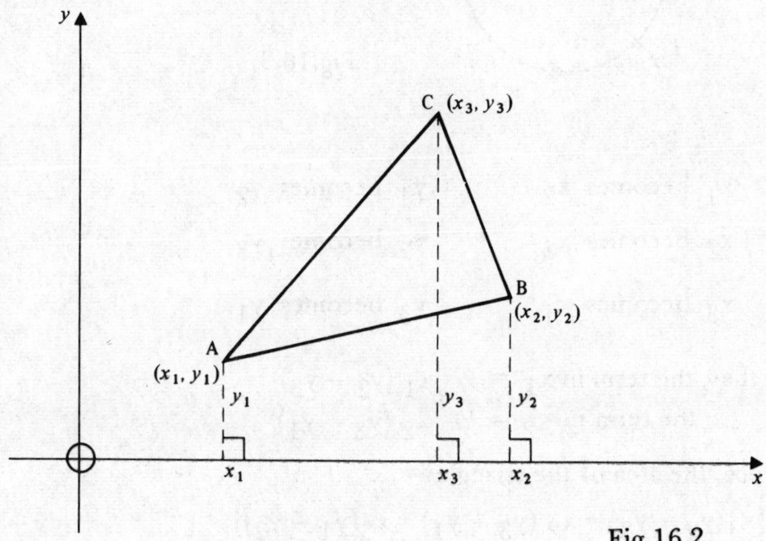

Fig.16.2.

Using the same method as before:

$$\Delta ABC = ½ [(x_3 - x_1)(y_1 + y_3) + (x_2 - x_3)(y_2 + y_3) - (x_2 - x_1)(y_1 + y_2)]$$

To simplify this, consider the term in x_3.

The term in x_3 (following the arrows) $= \frac{1}{2}[x_3 (y_1 + y_3) - x_3 (y_2 + y_3)]$

$= \frac{1}{2} x_3 (y_1 - y_2)$

Similarly, we can deduce the other terms in x_1 and x_2 by using the method of CYCLIC ORDER, following the arrows (Fig.16.3).

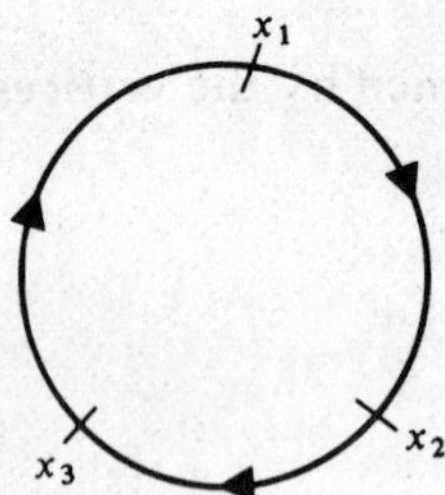

Fig.16.3.

i.e. x_1 becomes x_2 $\quad$ y_1 becomes y_2

x_2 becomes x_3 $\quad$ y_2 becomes y_3

x_3 becomes x_1 $\quad$ y_3 becomes y_1

So that, the term in $x_1 = \frac{1}{2} x_1 (y_2 - y_3)$
the term in $x_2 = \frac{1}{2} x_2 (y_3 - y_1)$

Hence, the area of the triangle =

$\frac{1}{2} [x_1(y_2 - y_3) + x_2 (y_3 - y_1) + x_3(y_1 - y_2)]$

This is a clumsy formula to remember, and is easier if written in **determinant** form as follows:

$$\Delta = \frac{1}{2} \begin{vmatrix} x_1 & y_1 & 1 \\ x_2 & y_2 & 1 \\ x_3 & y_3 & 1 \end{vmatrix}$$

This is a third-order determinant, having three rows and three columns.

Here we are implying that

$$x_1 \text{ multiplies } + \begin{vmatrix} y_2 & 1 \\ y_3 & 1 \end{vmatrix} \text{ which equals } (y_2 \times 1 - y_3 \times 1) = (y_2 - y_3)$$

Thus:

x_1 multiplies the small determinant obtained by missing out the row and column in which it stands.

Similarly *

$$x_2 \text{ multiplies } - \begin{vmatrix} y_1 & 1 \\ y_3 & 1 \end{vmatrix} \text{ which equals } -(y_1 \times 1 - y_3 \times 1) = (y_3 - y_1)$$

$$x_3 \text{ multiplies } + \begin{vmatrix} y_1 & 1 \\ y_2 & 1 \end{vmatrix} \text{ which equals } (y_1 \times 1 - y_2 \times 1) = (y_1 - y_2)$$

* Note that the second element of the first column, x_2, multiplies the small determinant obtained by missing out the row and column in which it stands but in working out determinants of any order, alternate signs of the smaller determinants must be taken as negative.

Let us check our first numerical example.

Here $(x_1, y_1) = (2, 1)$

$(x_2, y_2) = (5, 2) \quad \therefore \Delta = \frac{1}{2} \begin{vmatrix} 2 & 1 & 1 \\ 5 & 2 & 1 \\ 3 & 4 & 1 \end{vmatrix}$

$(x_3, y_3) = (3, 4)$

$$\begin{aligned} \therefore \Delta &= \tfrac{1}{2} [2 (2 - 4) - 5 (1 - 4) + 3 (1 - 2)] \\ &= \tfrac{1}{2} [2 \times (-2) - 5 \times (-3) + 3 \times (-1)] \\ &= \tfrac{1}{2} [-4 + 15 - 3] \\ &= 4 \text{ square units. Correct.} \end{aligned}$$

Example 3. The general solution of two simultaneous equations involving two unknowns may be worked out in the usual way as follows:

Suppose $\quad a_1 x + b_1 y + c_1 = 0 \quad$ ... [1]

and $\quad a_2 x + b_2 y + c_2 = 0 \quad$ ... [2]

where a_1, etc. are constants

To eliminate y : [1] x b_2: $a_1 b_2 x + b_1 b_2 y + c_1 b_2 = 0$

[2] x b_1: $a_2 b_1 x + b_1 b_2 y + c_2 b_1 = 0$

Subtracting : $x (a_1 b_2 - a_2 b_1) = c_2 b_1 - c_1 b_2$

$$\therefore x = \frac{c_2 b_1 - c_1 b_2}{a_1 b_2 - a_2 b_1}$$

Interchanging a's and b's to give the corresponding solution for y :

$$y = \frac{c_2 a_1 - c_1 a_2}{b_1 a_2 - b_2 a_1} \quad \text{or} \quad \frac{c_1 a_2 - a_1 c_2}{a_1 b_2 - a_2 b_1}$$

changing signs in numerator and denominator.

These solutions may be written :

$$\frac{x}{b_1 c_2 - b_2 c_1} = \frac{y}{c_1 a_2 - c_2 a_1} = \frac{1}{a_1 b_2 - a_2 b_1}$$

or

$$\frac{x}{\begin{vmatrix} b_1 & c_1 \\ b_2 & c_2 \end{vmatrix}} = \frac{y}{\begin{vmatrix} c_1 & a_1 \\ c_2 & a_2 \end{vmatrix}} = \frac{1}{\begin{vmatrix} a_1 & b_1 \\ a_2 & b_2 \end{vmatrix}}$$

each of the denominators being formed by cutting out the column of the corresponding variable in [1] and [2] and following on in cyclic order.

Numerical Example. If we wish to solve:

$$3x - 4y + 7 = 0$$
$$2x + 3y - 1 = 0$$

we write:

$$\frac{x}{\begin{vmatrix} -4 & 7 \\ +3 & -1 \end{vmatrix}} = \frac{y}{\begin{vmatrix} 7 & 3 \\ -1 & 2 \end{vmatrix}} = \frac{1}{\begin{vmatrix} 3 & -4 \\ 2 & +3 \end{vmatrix}}$$

$$\therefore \quad \frac{x}{-17} = \frac{y}{17} = \frac{1}{17}$$

$$\therefore \quad x = -1 \qquad y = 1$$

Exercise 47. Evaluate the determinants :

1. $\Delta_1 = \begin{vmatrix} 2 & 6 \\ 4 & 9 \end{vmatrix}$ $\qquad \Delta_2 = \begin{vmatrix} 3 & -1 \\ 2 & 5 \end{vmatrix}$ $\qquad \Delta_3 = \begin{vmatrix} -1 & 2 \\ 5 & -4 \end{vmatrix}$

2. $\Delta = \begin{vmatrix} 3 & -4 & 3 \\ 2 & 7 & 0 \\ 5 & -1 & 2 \end{vmatrix}$ $\qquad$ 3. $\Delta = \begin{vmatrix} 1 & 3 & 5 \\ 2 & 4 & 6 \\ 3 & 5 & 7 \end{vmatrix}$

Chapter 17
Imaginary and complex numbers

The greatest difficulty about this section of mathematics is the unfortunate terminology - 'imaginary' and 'complex' numbers. These numbers are no more imaginary or complex than the so-called ordinary numbers, with which we have become familiar since childhood. Numbers were in early times (and still are in some primitive tribes) represented by notches on a stick or scratches on a stone, probably representing the fingers held up, i.e. 1, 11, 111, 1111, with special marks for 5 and 10. Even today we use the same method very often for scoring, the fifth mark being a diagonal making a 'gate', 1111.

As children, we hold up one finger and say 'one' , and another finger and say 'two', and so on. But this 'one' is not the number one - it is one finger, and the 'two' is a completely different finger, so that the first 'one' is not the same as the second 'one', which we happily add together to make two. So what does this mean? It means that the idea of the number one as distinct from one thing is an abstract idea with which we work quite easily and accept as being a useful, in fact indispensible, tool with which to carry on our modern life. As a matter of fact these numbers are completely imaginary.

We say: one apple plus one apple = two apples

$$\therefore \quad 1 + 1 = 2$$

But the first apple is different from the second apple in size, shape, colour and yet we happily talk of two apples, quite sensibly, of course, and we have an idea in our own mind about the number two.

But 1 + 1 = 2 implies that the first 'one' is exactly the same as the second 'one', and we use this abstract idea of two exact things to add different things together.

For example, 5000 people plus 55,000 people make 60,000 people.

We know what we mean,

$$\text{But} \quad 5000 + 55{,}000 = 60{,}000$$

is an abstract representation of the above fact, i.e. imaginary. So don't be put off by the terrifying words, 'imaginary' and 'complex'. They are just as real as any other symbols.

For example, what do we mean by $\sqrt{2}$ or π or $0.\dot{7}$ recurring ? You may say $\sqrt{2} = 1.414$, but does it? Only approximately. And yet we use the symbol $\sqrt{2}$ and say $\sqrt{2} \times \sqrt{2} = \sqrt{4} = 2$. These things seem to work in solving problems and that is the real test of their usefulness.

A LITTLE HISTORY

Several claims have been made as to the origin of our present numerals, commonly referred to as Arabic numerals. These include the claims that they were originally found among the Arabs, Persians or Hindus. It is probable that they were a mixture obtained from all these sources, as numbers were needed mainly for trading, but India seems to have yielded the greatest number of our symbols. From whatever source they were derived, the decimal system, i.e. reckoning in 10's, used originally in counting large flocks of sheep, cows, camels, etc., by the nomadic herdsmen, was a great jump forward in mathematics. Imagine reckoning up with Roman numerals!

It seems inconceivable to us, now, that negative numbers were not used until the middle of the sixteenth century, and it wasn't until the beginning of the seventeenth century that they were used with any confidence. They arose as negative roots of an equation, and were rejected as being 'absurd' numbers, and having no meaning. Today, however, every schoolchild knows the meaning of a temperature of -2°C, when listening to a weather forecast.

In the same way, 'imaginary' roots of an equation first arose in the solution of cubic equations, and were viewed with great suspicion as meaningless, but in the seventeenth and eighteenth centuries mathematics made great strides and the importance of complex numbers gradually became recognised, until, today, no electrical engineer can manage without them. It appears that their application to electrical engineering was developed by Heaviside and others towards the end of the last century.

WHAT IS AN IMAGINARY NUMBER?

Taking three examples of quadratic equations:

1. $x^2 + 1 = 0$ ... [1]

i.e. $x^2 = -1$

$x = \pm\sqrt{-1}$

Now $\sqrt{-1}$ is not an ordinary number since the square of every ordinary number is positive. Up to the present we have avoided such numbers, which from their early history gained the unfortunate name of imaginary numbers. It is often denoted by i but electrical engineers use the symbol j , as the symbol i is often used for current. We shall therefore use j which is more widely used these days.

We say, therefore, that the solution of equation [1] is

$$x = \pm j \text{ where } j^2 = -1$$

2. $5x^2 + 20 = 0$

Divide through by 5:

$\therefore\ x^2 + 4 = 0$

$x = \pm\sqrt{-4}$

$= \pm\sqrt{4} \times \sqrt{-1}$

$x = \pm 2j$ both roots 'imaginary'

3. $x^2 - 4x + 13 = 0$

Using the formula $x = \dfrac{-b \pm\sqrt{b^2 - 4ac}}{2a}$ $a = 1$

$\therefore\ x = \dfrac{4 \pm\sqrt{16 - 4 \cdot 1 \cdot 13}}{2}$ $b = -4$, $c = 13$

$= \dfrac{4 \pm\sqrt{-36}}{2}$

$= \dfrac{4 \pm 6\sqrt{-1}}{2}$

$\therefore\ x = 2 \pm 3j$ both roots 'complex'

This solution, which is a combination of a so-called 'real' part, 2, and a so-called 'imaginary' part 3j, is called a *complex number.*

GRAPHICAL REPRESENTATION OF NUMBERS

We are already familiar with the 'thermometer scale' method of representing numbers, and we often represent the real numbers by a horizontal line. By convention, we take positive numbers measured to the right of a fixed point 0, and negative numbers to the left (Fig.17.1).

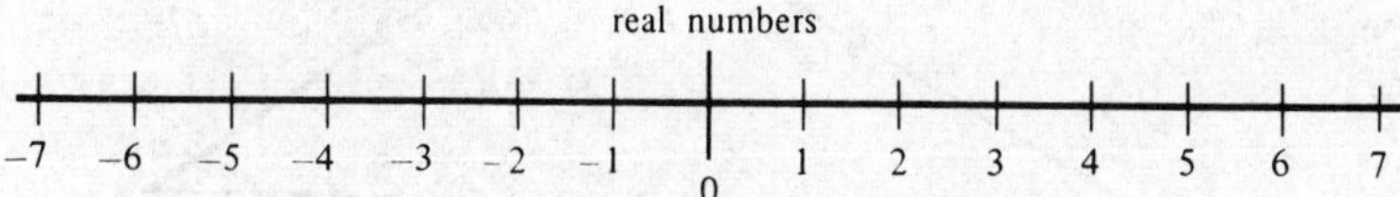

Fig.17.1.

Such numbers as $\sqrt{3}$ or $\frac{2}{11}$ can only be represented approximately, but all points represent some number, either positive or negative.

The next question arises;

What is represented by points *not* on this straight line?

Do not confuse this with the graphical method of representing a pair of real numbers, and using two axes at right angles. Here we are speaking of the graphical representation of only one number, which up to the present stage has only needed one axis, representing all real numbers from $+\infty$ to $-\infty$.

Do the points *off the line* represent anything at all?

Here we must branch aside to define a **vector** quantity.

Some physical quantities such as force, velocity, distance, acceleration, etc., are only completely specified when their direction as well as their magnitude is specified. Other quantities which involve no sense of direction are called **scalars.** Examples of these are volume, mass, density, etc.

A vector is represented graphically by a line drawn in the direction of the vector and proportional in length to its magnitude.

For example, we represent the vector $\vec{AB}$ by a line from A to B with an arrow indicating direction (Fig. 17.2).

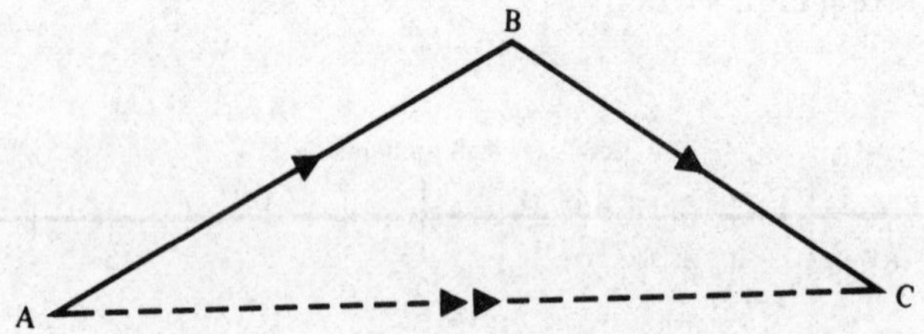

Fig.17.2.

and the line $\vec{BC}$ represents vector $\vec{BC}$.

And we say in **vector addition**, that

the vector $\vec{AC}$ = vector $\vec{AB}$ + vector $\vec{BC}$

or simply $\vec{AC} = \vec{AB} + \vec{BC}$

and we call $\vec{AC}$ the **resultant** of $\vec{AB}$ and $\vec{BC}$.

This is merely saying in symbols: 'If one goes from A to B and then from B to C, the result is the same as if one went straight from A to C'.

(We do *not* mean that the length of AC = the sum of the lengths of AB and BC).

Now let us consider our straight line representing real numbers once more (Fig. 17.3).

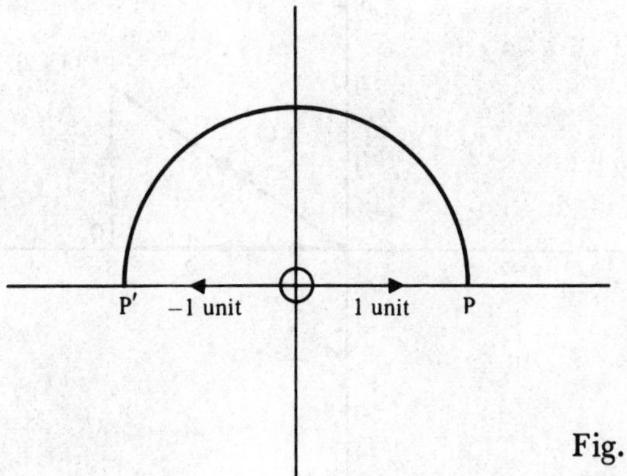

Fig.17.3.

The vector $\vec{OP}$ represents +1 unit

The vector $\vec{OP^1}$ represents −1 unit

If we rotate the vector $\vec{OP}$ through 180° or π radians we change the vector from +1 to −1, i.e. we multiply it by −1. But $-1 = j^2$.

Rotating a vector through 180° changes the vector from + to − or vice versa. So the question arises: if a rotation of 180° multiplies a vector by j x j, what does a rotation of 90° do? It seems natural to suggest that each 90° rotation multiplies by j, so that:

a 90° rotation multiplies the vector by j
a 180° " " " " by j x j i.e. −1
a 270° " " " " by j^3 i.e. −j
a 360° " " " " by j^4 i.e. + 1

and returns the vector unaltered to its original position.

We now have a representation for j, 2j, 3j, etc., as shown in Fig.17.4.

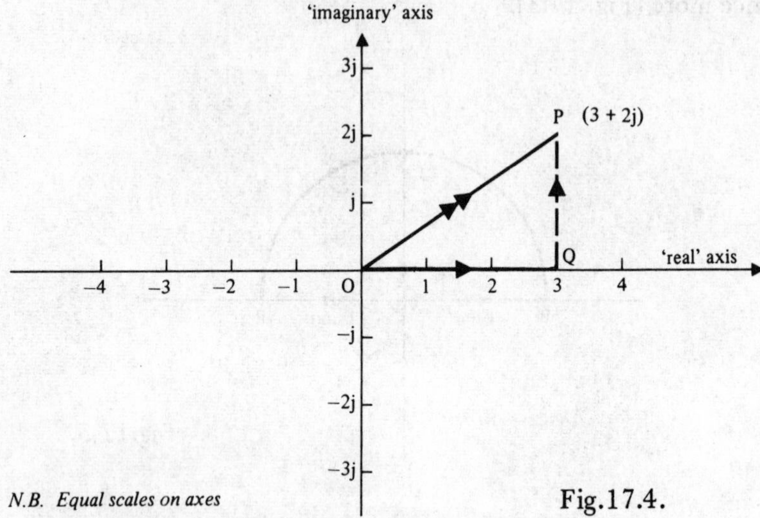

Fig.17.4.

This diagram is called the *Argand diagram.*

A vector such as $\vec{OP}$ is the resultant of two vectors $\vec{OQ}$ and $\vec{QP}$, one part real and one part imaginary, although we must always remember that both these are equally abstract representations of vectors.

In Figure 17.4. $\vec{OP} = 3 + 2j$

Similarly for vectors in the other quadrants.

We sometimes say that the vector (3 + 2j) is represented by the point P, meaning that the position of this point P relative to O represents the vector.

It must be clearly understood that the numbers j, 2j, 3j, etc., and −j, −2j, −3j, etc., marked on the vertical axis do not mean that the lengths are imaginary, for example, 3j means the vector OA (see Fig.17.5), not its length. The length is 3 units. Just as a vector of −3 along the real axis indicates a length of 3 units in the negative direction, so a vector 3j indicates a vector of length 3 in the 'j direction'.

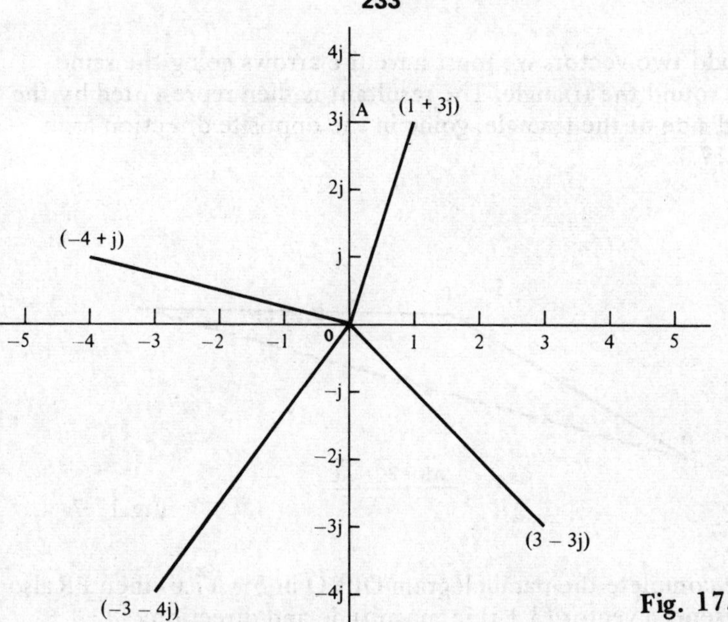

Fig. 17.5

In fact, one can think of $+j$ as due north
$-j$ as due south
$+1$ as due east
-1 as due west

DEALING WITH COMPLEX NUMBERS

Addition and subtraction

Example. Add the vectors $(1 + 2j)$ and $(3 + j)$.

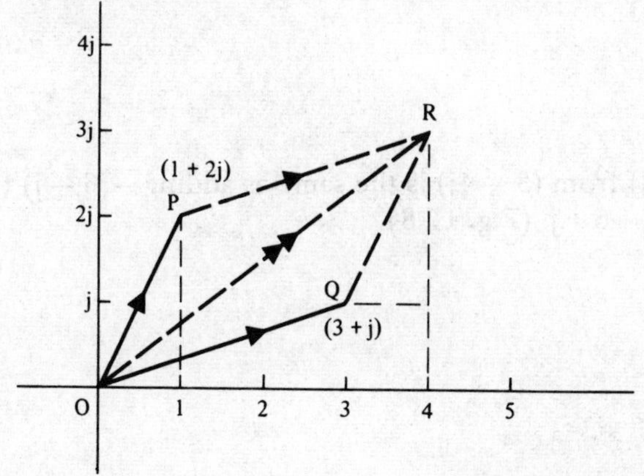

Fig.17.6.

To add two vectors we must have the arrows going the same way round the triangle. The resultant is then represented by the third side of the triangle, going in the opposite direction as in Fig.17.7.

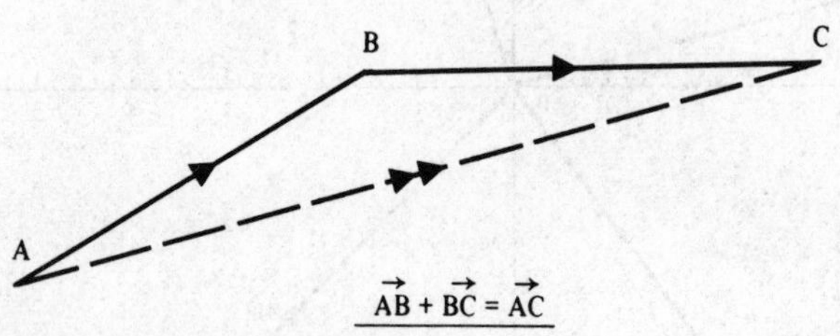

Fig.17.7.

If we complete the parallelogram OPRQ in Fig.17.6. then $\vec{PR}$ also represents a vector (3 + j) in magnitude and direction.

But $\vec{OP} + \vec{PR} = \vec{OR}$ (vector addition)

But R is the point (4 + 3j) by the 'step' method

$\therefore\ 1 + 2j + 3 + j = 4 + 3j$

In other words, we add (or subtract) the real parts and the imaginary parts just in the normal algebraic way.

Example. Simplify (3 – 4j) – (6 – j).

$$
\begin{aligned}
& (3 - 4j) - (6 - j) \\
= \quad & 3 - 4j - 6 + j \\
= \quad & -3 - 3j
\end{aligned}
$$

Subtracting (6 – j) from (3 – 4j) is the same as adding –(6 – j) to 3 – 4j, i.e. adding –6 + j (Fig. 17.8).

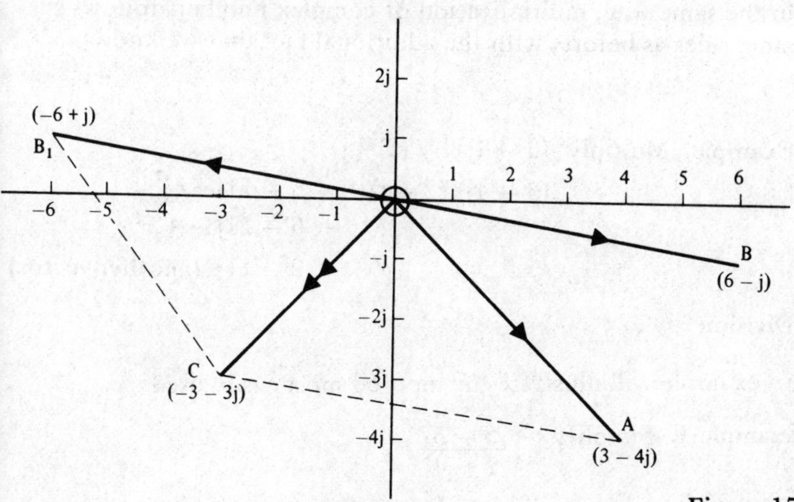

Figure 17.8

$\vec{OB_1} = -\vec{OB} = -6 + j$

$\vec{OA} = 3 - 4j$

$\therefore \vec{OA} - \vec{OB} = \vec{OA} + \vec{OB_1} = \vec{OC}$ (vector addition)

$\therefore (3 - 4j) - (6 - j) = -3 - 3j$

Exercise 48. Examples on Addition and Subtraction of Vectors.

Evaluate the following, representing each one on a separate Argand diagram.

1. $(3 + 2j) + (5 - 6j)$
2. $(-3 - j) - (2 + 3j)$
3. $(a + bj) + (c + dj)$
4. $(1.1 + 0.3j) - (0.9 + 0.3j)$
5. $5 + 2j + (-5 - 2j)$

Multiplication

In the same way, multiplication of complex numbers follows the same rules as before, with the additional fact that we know

$$j^2 = -1$$

Example. Multiply $(3 - 4j)$ by $(2 - j)$

$$\begin{aligned}(3 - 4j)(2 - j) &= 6 - 11j + 4j^2 \\ &= 6 - 11j - 4 \\ &= 2 - 11j \quad \textbf{(another vector)}\end{aligned}$$

Division

An example will illustrate the method most easily used.

Example 1. Simplify : $\dfrac{3 - 5j}{2 + 4j}$

This looks more complicated, but we can get rid of the j in the denominator by multiplying numerator and denominator by the conjugate vector $(2 - 4j)$ to obtain

$$\frac{(3 - 5j)}{(2 + 4j)} \times \frac{(2 - 4j)}{(2 - 4j)}$$

N.B. Both top line and bottom line must be multiplied by the same vector, otherwise the quantity is altered in value. (This is the reverse process of cancelling by the same quantity).

$$\frac{(3 - 5j)}{(2 + 4j)} \times \frac{(2 - 4j)}{(2 - 4j)}$$

$= \dfrac{6 - 22j + 20j^2}{4 - 16j^2}$ since $(2 + 4j)(2 - 4j)$ are factors of a 'difference of two squares'.

$= \dfrac{-14 - 22j}{20}$ putting $j^2 = -1$

$= -\dfrac{14}{20} - \dfrac{22}{20}j$

$= \mathbf{-0.7 - 1.1j}$

Example 2. Simplify : $\dfrac{4}{8 - 7j} - \dfrac{2}{1 - j}$

$= \dfrac{4(1 - j) - 2(8 - 7j)}{(8 - 7j)(1 - j)}$ putting over a common denominator

$= \dfrac{4 - 4j - 16 + 14j}{8 - 15j + 7j^2}$

$$= \frac{-12 + 10j}{1 - 15j} \quad \text{putting } j^2 = -1$$

$$= \frac{(-12 + 10j)}{(1 - 15j)} \times \frac{(1 + 15j)}{(1 + 15j)} \quad \text{rationalising the denominator}$$

$$= \frac{-12 - 170j + 150j^2}{1 - 225j^2}$$

$$= \frac{-162 - 170j}{226} \quad \text{putting } j^2 = -1$$

$$= -\frac{81}{113} - \frac{85}{113}j$$

Note: This method of rationalising the denominator is very similar to the method of dealing with surds, i.e. numbers involving square roots.

Example. Simplify : (i) $\frac{1}{\sqrt{3}}$; (ii) $\frac{1}{3 - 2\sqrt{2}}$

(i) Multiply by $\frac{\sqrt{3}}{\sqrt{3}}$

$$\therefore \frac{1}{\sqrt{3}} = \frac{1}{\sqrt{3}} \times \frac{\sqrt{3}}{\sqrt{3}}$$

$$= \frac{\sqrt{3}}{3}$$

(ii) Multiply by $\frac{3 + 2\sqrt{2}}{3 + 2\sqrt{2}}$

$$\therefore \frac{1}{3 - 2\sqrt{2}} = \frac{1}{(3 - 2\sqrt{2})} \times \frac{(3 + 2\sqrt{2})}{(3 + 2\sqrt{2})}$$

$$= \frac{3 + 2\sqrt{2}}{9 - 8}$$

(since $2\sqrt{2} \times 2\sqrt{2} = 4 \times 2 = 8$)

$$\therefore \frac{1}{3 - 2\sqrt{2}} = 3 + 2\sqrt{2}$$

These latter expressions are easier to evaluate than the given expressions.

Examples of multiplication and division of vectors by complex numbers.

Exercise 49.

Simplify the following :

1. $(8 - j)(2 + j)$
2. $(3 - 4j)(1 - 2j)$
3. $(3 + 4j)^2$
4. $(3 - 4j)(3 + 4j)$
5. $(1 + 2j)(3 - 2j)(1 + j)$ [Hint: substitute $j^2 = -1$ as soon as it occurs.]
6. $(-1 + j)^4$ [Hint: Find $(-1 + j)^2$ and then square the answer.]

Evaluate:

7. $\dfrac{5 - 6j}{4 - 2j}$
8. $\dfrac{3 + 7j}{3 - 7j}$
9. $\dfrac{3 - 7j}{3 + 7j}$
10. $\dfrac{(3 - 5j)(1 + j)}{4 + 2j}$
11. Find the value of $\dfrac{E_m}{R + jX}$ when $E_m = 250$, $R = 50$, $X = 4$
12. Find the value of z if

$$\frac{1}{z} = \frac{1}{6 + 2j} + \frac{1}{3 + 4j}$$

13. Solve the equation

$$x^2 - 6x + 13 = 0$$

QUADRATIC EQUATIONS

We have now extended our knowledge of quadratic equations. The solution of

$$ax^2 + bx + c = 0$$

is

$$x = \frac{-b \pm \sqrt{b^2 - 4ac}}{2a}$$

From this we can see that $\sqrt{b^2 - 4ac}$ decides the type of solution we obtain:

(i) **if $b^2 - 4ac$ is positive roots are real**

(ii) **if $b^2 - 4ac$ is zero roots are equal**

(iii) **if $b^2 - 4ac$ is negative roots are complex.**

It is evident, also, that if the roots are **complex** they are **conjugate complex**, i.e. of the form (c + dj) and (c – dj).

Summary

$b^2 - 4ac$	Type of root
Positive	Real, unequal
Zero	Real, equal
Negative	Complex, conjugate

Problem. When a capacitor of capacitance C farads discharges through a resistance of R ohms and an inductance of L henrys in series, the discharge is direct or oscillatory according as the roots of the equation :

$$Lp^2 + Rp + \frac{1}{C} = 0 \text{ are real or complex.}$$

(i) If $L = 0.01$; $R = 300$; $C = 0.4 \times 10^{-6}$

what type of discharge takes place?

(ii) If R is increased to 400 ohms does this affect the type of discharge?

COMPLEX NUMBERS IN POLAR CO-ORDINATES

We need another system of representing a vector, as distinct from the rectangular co-ordinate notation used so far. This notation is needed in order to deal with rotating vectors more easily.

Polar Co-ordinates

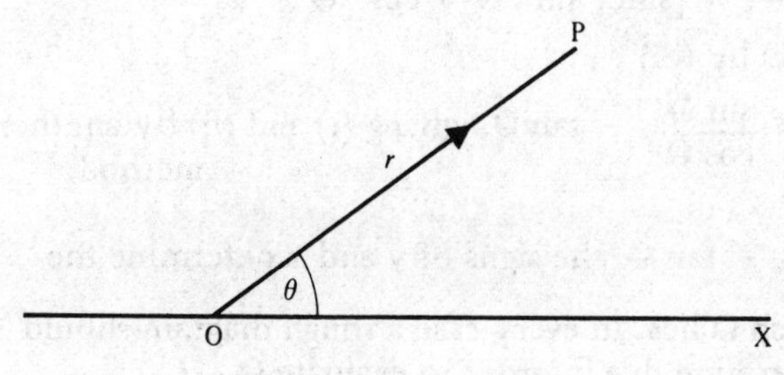

Figure 17.9

A vector $\vec{OP}$ can be completely defined if we know its magnitude r and the angle Θ which it makes with a fixed direction, OX (fig. 17.9).
We call these co-ordinates (r,Θ) the polar co-ordinates of the vector $\vec{OP}$.
It is quite easy to transform the (r, Θ) co-ordinates to (x,y) co-ordinates, and vice versa, by simple geometry.

Polar co-ordinates and rectangular co-ordinates

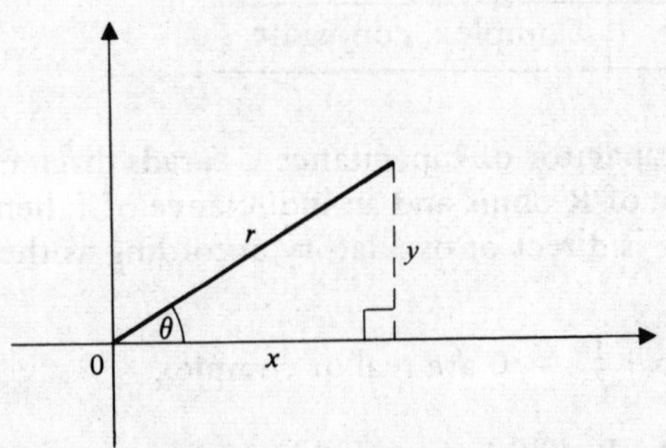

Figure 17.10

In Fig. 17.10, by simple geometry:

$$x^2 + y^2 = r^2 \qquad \text{... (i)}$$

$$\frac{y}{x} = \tan\Theta \qquad \text{... (ii)}$$

Equations (i) and (ii) give r and Θ in terms of x and y.
Also:

$$x = r\cos\Theta \qquad \text{... (iii)}$$
$$y = r\sin\Theta \qquad \text{... (iv)}$$

Equations (iii) and (iv) give x and y in terms of r and Θ..

Squaring and adding (iii) and (iv) :

$$x^2 + y^2 = r^2\,(\sin^2\Theta + \cos^2\Theta)$$

$$\therefore\ x^2 + y^2 = r^2 \quad [\text{since } \sin^2\Theta + \cos^2\Theta = 1]$$

Also, dividing (iv) by (iii) :

$$\frac{y}{x} = \frac{\sin\Theta}{\cos\Theta} = \tan\Theta,$$ giving (i) and (ii) by another method.

Note: In using $\frac{y}{x} = \tan\Theta$, the signs of y and x determine the quadrant in which Θ lies. In every case a rough diagram should be drawn to determine this in order to evaluate Θ.

Example. Find the polar co-ordinates of the point whose rectangular co-ordinates are (–3, 4).

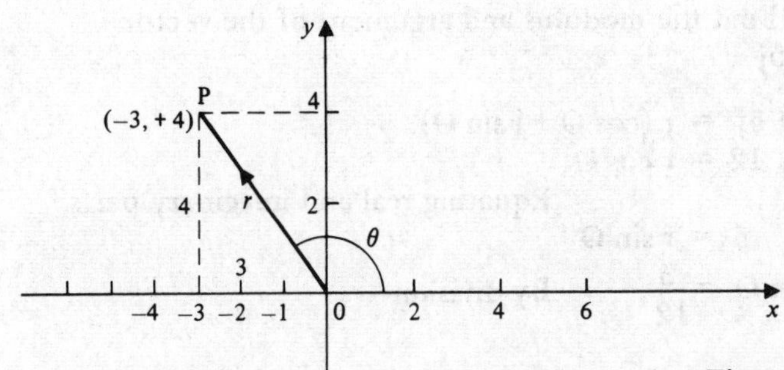

Figure 17.11

$r^2 = x^2 + y^2$

$= 3^2 + 4^2$

$\therefore r = 5$ (r is always positive)

Θ is in the second quadrant

$\tan^{-1}\frac{4}{3} = 53^o8$

$\therefore \Theta = 180^o - 53^o8$

$\Theta = 126^o52$

∴ Polar co-ordinates are $(5, 126^o52)$

Modulus and argument

When a complex number is expressed in polar co-ordinates (r, Θ)

r is called the *modulus* of the complex number
Θ is called the *argument* of the complex number

If $\vec{z} = a + jb$ where $a = r\cos\Theta$

$b = r\sin\Theta$

then $\vec{z} = r(\cos\Theta + j\sin\Theta)$

The modulus of z, i.e. r, is often expressed as mod z or $|z|$ and the argument by arg z

Cis Θ

$z = r \text{ cis } \Theta$ is often used as an abbreviation derived from $i = \sqrt{-1}$

i.e. $z = \underline{r}(\underline{c}os\ \Theta + \underline{i}\ \underline{s}in\ \underline{\Theta})$

Example. Find the modulus and argument of the vector $z = 12 + 5j$

Let $12 + 5j = r(\cos\Theta + j\sin\Theta)$

$\therefore$ (i) $12 = r\cos\Theta$

Equating real and imaginary parts

(ii) $5 = r\sin\Theta$

$\therefore \tan\Theta = \frac{5}{12}$ By division

$\therefore r^2 = 5^2 + 12^2$ By squaring and adding

$\therefore$ **r = 13 = modulus (r always taken positive)**

and Θ = 22°37 = argument

N.B. $\tan\Theta = \frac{5}{12}$ does not define the angle completely, as tan Θ is positive in both first and third quadrants. However, in this case both sin Θ and cos Θ are positive, so Θ must lie in the first quadrant.

Multiplication of complex numbers in polar form.

Multiplication and division of vectors is most easily done in this form.

Let two vectors be $r_1(\cos\Theta_1 + j\sin\Theta_1) = (r_1, \Theta_1)$

$r_2(\cos\Theta_2 + j\sin\Theta_2) = (r_2, \Theta_2)$

Then $(r_1, \Theta_1) \times (r_2, \Theta_2) = r_1(\cos\Theta_1 + j\sin\Theta_1) \times r_2(\cos\Theta_2 + j\sin\Theta_2)$

$= r_1 r_2 (\cos\Theta_1\cos\Theta_2 - \sin\Theta_1\sin\Theta_2)$

$+ j(\sin\Theta_1\cos\Theta_2 + \cos\Theta_1\sin\Theta_2)$

using $j^2 = -1$

But $\cos(\Theta_1 \pm \Theta_2) = \cos\Theta_1 \cos\Theta_2 \mp \sin\Theta_1 \sin\Theta_2$
and $\sin(\Theta_1 \pm \Theta_2) = \sin\Theta_1 \cos\Theta_2 \pm \cos\Theta_1 \sin\Theta_2$ .... [1]

(See Appendix 3)

$$\therefore (r_1, \Theta_1) \times (r_2, \Theta_2) = r_1 r_2[\cos(\Theta_1 + \Theta_2) + j\sin(\Theta_1 + \Theta_2)]$$
$$= (r_1 r_2, \Theta_1 + \Theta_2)$$

Hence, to **multiply** two vectors together in polar form:

(i) **multiply their moduli;**

(ii) **add their arguments.**

Division in polar form

$$\frac{(r_1, \Theta_1)}{(r_2, \Theta_2)} = \frac{r_1(\cos\Theta_1 + j\sin\Theta_1)}{r_2(\cos\Theta_2 + j\sin\Theta_2)}$$

Rationalising the denominator by multiplying by $\dfrac{\cos\Theta_2 - j\sin\Theta_2}{\cos\Theta_2 - j\sin\Theta_2}$ we obtain:

$$\frac{r_1}{r_2} \cdot \frac{(\cos\Theta_1 + j\sin\Theta_1)(\cos\Theta_2 - j\sin\Theta_2)}{\cos^2\Theta_2 - j^2\sin^2\Theta_2}$$

$$= \frac{r_1}{r_2}(\cos\Theta_1 + j\sin\Theta_1)(\cos\Theta_2 - j\sin\Theta_2)$$

$$[\text{since } \cos^2\Theta_2 + \sin^2\Theta_2 = 1]$$

$$= \frac{r_1}{r_2}[\cos\Theta_1 \cos\Theta_2 + \sin\Theta_1 \sin\Theta_2 + j(\sin\Theta_1 \cos\Theta_2 - \cos\Theta_1 \sin\Theta_2)]$$

$$= \frac{r_1}{r_2}[\cos(\Theta_1 - \Theta_2) + j\sin(\Theta_1 - \Theta_2)]$$ by using identities [1] again.

$$= \frac{r_1}{r_2}, (\Theta_1 - \Theta_2)$$

Hence, to **divide** two vectors in polar form:

(i) **divide their moduli;**

(ii) **subtract their arguments.**

Corollary

To find the effect of multiplying any complex number by j :

Since $j = 1 \ (\cos 90^{\circ} + j \sin 90^{\circ}) \quad [\cos 90^{\circ} = 0, \ \sin 90^{\circ} = 1]$

if we multiply $(r, \Theta) = r(\cos \Theta + j \sin \Theta)$ by j

we get $\quad r.1 \ [\cos(\Theta + 90^{\circ}) + j \sin (\Theta + 90^{\circ})]$

$$= r \ [\cos (\Theta + 90^{\circ}) + j \sin (\Theta + 90^{\circ})]$$

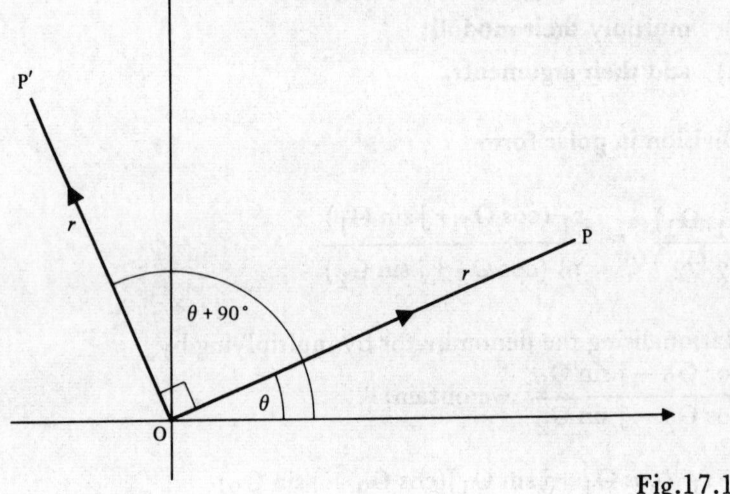

Fig.17.12.

So that OP is changed to OP[1] (Fig.17.12).

In other words, the effect of multiplying a vector by j is to rotate the vector through 90° anti-clockwise without altering its modulus.

Exercise 50. Draw the following vectors on a diagram and express them in the polar form (r,Θ).

1. $3 + 4j$
2. $12 - 5j$
3. $-8 + 15j$
4. $-73 + 40j$

Express each of the following vectors in the form a + bj :

5. $(5, 36^{\circ})$ 6. $(0.8, 120^{\circ})$ 7. $(6, -10^{\circ})$

RELATIONSHIP BETWEEN COMPLEX NUMBERS AND e.

To prove

$r(\cos\Theta + j\sin\Theta) = re^{j\Theta}$

Let $z = \cos\Theta + j\sin\Theta$ ... [1]

$\therefore \dfrac{dz}{d\Theta} = -\sin\Theta + j\cos\Theta$

$= j^2 \sin\Theta + j\cos\Theta$ putting $j^2 = -1$

$= j(\cos\Theta + j\sin\Theta)$

$= jz$

Inverting both sides:

$$\frac{d\Theta}{dz} = \frac{1}{jz}$$

Integrating w.r.t. z :

$$\Theta = \frac{1}{j}\int \frac{1}{z}\,dz$$

$$= \frac{1}{j}\log_e z + c$$

But from [1], when $\Theta = 0$, $\cos\Theta = 1$, $\sin\Theta = 0$, i.e. $z = 1$

$\therefore \quad \Theta = \frac{1}{j}\log_e 1 + c$

But log 1 = 0 to any base

$\therefore \quad c = 0$

$\therefore \quad \Theta = \frac{1}{j}\log_e z$

$\therefore \quad j\Theta = \log_e z$

$\therefore \quad e^{j\Theta} = z$ (definition of Logs)

$\therefore$ **$r(\cos\Theta + j\sin\Theta) = re^{j\Theta}$**

ROTATING VECTORS

One of the most important applications of the theory of vectors is its application to the theory of alternating currents in electricity.

An alternating current i may be expressed by a sine wave of the form:

$i = I_m \sin\omega t$ where I_m is the maximum current

ω is constant

t is time

Take a vector I whose magnitude, i.e. modulus, is I_m making angle ωt with the real axis at time t.

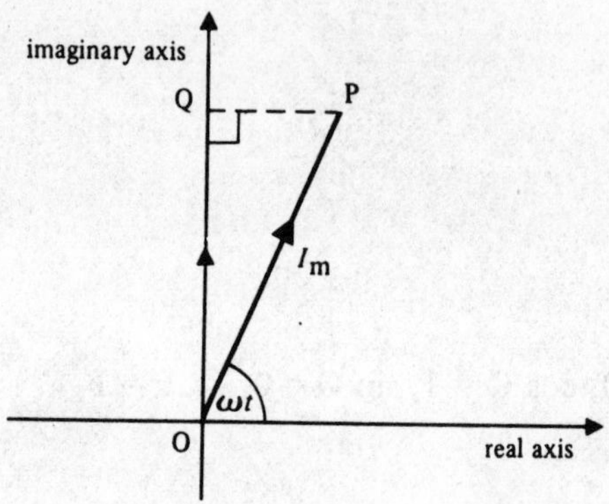

Fig.17.13.

Then $i = I_m \sin \omega t$ is the projection of I_m on the imaginary axis. Therefore, the current i is the coefficient of j in the vector I (represented by OP,) and is represented by vector OQ. Although we call OQ the 'imaginary part' of vector OP, we must always remember that it is *real.*

De Moivre's theorem

This states that:

For all rational values of n
$(\cos \Theta + j \sin \Theta)^n = \cos n\Theta + j \sin n\Theta$.

We have already shown that :
$r_1(\cos \Theta_1 + j \sin \Theta_1) \times r_2(\cos \Theta_2 + j \sin \Theta_2) =$
$r_1 r_2 [\cos(\Theta_1 + \Theta_2) + j \sin (\Theta_1 + \Theta_2)]$

Put $\Theta_1 = \Theta_2 = \Theta$ and $r_1 = r_2 = 1$ and we get
$(\cos \Theta + j \sin \Theta)^2 = \cos 2\Theta + j \sin 2\Theta$

This method may be continued by multiplying by $(\cos \Theta + j \sin \Theta)$ and we obtain

$(\cos \Theta + j \sin \Theta)^3 = (\cos 2\Theta + j \sin 2\Theta)(\cos \Theta + j \sin \Theta)$
$= \cos 3\Theta + j \sin 3\Theta$ and so on.

This proves the theorem for n a positive integer.

Proof of De Moivre's theorem for any value of n

$$\cos \Theta + j \sin \Theta = e^{j\Theta} \quad \text{... [1]}$$

$$\therefore (\cos \Theta + j \sin \Theta)^n = (e^{j\Theta})^n$$
$$= e^{jn\Theta}$$
$$= e^{j(n\Theta)}$$

But $e^{j(n\Theta)} = \cos n\Theta + j \sin n\Theta$ from [1], replacing Θ by $n\Theta$.
$\therefore (\cos \Theta + j \sin \Theta)^n = \cos n\Theta + j \sin n\Theta$

Example. Find the square root of the vector $r(\cos\Theta + j\sin\Theta)$

$$\begin{aligned}\sqrt{r(\cos\Theta + j\sin\Theta)} &= [r(\cos\Theta + j\sin\Theta)]^{1/2}\\ &= r^{1/2}(\cos\Theta + j\sin\Theta)^{1/2}\\ &= r^{1/2}\left(\cos\frac{\Theta}{2} + j\sin\frac{\Theta}{2}\right) \quad \text{(De Moivre's theorem)}\end{aligned}$$

This gives the square root of a vector quantity

Exercise 5l. If $z = 4(\cos 30^{o} + j\sin 30^{o})$ find z^2 and $\sqrt{z}$.

Chapter 18

Partial fractions

INTRODUCTION

If we are given

(i) $3x + 2 = 5$

(ii) $x^2 - 3x + 2 = 0$

(iii) $(2x - 5)(x + 4) = 0$

(iv) $\frac{x + 2}{3} = 4$

(v) $3x + 2 = x + 2x + 2$

would we say these are all 'equations' in the normal sense?

We note that

(i) is a linear equation with a solution $x = 1$

(ii) is a quadratic equation with solutions $x = 1$ and 2

(iii) is also quadratic with solutions $x = 2\frac{1}{2}$ and -4

(iv) is linear with a solution $x = 10$

But what is (v)? It is not an equation in the sense that the others are equations. What is the difference? Yes, the left-hand side is just a tidier way of writing the right-hand side, or putting it another way, the statement that

$$3x + 2 = x + 2x + 2 \text{ is}$$

Always true for any value of x

whereas an 'equation' is only true for particular values of x. We call this type of 'equation' an *identity* which we should denote by the sign ≡. (Read: 'identically equal to').

Strictly speaking, for example, we should write

$$2x + 3x + x \equiv 6x$$

since it is true for all values of x. This is merely a 'tidying up' process.

We need to recognise this distinction when we wish to split up a complicated fraction, which we want to integrate, into simpler fractions which are more easily dealt with. We shall see later why we need to do this, but first let us look at the reverse process as a revision exercise.

Example 1. Simplify:

$$\frac{3}{(x+2)} + \frac{1}{(x-3)}$$

$$\equiv \frac{3(x-3) + 1(x+2)}{(x+2)(x-3)} \quad \text{common denominator} = (x+2)(x-3)$$

$$\equiv \frac{4x-7}{(x+2)(x-3)}$$

Note: The identically equal sign is used since the result is exactly equivalent to what we were given.

Now suppose we need to find

$$\int \frac{(4x-7)\,dx}{(x+2)\,(x-3)}$$

The expression under the integral sign has never occurred as the differential of any function we have encountered so far. Hence we are unable to integrate it in this form. But if we can reverse the tidying up process in Example 1, to obtain

$$\frac{4x-7}{(x+2)(x-3)} \equiv \frac{3}{(x+2)} + \frac{1}{(x-3)}$$

i.e. split a complicated fraction into two or more simple fractions, we can then integrate each part separately. We know that

$$\int \frac{3}{(x+2)}\,dx = 3 \log_e (x+2) + \text{a constant}$$

and

$$\int \frac{1}{(x-3)}\,dx = \log_e (x-3) + \text{a constant}$$

$$\therefore \quad \int \frac{(4x-7)\,dx}{(x+2)(x-3)} = \int \frac{3}{(x+2)}\,dx + \int \frac{1}{(x-3)}\,dx$$
$$= 3\log_e(x+2) + \log_e(x-3) + \text{a constant}$$

This method of splitting a complicated fraction into simpler ones is called the method of *partial fractions.*

Suppose we now work Example 1 in reverse, to illustrate the method used to obtain the required partial fractions.

Example 2. Express

$$\frac{4x-7}{(x+2)(x-3)} \text{ in partial fractions.}$$

Suppose $\frac{4x-7}{(x+2)(x-3)}$ can be split into fractions

$\frac{A}{(x+2)} + \frac{B}{(x-3)}$ where A and B are constants to be evaluated.

Then we know that $\frac{4x-7}{(x+2)(x-3)}$ and $\frac{A}{(x+2)} + \frac{B}{(x-3)}$

must be exactly equivalent to each other. One is merely a tidier form of the other. Hence they are identically equal.

Let $\frac{4x-7}{(x+2)(x-3)} \equiv \frac{A}{(x+2)} + \frac{B}{(x-3)}$ .... (1)

An identity is true for all values of x.

Multiply by the common denominator $(x+2)(x-3)$:

$\therefore \quad 4x-7 \equiv A(x-3) + B(x+2)$ .... (2)

Since this is an identity we can choose any values of x to substitute in (2) to evaluate A and B. Can we choose a value of x which makes A disappear? x = 3 ?
Put x = 3 in (2) :

$$12 - 7 = A.0 + B(5) \quad \text{(Note the equals sign now)}$$
$$\therefore \quad 5 = 5B$$
$$\therefore \quad \mathbf{B = 1}$$

Put x = −2 in (2) (to make B disappear):

$$-8-7 = A(-2-3) + B.0$$
$$\therefore \quad -15 = -5A$$
$$\therefore \quad \mathbf{A = 3}$$

Hence $\frac{4x-7}{(x+2)(x-3)} \equiv \frac{3}{(x+2)} + \frac{1}{(x-3)}$ from (1)

We do not need to check this by simplifying the R.H.S. since we have already done so in Example 1.

Example 3. Find $\int \frac{x}{1-x^2}\,dx$

Let $\frac{x}{1-x^2} \equiv \frac{A}{(1-x)} + \frac{B}{(1+x)}$ since $1-x^2 = (1-x)(1+x)$

Multiply by $(1-x)(1+x)$:

$$x \equiv A(1+x) + B(1-x) \quad \text{(true for all values of x).}$$

Put $x = -1$; $-1 = +2B$ $\quad \therefore \mathbf{B} = -\frac{1}{2}$

Put $x = +1$; $+1 = 2A$ $\quad \therefore \mathbf{A} = \frac{1}{2}$

$$\therefore \int \frac{x}{1-x^2}\,dx \equiv \tfrac{1}{2}\int \frac{1}{1-x}\,dx - \tfrac{1}{2}\int \frac{1}{1+x}\,dx$$

$$= -\tfrac{1}{2}\log_e(1-x) - \tfrac{1}{2}\log_e(1+x) + c$$

$$= -\tfrac{1}{2}\log_e(1-x)(1+x) + c \quad \text{(theory of logs)}$$

Exercise 52. Find the following integrals by first expressing the integrand in partial fractions:

1. $\int \frac{dx}{x^2-1}$ 2. $\int \frac{dx}{1-x^2}$ 3. $\int \frac{dx}{4x^2-9}$ 4. $\int \frac{3x-1}{x^2+x-6}\,dx$

IMPROPER FRACTIONS

We note that in the previous examples the degree of the numerator is less than that of the denominator. This type of fraction, as in arithmetic, is called a simple or proper fraction. In algebra, an improper fraction has a numerator of degree equal to or greater than that of the denominator.

If it is necessary to convert an improper fraction into partial fractions, either for purposes of integration or for expansion by the Binomial theorem (see page 307) we must separate out the whole number part of the fraction first. This avoids complications at a later stage. The simple fraction which remains is converted into partial fractions in the normal way. The next two examples will illustrate the method.

Example 4. Degree of numerator equal to that of denominator.

Express $\dfrac{3x^2 + x}{x^2 + 5x + 6}$ in partial fractions.

Here we see that the highest powers of x in both numerator and denominator are the same, i.e. x^2. This means that the denominator will divide into the numerator a certain number of times.

By long division:

$$\begin{array}{r|l} & \quad 3 \\ x^2 + 5x + 6 & 3x^2 + x \\ & 3x^2 + 15x + 18 \quad \text{(multiplying the divisor by 3)} \\ \hline & \quad - 14x - 18 \quad \text{(subtracting)} \end{array}$$

$$\therefore \frac{3x^2 + x}{x^2 + 5x + 6} \equiv 3 - \frac{(14x + 18)}{x^2 + 5x + 6} \qquad \text{.... (1)}$$

Now we express the algebraic proper fraction in partial fractions.

$$\frac{14x + 18}{x^2 + 5x + 6} \equiv \frac{14x + 18}{(x + 3)(x + 2)} \quad \text{(factorising the denominator)}$$

Let $\dfrac{14x + 18}{(x + 3)(x + 2)} \equiv \dfrac{A}{(x + 3)} + \dfrac{B}{(x + 2)}$

Multiply by $(x + 3)(x + 2)$:

$\therefore\ 14x + 18 \equiv A(x + 2) + B(x + 3)$ (true for all values of x)

Put $x = -2$; $-28 + 18 = B(1)$ $\qquad \left[\ \therefore\ \mathbf{B = -10}\right.$

Put $x = -3$; $-42 + 18 = A(-1)$ $\qquad \left.\ \therefore\ \mathbf{A = 24}\ \right]$

$$\therefore \frac{14x + 18}{x^2 + 5x + 6} \equiv \frac{24}{(x + 3)} - \frac{10}{(x + 2)}$$

and from (1) :

$$\frac{3x^2 + x}{x^2 + 5x + 6} \equiv 3 - \frac{24}{(x + 3)} + \frac{10}{(x + 2)}$$

Check: Putting the R.H.S. on the common denominator $(x + 3)(x + 2)$:

$$\text{R.H.S.} = 3 - \frac{24}{(x+3)} + \frac{10}{(x+2)} = \frac{3(x+3)(x+2) - 24(x+2) + 10(x+3)}{(x+3)(x+2)}$$

$$= \frac{3x^2 + 15x + 18 - 24x - 48 + 10x + 30}{(x+3)(x+2)}$$

$$= \frac{3x^2 + x}{(x+3)(x+2)} = \text{L.H.S.} \qquad \text{Correct.}$$

Example 5. Degree of numerator greater than that of denominator

Express $\frac{2x^3 - 25x + 22}{x^2 + 2x - 8}$ in partial fractions and find the integral of the result.

Here we note that the highest power of x in the numerator is x^3 and in the denominator is x^2. Hence the denominator will divide into the numerator, and this must be done first.

This operation is performed as follows (see 'long division,' page 32

$$\begin{array}{lrl}
 & 2x - 4 & \\
x^2 + 2x - 8 & \overline{)\,2x^3 \qquad\quad - 25x + 22} & \\
\text{line (i)} & \underline{2x^3 + 4x^2 - 16x} & \text{(multiplying the divisor by 2} \\
 & -4x^2 - 9x + 22 & \text{(subtracting and bringing do} \\
 & & \text{the 22} \\
 & \underline{-4x^2 - 8x + 32} & \text{(multiplying the divisor by -} \\
\text{Remainder} = & \underline{-x - 10} & \text{(subtracting)}
\end{array}$$

Hence, $\frac{2x^3 - 25x + 22}{x^2 + 2x - 8} \equiv 2x - 4 + \frac{-x - 10}{(x+4)(x-2)} \equiv E$ (say

Let $\frac{-x - 10}{(x+4)(x-2)} \equiv \frac{A}{(x+4)} + \frac{B}{(x-2)}$

Multiply by $(x + 4)(x - 2)$:

$$-x - 10 \equiv A(x-2) + B(x+4)$$

Put $x = 2$: $\quad -12 = 6B \qquad B = -2$

Put $x = -4$: $\quad -6 = -6A \qquad A = 1$

$$\therefore\ E \equiv 2x - 4 + \frac{1}{(x+4)} - \frac{2}{(x-2)}$$

Check:

$$2x - 4 + \frac{1}{(x+4)} \quad - \quad \frac{2}{(x-2)}$$

$$= \quad \frac{(2x-4)(x+4)(x-2) + (x-2) - 2(x+4)}{(x+4)(x-2)}$$

$$= \quad \frac{(2x-4)(x^2 + 2x - 8) + (x-2) - 2(x+4)}{(x+4)(x-2)}$$

$$= \quad \frac{2x^3 - 24x + 32 + x - 2 - 2x - 8}{(x+4)(x-2)}$$

$$= \quad \frac{2x^3 - 25x + 22}{x^2 + 2x - 8} \qquad \text{Correct}$$

$$\begin{array}{rrrr}
 & x^2 + & 2x & - 8 \\
 & & 2x & - 4 \\
\hline
 & -4x^2 & - 8x & + 32 \\
2x^3 & + 4x^2 & - 16x & \\
\hline
2x^3 & & - 24x & + 32 \\
\hline
\end{array}$$

And

$$\int E\,dx = x^2 - 4x + \log_e(x+4) - 2\log_e(x-2) + c$$

Exercise 53. By first dividing the denominator into the numerator, express each of the following as a whole number plus partial fractions. Integrate the results.

1. $\dfrac{x^2}{(x^2 - 1)}$ 2. $\dfrac{2x^2}{(x-4)(x+2)}$ 3. $\dfrac{2x^3 + 2x^2 - 12x + 5}{x^2 + x - 6}$

QUADRATIC FACTORS IN THE DENOMINATOR

Let us now consider what happens if one of the factors of the denominator is not a simple factor such as $(x - 3)$ or $(2x + 1)$, but is of the second degree, for example $(x^2 + 1)$, which will not factorise.

Before proceeding to the method for dealing with this type, consider what happens in the reverse process. This will help us to understand why we need the partial fractions to be expressed in a certain way.

Example 6. Simplify:

$$\frac{2}{(x-1)} + \frac{3x+2}{(x^2+1)}$$ (neither denominator will divide into the numerator)

$$\equiv \frac{2(x^2+1)+(3x+2)(x-1)}{(x-1)(x^2+1)}$$

$$\equiv \frac{2x^2+2+3x^2-x-2}{(x-1)(x^2+1)}$$

$$\equiv \frac{5x^2-x}{(x-1)(x^2+1)}$$

Now let us reverse the process. With hindsight can we assume that

$$\frac{5x^2-x}{(x-1)(x^2+1)} \text{ will split up into } \frac{A}{(x-1)} + \frac{B}{(x^2+1)} \quad ?$$

Obviously not. The numerator of (x^2+1) can possibly contain a term in x as well as a constant, as we see above.

We must allow for this, and put in $\frac{Bx+C}{x^2+1}$ as our second fraction. In some cases, either B or C can be zero, but we must not assume this.

Hence:

Let $$\frac{5x^2-x}{(x-1)(x^2+1)} \equiv \frac{A}{(x-1)} + \frac{(Bx+C)}{(x^2+1)}$$

Multiply by $(x-1)(x^2+1)$:

$$5x^2 - x \equiv A(x^2+1) + (Bx+C)(x-1) \quad \text{... [}$$

Put $x = 1$: $\quad 4 \equiv 2A \quad \therefore A = 2$

(There are no more obvious values to substitute, but in an identity we can let x have *any* value. A useful value is $x = 0$).

Put $x = 0$ in [1]: $\quad 0 = A + C(-1)$

$0 = A - C \qquad \therefore C = 2$

Another useful method is to equate like terms on either side of the identity, i.e. x^2 terms with x^2 terms or x terms with x terms or constants with constants. * In this case, to bring in B, equate terms in x^2 :

$$5x^2 = Ax^2 + Bx^2$$

$$\therefore \quad 5 = A + B$$

We call this 'equating coefficients of x^2'.

Since $A = 2, \qquad B = 3$

$$\therefore \quad \frac{5x^2 - x}{(x-1)(x^2+1)} \equiv \frac{2}{(x+1)} + \frac{3x+2}{(x^2+1)}$$ as we expected.

* A simple example of this will illustrate the point.

We know that: $\quad 3x^2 + 2x^2 - 3x + 6x \equiv 5x^2 + 3x$

Equate coefficients of x^2: $\quad 3 + 2 = 5$

Equate coefficients of x : $\quad -3 + 6 = +3$

Thus in an identity the terms of *any power* on the L.H.S. must balance the terms of the same power on the R.H.S.

Example 7. Express

$\frac{x-1}{(x+1)(x^2+1)}$ in partial fractions.

Let $\frac{x-1}{(x+1)(x^2+1)} \equiv \frac{A}{(x+1)} + \frac{Bx+C}{(x^2+1)}$ where A, B, C are constants.

Multiply by $(x+1)(x^2+1)$:

$$x - 1 \equiv A(x^2+1) + (Bx+C)(x+1)$$

Put $x = -1$: $\quad -2 = A.2 \qquad \therefore A = -1$

Put $x = 0$: $\quad -1 = A + C \qquad \therefore C = 0$

Equate coefficients of x^2 : $\quad 0 = A + B$

$\therefore \quad B = -A \qquad \therefore\ B = 1$

Hence $$\frac{x-1}{(x+1)(x^2+1)} \equiv -\frac{1}{(x+1)} + \frac{x}{(x^2+1)}$$

Check:

$$-\frac{1}{(x+1)} + \frac{x}{(x^2+1)}$$

$$= \frac{-(x^2+1)+x(x+1)}{(x+1)(x^2+1)}$$

$$= \frac{-x^2-1+x^2+x}{(x+1)(x^2+1)}$$

$$= \frac{x-1}{(x+1)(x^2+1)} \quad \text{Correct}$$

Exercise 54. Express the following in partial fractions:

1. $\dfrac{1}{x(x^2+1)}$ 2. $\dfrac{1}{(x^2+1)(x-2)}$ 3. $\dfrac{x}{(x+1)(x^2+4)}$

REPEATED LINEAR FACTORS

In the examples given so far, each factor in the denominator is different, and has become the denominator of one of the partial fractions,

e.g. $\dfrac{2x-1}{(x+2)(x+1)}$ can be obtained from fractions with denominators $(x + 2)$ and $(x + 1)$.

What do we do about a fraction such as $\dfrac{3}{(x-2)(x-1)^2}$?

Do we express it as $\dfrac{A}{(x-2)} + \dfrac{B}{(x-1)} + \dfrac{C}{(x-1)}$?

This seems stupid, as the last two fractions could be combined to give

$$\frac{B+C}{(x-1)} \quad \text{i.e.} \quad \frac{D}{(x-1)}$$

and it is obvious that

$$\frac{A}{(x-2)} + \frac{D}{(x-1)}$$

has a common denominator of $(x-2)(x-1)$, not $(x-2)(x-1)^2$ which we need. In fact, we need to have a fraction with a denominator $(x-1)^2$ in order to derive our common denominator.

Thus we take $\frac{3}{(x-2)(x-1)^2} \equiv \frac{A}{(x-2)} + \frac{B}{(x-1)} + \frac{C}{(x-1)^2}$

We must include $\frac{B}{(x-1)}$ as this could be included to give our common denominator. It may be superfluous, but if it is we shall find that B equals zero; *but we cannot omit it.*

Note also, that although the denominator $(x-1)^2$ is quadratic it *does not need a numerator* $(Cx + D)$.

This is compensated for by the fraction $\frac{B}{(x-1)}$

Let us complete the example given.

Let $\frac{3}{(x-2)(x-1)^2} \equiv \frac{A}{(x-2)} + \frac{B}{(x-1)} + \frac{C}{(x-1)^2} \equiv E$ (say)

Multiply by $(x-2)(x-1)^2$:

$$\therefore \quad 3 \equiv A(x-1)^2 + B(x-1)(x-2) + C(x-2)$$

Put $x = 1$: $\quad 3 = C(-1) \qquad C = -3$

Put $x = 2$: $\quad 3 = A.1 \qquad A = 3$

Equate coefficients of x^2 :

By inspection: $\quad 0 = A + B \qquad B = -3$

Hence

$$E \equiv \frac{3}{(x-2)} - \frac{3}{(x-1)} - \frac{3}{(x-1)^2}$$

Check:

$$\frac{3}{(x-2)} - \frac{3}{(x-1)} - \frac{3}{(x-1)^2}$$

$$= \frac{3(x-1)^2 - 3(x-2)(x-1) - 3(x-2)}{(x-2)(x-1)^2}$$

$$= \frac{3(x^2 - 2x + 1) - 3(x^2 - 3x + 2) - 3(x-2)}{(x-2)(x-1)^2}$$

$$= \frac{3x^2 - 6x + 3 - 3x^2 + 9x - 6 - 3x + 6}{(x-2)(x-1)^2}$$

$$= \frac{3}{(x-2)(x-1)^2} \qquad \text{Correct}$$

Exercise 55.

(a) What should be the form of the partial fractions in the following examples?

(b) Complete the solutions.

1. $\dfrac{2x+7}{(x-3)(x^2+4)}$

2. $\dfrac{x^2+9}{(x-2)(x^2+2x+5)}$

3. $\dfrac{6x+3}{(x-1)(x+2)^2}$

4. $\dfrac{-2x^2+3x+2}{x^2(x+1)}$

Chapter 19
Elementary differential equations

What is a differential equation ?

We have already come across several differential equations (D.E.'s for short) although we have not given them any special name. D.E.'s arise in very many practical problems and their solution is important for every branch of science. They arise because one of the most important aspects of science is concerned with how things are changing, either developing or dying away.

Example 1. A circuit is set up as shown (Fig.19.1), where

R ohms is a resistance
L henrys is an inductance
E_o is a battery voltage
i amps is the current flowing
t secs after closing the circuit.

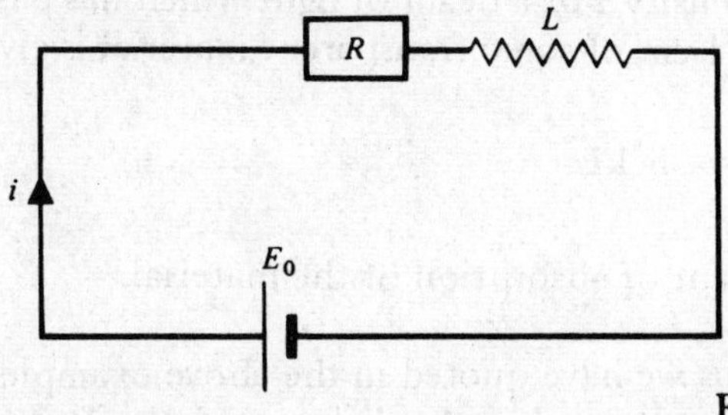

Fig.19.1.

The relation between these is the D.E.

$$L\frac{di}{dt} + Ri = E_o$$

Note: On p. 188 we obtained the special solution (when $E_o = 0$)

$$i = i_o e^{-\frac{R}{L}t}$$

Example 2. When a space vehicle is launched vertically, it is necessary to find the minimum velocity of launch required for it to escape from the Earth's gravitational field (the escape velocity).

The equation of motion is

$$-v\frac{dv}{dx} = \frac{gR^2}{x^2}$$

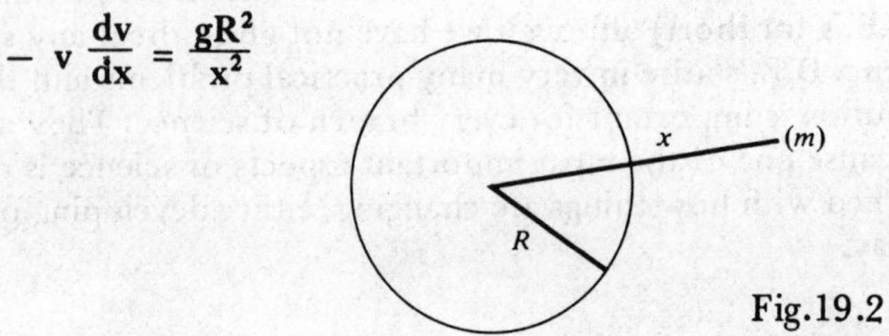

Fig.19.2

where v = velocity at distance x from the Earth's centre

g = acceleration towards the centre of the earth due to gravity.

R = the radius of the Earth (See Fig.19.2).

Example 3. The intensity I of a beam of light which has passed through a thickness l cm of some transparent material is given by

$$\frac{dI}{dl} = -kI$$

where k is the constant of absorption of the material.

Each of the equations we have quoted in the above examples is a *differential equation.* It involves the differential coefficient of one variable with respect to another.

We shall return to these examples again, when you will be able to solve them for yourself.

Meanwhile, let us look at a simpler case.

Example 4. If $\frac{dy}{dx} = x$ what is y equal to?

When we have answered this we have 'solved' the D.E.

In this case $y = \frac{x^2}{2} + c \qquad c = \text{a constant} \qquad \ldots [1]$

If we are told (say) in addition that y = 2 when x = 1 we can evaluate c.

Substituting: $2 = \frac{1}{2} + c$

$\therefore c = 1\frac{1}{2}$

$\therefore y = \frac{x^2}{2} + 1\frac{1}{2} \qquad \ldots [2]$

[1] is called the *general solution* (for obvious reasons)
[2] is called a *particular solution.*

Our original equation $\frac{dy}{dx} = x$ is a *first order* differential equation as $\frac{dy}{dx}$ is the highest differential involved. If we look at the other examples previously quoted we see that they are all first-order D.E.'s.

INITIAL CONDITIONS and BOUNDARY CONDITIONS

Differential equations arise in practical problems and their solution involves satisfying specific conditions. These conditions are fundamental to the complete solution of the problem.

For example, if you are travelling by car and can get a performance of (say) 10 km per litre of petrol, you need to know how full the tank is now in order to estimate how far you can travel before looking for a petrol station. This is the required *initial condition* which is necessary to answer the question. The problem would have a different answer if the tank were nearly empty instead of being full. It would also be different if one could get 15 km to the litre, i.e. a different rate of consumption. Hence it can be seen that we need to know two facts:

1. The rate of decrease (or increase) of the varying quantity.
2. The conditions at the start.

In other cases, knowing the final condition will enable us to solve the problem. For example, if we know we have to reach a certain destination at a particular time we can adjust our plans accordingly. We can speed up or slow down to suit this fact. This is a boundary condition which has to be satisfied in order to do what we are asked.

What have we learned from this very simple example?

1. When we solve a first-order D.E. we have **one arbitrary constant** coming in. (c in this case)
2. To evaluate this constant we must know some **initial condition** or **boundary condition** such as the one we used, i.e. $y = 2$ when $x = 1$.

Note: Every physical problem which translates into a D.E. involves additional conditions not expressed in the D.E. itself. In Example 1, 'i amps is the current flowing t sec after the circuit is closed' implies that when $t = 0$, $i = 0$ since no current flows until the circuit is closed. This condition enables us to evaluate the arbitrary constant involved.

Another way of viewing this is as follows:

In the 'family' of curves $y = \frac{x^2}{2} + c$ (Fig. 19.3) where c can have any value positive or negative, we have a set of parabolas cutting the y axis at $y = c$ (i.e. where $x = 0$). We have to pick out the particular curve which passes through the point (1, 2). This is our particular solution. (See equation [2] p. 263).

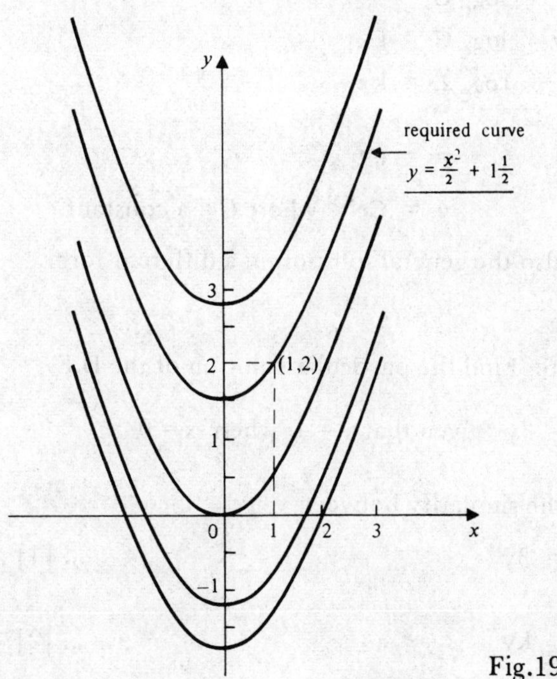

Fig.19.3.

Example 5. On page 186 when dealing with the exponential function we solved the equation

$$\frac{dy}{dx} = ky$$

and obtained the solution $y = C\,e^{kx}$ where C = constant.

Let us state this another way. Separate the variables, y with dy, and x with dx.

$$\frac{dy}{y} = k\,dx$$

Integrate both sides: $\int \frac{dy}{y} = k \int dx$

$$\therefore \log_e y = kx + c$$ is the general solution where c is a constant.

We obtain a simpler form of the solution if we make the following substitution:

Put $c = \log_e C$

$\therefore \quad \log_e y - \log_e C = kx$

$\therefore \quad \log_e \frac{y}{C} = kx$

$\therefore \quad \frac{y}{C} = e^{kx}$

$\therefore \quad y = Ce^{kx}$ where C = a constant.

which is also the general solution in a different form.

Example 6. Find the particular solution of the D.E.

$$\frac{dy}{dx} = 3y \quad \text{given that } y = 4 \text{ when } x = 0$$

We note the similarity between

$$\frac{dy}{dx} = 3y \qquad \text{... [1]}$$

and $\frac{dy}{dx} = ky$ ... [2]

i.e. $k = 3$.

The general solution of [2] is

$y = Ce^{kx}$ where C is a constant (see Example 5)

Hence, the general solution of [1] is

$y = Ce^{3x}$ where C is a constant ... [3]

To evaluate C we use the fact that $y = 4$ when $x = 0$

Substituting in [3]:

$4 = Ce^0$

But $e^0 = 1$

$\therefore \quad C = 4$

Hence the particular solution of the D.E. is

$$y = 4e^{3x}$$

Example 7. A heavy particle falls from rest from a height of 20 m. Find:

(i) the velocity with which it strikes the ground;

(ii) the time taken to fall.

Take $g = 10\ m/sec^2$

Acceleration $= \dfrac{d^2x}{dt^2} = g$

where x = distance fallen (Fig.19.4).

This is a second-order differential equation since $\dfrac{d^2x}{dt^2}$ is the highest differential involved.

Integrate w.r.t. t :

$\dfrac{dx}{dt} = gt + a$ (a = constant)

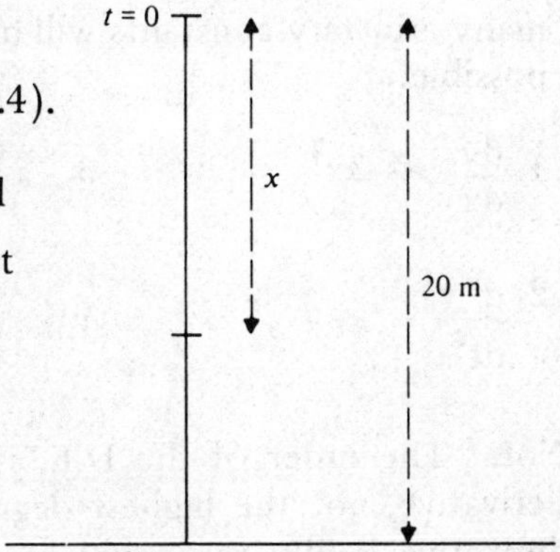

Fig.19.4.

This gives the velocity at any time :

$\therefore\ v = gt + a$ (general solution)

But when t = 0, x = 0 and v = 0 (particle falls from rest) (initial condition)

$\therefore\quad a = 0$

$\therefore\quad v\ (= \dfrac{dx}{dt}) = gt$ (particular solution) ... [1]

Integrate again w.r.t. t :

$x = \frac{1}{2}gt^2 + b$ where b is a constant (general solution)

But when t = 0, x = 0 (initial condition)

$\therefore\quad b = 0$

giving $x = \frac{1}{2}gt^2$ (particular solution) ... [2]

When particle reaches the ground $x = 20$ and $g = 10$

$\therefore t = 2$ ($t = -2$ is meaningless here)

and $v = 20$ from [1]

Note: In a second-order D.E. two arbitrary constants are involved: two initial conditions are required to find them.

Exercise 56. State the order of the following D.E.'s and say how many arbitrary constants will be involved in each case. Solve if possible.

1. $\frac{dy}{dx} = 3x^2$

2. $\frac{d^2y}{dt^2} = 8t + 3$

3. $\left(\frac{dy}{dx}\right)^2 = 9x$

4. $x\frac{d^3y}{dx^3} + \frac{d^2y}{dx^2} + \left(\frac{dy}{dx}\right)^4 = 0$

Note: The order of the D.E. is the order of the highest derivative, not the highest degree. For example, if the highest derivative is $\frac{d^ny}{dx^n}$ the equation is said to be of order n. The degree of a D.E. is the power to which the highest derivative is raised.

TYPES OF FIRST-ORDER DIFFERENTIAL EQUATIONS

We shall study these in four main groups:

I.. variables separable;
II. homogeneous;
III. linear;
IV. exact (may be omitted on first reading).

Type I.

(Since we are dealing with first order D.E.'s, only $\frac{dy}{dx}$ occurs.)

In this type $\frac{dy}{dx}$ can be separated out giving

$$\frac{dy}{dx} = \text{some function of } x \text{ and/or } y.$$

If this function can be expressed as (a function of x) multiplied by (a function of y) the variables can be separated.

Example.

$$(2 + 3y)\frac{dy}{dx} = 2 + x - x^2$$

$$\therefore \quad \frac{dy}{dx} = \frac{1}{2 + 3y} \cdot (2 + x - x^2)$$
$$= (\text{function of } y) \times (\text{function of } x)$$

Exercise 57. In which of the following are the variables separable? Separate out the variables ready for integration, if this is possible. For this type of D.E. we separate the x terms with dx and the y terms with dy.

1. $3\cos^2 x \dfrac{dy}{dx} = \cos^2 y$
2. $(1 + y^2)\dfrac{dy}{dx} = (1 + x^2)$
3. $(1 + x^2)\dfrac{dy}{dx} = = (1 + y^2)$
4. $\dfrac{dy}{dx} = \dfrac{3x + y}{x}$
5. $x(1 + y)\dfrac{dy}{dx} + (1 + x)y^2 = 0$
6. $2\cos x \sin y \dfrac{dy}{dx} + \sin x \cos y = 0$
7. $x\dfrac{dy}{dx} + 3xy + \sin x = 0$
8. $y(1 - x^2)\dfrac{dy}{dx} = 2xy + 2x$
9. $\dfrac{dy}{dx} = e^{x-y}$
10. $\sqrt{2xy}.\dfrac{dy}{dx} = 1$

Technique
To complete the solution we integrate both parts separately.

Question: Do we need two constants of integration, one for each integration performed?

Consider $$\frac{dy}{dx} = (3x^2 - 2)(y + 1)$$

$$\therefore \quad \frac{dy}{y+1} = (3x^2 - 2)\,dx$$

$$\therefore \quad \int \frac{dy}{y+1} = \int (3x^2 - 2)\,dx$$

$\therefore \log_e(1 + y) + a = x^3 - 2x + b$ where a and b are constants or $\log_e(1 + y) \quad = \quad x^3 - 2x + b - a$

but $b - a$ is a constant which we can call c

$$\therefore \log_e(1 + y) = x^3 - 2x + c$$

This shows that only one constant is needed even though the integration is performed in two parts.

Exercise 58. Complete the solutions of the separable examples in Exercise 57 with the help of the following hints:

1. Use $\frac{1}{\cos^2 x} = \sec^2 x$ and $\frac{d}{dx}(\tan x) = \sec^2 x$

3. Use $\int \frac{dx}{1 + x^2} = \tan^{-1} x$

5. Separate the terms: e.g. $\frac{1 + y}{y^2} = \frac{1}{y^2} + \frac{1}{y}$

6. Use $\frac{d}{dx}(\log_e \cos x) = \frac{1}{\cos x} \times$ (differential of cos x)

$$= -\frac{\sin x}{\cos x}$$

8. Use $\frac{y}{y + 1} = 1 - \frac{1}{y + 1}$ and $\frac{2x}{1 - x^2} = \frac{1}{1 - x} - \frac{1}{1 + x}$

or use $\frac{2x}{1 - x^2} = -\frac{d(1 - x^2)}{(1 - x^2)}$

The general solutions of D.E.'s can often be written in different forms by choosing a different form for the arbitrary constant(s). But the different forms are entirely equivalent. For example, when solving the D.E. $\frac{dy}{dx} = k\,y$ (see page 265) we have two forms for the solution,

either $\log_e y = kx + c$
or $\quad y = Ae^{kx}$

These are equivalent forms.

Exercise 59. Find the particular solution of the examples in Exercise 57 by using the following boundary conditions respectively:

1. $y = 0$ when $x = \frac{\pi}{4}$
2. $y = 0$ when $x = 0$
3. $y = 0$ when $x = 1$
5. $y = 2$ when $x = 1$
6. $y = 0$ when $x = 0$
8. $y = 1$ when $x = 0$
9. $y = 1$ when $x = 0$
10. $y = 1$ when $x = 2$

Substitution to reduce certain types to type 1.

Sometimes examples in which it is impossible to separate the variables may be reduced to this form by a simple substitution As in most cases of this type of work, there are no hard and fast rules - one can only try.

Consider $\frac{dx}{dt} = \cos(x + t)$, where it is impossible to separate the variables.

Put $x + t = z$ (say) and differentiate w.r.t. t.

$$\therefore \frac{dx}{dt} + 1 = \frac{dz}{dt}$$

Substituting:

$$\frac{dz}{dt} - 1 = \cos z$$

Can you separate the variables now? If so, integrate and then substitute back to obtain the general solution.

Hint: use the substitution $\cos z = 2\cos^2 \frac{z}{2} - 1$

and remember $\frac{d}{dx}(\tan x) = \sec^2 x$.

Did you get $x = 2\tan^{-1}(t + c) - t$?

Solution

$$\frac{dx}{dt} = \cos(x + t) \qquad \text{Put } z = x + t$$

$$\therefore \frac{dz}{dt} = \frac{dx}{dt} + 1$$

$$\therefore \frac{dz}{dt} - 1 = \cos z$$

$$\therefore \int \frac{dz}{1 + \cos z} = \int dt$$

$$\therefore \int \frac{dz}{2\cos^2 \frac{z}{2}} = t + c$$

$$\therefore \quad \tfrac{1}{2} \int \sec^2 \frac{z}{2}\, dz = t + c$$

$$\tfrac{1}{2} . 2 \tan \frac{z}{2} = t + c$$

$$z = 2 \tan^{-1} (t + c)$$

$$\therefore \quad x = 2 \tan^{-1} (t + c) - t.$$

Example 1. We have mentioned previously the equation

$$L\frac{di}{dt} + Ri = E_o$$ (see page 261)

obtained from the circuit of Fig. 19.5, where R ohms is a resistance, L henrys is an inductance, E_o is a battery voltage, i amps is the current flowing t secs after the circuit is closed.

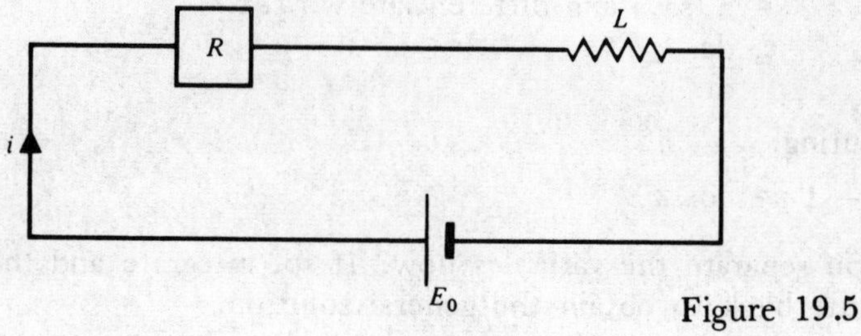

Figure 19.5

Equating the total potential drop across the components we get

$$E_o = L\frac{di}{dt} + Ri$$ where E_o, L and R are constants.

$$\therefore E_o - Ri = L\frac{di}{dt}$$

Separating the variables, i and t :

$$dt = \frac{L\, di}{E_o - Ri}$$

Integrating each side:

$$\int dt = \int \frac{L}{E_o - Ri}\, di$$

$$\therefore \quad t = -\frac{L}{R} \log_e (E_o - Ri) + c$$

But i = 0 when t = 0 (initial condition) since t is measured from closure of circuit.

$$\therefore c = \frac{L}{R} \log_e E_o$$

$$\therefore t = -\frac{L}{R} \log_e (E_o - Ri) + \frac{L}{R} \log E_o$$

$$\therefore t = -\frac{L}{R} \log_e \frac{E_o - Ri}{E_o} \quad \text{(theory of logs)}$$

Multiply by $-\frac{R}{L}$:

$$\therefore -\frac{Rt}{L} = \log_e \frac{E_o - Ri}{E_o} = \log_e (1 - \frac{Ri}{E_o})$$

$$\therefore e^{-\frac{Rt}{L}} = 1 - \frac{Ri}{E_o}$$

$$\therefore \frac{Ri}{E_o} = 1 - e^{-\frac{Rt}{L}} \qquad i = \frac{E_o}{R} [1 - e^{-\frac{Rt}{L}}]$$

You can check this solution by differentiating and substituting in the original equation.

Example 2. Velocity of space launch.

One very interesting example is taken from space travel and is concerned with the velocity with which a space vehicle must be launched in order to escape the Earth's gravity. (We neglect air resistance at this stage.) See Figure 19.2.

The attraction of gravity at a point outside the Earth obeys the inverse square law, i.e. it varies inversely as the square of the distance from the centre of the Earth. Let mg = attraction due to gravity on mass m at the surface of the Earth. Then at a distance x, gravitational force = $\frac{mg R^2}{x^2}$ where R = radius of Earth.

But since force = mass × acceleration

$$\frac{mg R^2}{x^2} = - m f$$ (negative sign since the acceleration and distance increase in opposite directions).

But acceleration $= f = \frac{dv}{dt}$ or $\frac{dv}{dx} \cdot \frac{dx}{dt} = v \frac{dv}{dx}$

Note: We have usually used the form $f = \frac{d^2 x}{dt^2}$, but here we need to express f in terms of x not t.)

$$\therefore \frac{\not{m} g R^2}{x^2} = -\not{m}\, v \frac{dv}{dx}$$

$$\therefore v \frac{dv}{dx} = -\frac{g R^2}{x^2}$$

Separate the variables and integrate:

$$\therefore \int v\, dv = -\int gR^2 \cdot \frac{1}{x^2}\, dx$$

$$\therefore \frac{v^2}{2} = gR^2 \cdot \frac{1}{x} + c$$

$$\text{or} \quad v^2 = \frac{2gR^2}{x} + C \qquad \text{where } C = 2c$$

Let V = velocity of launch, i.e. v = V when x = R.

Substituting:

$$V^2 = 2gR + C$$

$$\therefore C = -2gR + V^2$$

$$\text{giving } v^2 = \frac{2gR^2}{x} - 2gR + V^2$$

This gives the velocity at any point in space at a distance of x from the centre of the Earth. But if the vehicle is to overcome the gravity of the Earth, v must always be positive even for very large values of x. When x is very large $\frac{2gR^2}{x}$ becomes negligible but v^2 must still be positive.

$\therefore V^2 - 2gR$ must always be greater than 0.

$\therefore V^2$ must be greater than 2gR.

g = 9.81 m/sec, R = 6380 km approximately

$\therefore$ V must be greater than $\sqrt{2 . 9.81 . 6380 . 10^3}$ m/sec

Minimum velocity = 11.2 km/sec approx.

Type II. Homogeneous equations

An equation or expression is said to be homogeneous if each term is of the same degree. For example, $x^2 y$, xy^2, y^3 are all of degree 3 since each is the product of three letters, so that

$4x^2 y + 2xy^2 - x^3 + 3y^3$ is homogeneous of degree 3

Similarly, if a D.E. of first order can be written in the form

$$\frac{dy}{dx} = \frac{F(x,y)}{G(x,y)}$$

where F and G are homogeneous functions of x and y of the same degree, the equation is said to be homogeneous.

For example, the equation

$$\frac{dy}{dx} = \frac{2xy}{3x^2 + y^2}$$ is homogeneous of second degree

Exercise 60. Which of the following D.E.'s are homogeneous?

1. $(x + y)\,dy + (x - y)\,dx = 0$
2. $(x^2 + y^2)\frac{dy}{dx} = xy$
3. $x^2\,dy + (y^2 - xy)\,dx = 0$
4. $(x^2 + y)\frac{dy}{dx} = xy$
5. $xy\,dy = (x^2 + 2y^2)\,dx$
   $y = 0$ when $x = 1$
6. $\frac{dy}{dx} = \frac{y(3x^2 + 2y^2)}{x(x + 2y)}$
7. $\frac{dy}{dx} = \frac{y(x + 2y)}{x(2x + y)}$
8. $\frac{dx}{dy} = \frac{2x^3y}{x^4 + y^4}$

Technique

An example will give the method of solution.

Example (No. 2 in Exercise 60)

$$\frac{dy}{dx} = \frac{xy}{x^2 + y^2} \quad \text{degree 2} \quad .... [1]$$

Divide numerator and denominator by x^2 (since of degree 2)

$$\frac{dy}{dx} = \frac{y/x}{1 + (y/x)^2} \quad .... [2]$$

Put $\frac{y}{x} = v$ i.e. $y = v\,x$

Differentiating w.r.t. x, using the product rule,

$$dy = v\,dx + x\,dv$$

$$\therefore \frac{dy}{dx} = v + x\frac{dv}{dx}$$

Substituting for $\frac{y}{x}$ and $\frac{dy}{dx}$ in (2) :

$$v + x\frac{dv}{dx} = \frac{v}{1 + v^2}$$

$$\therefore \quad x\frac{dv}{dx} = \frac{v - (v + v^3)}{1 + v^2} = -\frac{v^3}{1 + v^2}$$

$$\therefore dv\left(\frac{1 + v^2}{v^3}\right) = -\frac{dx}{x}$$

Integrating: $-\frac{1}{2v^2} + \log_e v = -\log_e x + c$

Let $c = \log_e A$.

$$\therefore \log_e v + \log_e x - \log_e A + = \frac{1}{2v^2}$$

$$\log_e y - \log_e x + \log_e x - \log_e A = \frac{x^2}{2y^2} \qquad \text{(since } v = \frac{y}{x}\text{)}$$

$$\therefore \log_e \frac{y}{A} = \frac{x^2}{2y^2}$$

$$\therefore \quad \frac{y}{A} = e^{\frac{x^2}{2y^2}} \qquad \text{i.e. } y = Ae^{\frac{x^2}{2y^2}}$$

Exercise 61. Solve the other examples in Exercise 60 which are homogeneous.

Note: Certain equations of the form

$$\frac{dy}{dx} = \frac{ax + by + c}{dx + ey + f}$$

where a, b, c, d, e, f, are constants, may be reduced to the above form by substituting $Y = ax + by + c \quad X = dx + ey + f$

By finding dY and dX it may be shown (see example below) that

$$\frac{dY}{dX} = \frac{aX + bY}{dX + eY} \quad \text{which is homogeneous}$$

Example. Consider the equation $\frac{dy}{dx} = \frac{x - y + 6}{x + y - 1}$, which is not homogeneous

Put $\quad Y = x - y + 6 \qquad \ldots [1]$

$X = x + y - 1 \qquad \ldots [2]$

$\therefore \quad \frac{dy}{dx} = \frac{Y}{X} \qquad \ldots [3]$

Differentiate [1] and [2] :

$$\frac{dY}{dx} = 1 - \frac{dy}{dx}$$

$\therefore \quad dY = dx - dy \qquad \ldots [4]$

Similarly:

$dX = dx + dy \qquad \ldots [5]$

Add [4] and [5] : $dY + dX = 2dx$

Subtract [4] from [5] : $dX - dY = 2dy$

$\therefore \quad \frac{dy}{dx} = \frac{dX - dY}{dX + dY} \qquad \ldots [6]$

From [3] and [6] : $\frac{Y}{X} = \frac{dX - dY}{dX + dY}$

Now we need to rearrange this to obtain $\frac{dY}{dX}$

$\therefore$ Cross multiply :

$$Y(dX + dY) = X(dX - dY)$$

$\therefore \quad dX(Y - X) = dY(-X - Y)$

or $\quad dY(X + Y) = dX(X - Y)$

$\therefore \quad \frac{dY}{dX} = \frac{X - Y}{X + Y}$ (Compare with $\frac{dy}{dx} = \frac{x-y+6}{x+y-1}$; note the pattern)

This is homogeneous in X and Y and replaces the original equation. Having solved for Y in terms of X, we then use [1] and [2] to find the solution of the given D.E. as follows:

$$\frac{dY}{dX} = \frac{X - Y}{X + Y}$$ This is homogeneous of first order.

Divide numerator and denominator by X :

$$\text{Put } \frac{Y}{X} = V, \quad \text{i.e. } Y = VX \qquad \text{... [7]}$$

$$\therefore \quad \frac{dY}{dX} = \frac{1 - V}{1 + V}$$

Differentiate [7] w.r.t. X :

$$\frac{dY}{dX} = V + X\frac{dV}{dX}$$

$$\therefore \quad \frac{1 - V}{1 + V} = V + X\frac{dV}{dX}$$

$$\therefore \quad \frac{1 - V}{1 + V} - V = X\frac{dV}{dX}$$

$$\therefore \quad \frac{1 - V - V - V^2}{1 + V} = X\frac{dV}{dX}$$

$$\therefore \quad \frac{1 - 2V - V^2}{1 + V} = X\frac{dV}{dX}$$

$$\therefore \quad \frac{dX}{X} = \frac{1 + V}{1 - 2V - V^2}\,dV$$

$$\text{or } -\frac{dX}{X} = \frac{1 + V}{V^2 + 2V - 1}\,dV \quad \text{(changing signs on both sides)}$$

Now the differential of $V^2 + 2V - 1$ is $2V + 2$, which is twice the numerator on the R.H.S.

$$\therefore -\frac{dX}{X} = \tfrac{1}{2}\,\frac{d(V^2 + 2V - 1)}{V^2 + 2V - 1}$$

Integrating:

$$\therefore \quad -\log_e X = \tfrac{1}{2}\log(V^2 + 2V - 1) + C$$

or $\quad -2\log_e X + \log_e A = \log(V^2 + 2V - 1)$ where $\log_e A = -2C$

$$\therefore \quad \frac{A}{X^2} = V^2 + 2V - 1$$

$\therefore \quad A = X^2 \left(\frac{Y^2}{X^2} + 2\frac{Y}{X} - 1\right)$

$\therefore \quad A = Y^2 + 2XY - X^2$ is the required solution.

Substitute for X and Y :

$$A = (x - y + 6)^2 + 2(x + y - 1)(x - y + 6) - (x + y - 1)^2$$

is the solution of the original D.E.

Exercise 62. (Can be omitted on first reading.)

Try the following examples:

1. $\frac{dy}{dx} = \frac{x - y + 2}{x + y - 2}$ 2. $\frac{dy}{dx} = \frac{4x + y - 1}{x + y + 1}$

Type III. Linear equations

If a D.E. can be put in the form

$$\frac{dy}{dx} + Py = Q \qquad \ldots [1]$$

where P and Q are functions of x only, the equation is *linear* since $\frac{dy}{dx}$ and y are of first power only.

Example.

$$3x\frac{dy}{dx} + y = x^2$$

Divide by 3x:

$$\therefore \frac{dy}{dx} + \frac{1}{3x}y = \frac{x^2}{3x}$$

$$P = \frac{1}{3x} \quad Q = \frac{x}{3}$$

which are functions of x only. Therefore the D.E. is linear.

Exercise 63

(a) Can you identify the linear equations among the following?

(b) Do the others belong to any other type you know?

Note: You can consider $\frac{dx}{dy}$ and x, if the equation is non-linear in $\frac{dy}{dx}$ and y.

1. $\frac{dy}{dx} + y = e^x$
2. $x\frac{dy}{dx} - 3y = x^2$
3. $x\frac{dy}{dx} + 3y = \frac{\sin x}{x^2}$
4. $x^2\frac{dy}{dx} - y^2 = xy$
5. $x\,dy + y\,dx = y\,dy$
6. $x\,dy + y\,dx = \sin x\,dx$

Technique.

We are familiar with the formula for differentiation of a product, i.e.

$$d(uv) = v\,du + u\,dv$$

or $$\frac{d}{du}(uv) = v + u\frac{dv}{du}$$

Similarly $\frac{d}{dx}(xy) = y + x\frac{dy}{dx}$ or $x\frac{dy}{dx} + y$.

When we see $\frac{dy}{dx} + Py = Q$ the terms on the L.H.S. suggest some form of the differentiation of a product involving y and x.

But the above form, $\frac{dy}{dx} + Py = Q$ may be obtained after dividing through by some factor as in the example above. Therefore, we may need to multiply by some factor to make the L.H.S. the differential of a product. (We may not need to do this, but we don't know.) In order to find this *integrating factor* we try, experimentally, multiplying through by u (say), where u is some function of x which we shall determine later. This function of course is different for each D.E.

Multiply [1] by u :

$$u\frac{dy}{dx} + (Pu)\,y = Qu$$

[Pu and Qu are both functions of x only]

Add and subtract $y\frac{du}{dx}$ on the L.H.S. as follows :

$$u\frac{dy}{dx} + y\frac{du}{dx} + (Pu)\,y - y\frac{du}{dx} = Qu$$

which is $\underbrace{\frac{d}{dx}(u\,y)}_{\text{(we want this)}} + (Pu)\,y - y\frac{du}{dx} = Qu$

[since $\frac{d}{dx}(u\,y) = u\frac{dy}{dx} + y\frac{du}{dx}$]

i.e. $\frac{d}{dx}(u\,y) + y\,(Pu - \frac{du}{dx}) = Qu$

If we can choose u so that $(Pu - \frac{du}{dx})$ disappears, the equation can be integrated straight away.

So hopefully, put

$$Pu - \frac{du}{dx} = 0$$

$\therefore$ $\frac{du}{dx} = Pu$

$\therefore$ $\frac{du}{u} = P\,dx$

i.e. $\log_e u = \int P\,dx$

or $u = e^{\int P dx}$

is the integrating factor required. (Note: No constant of integration is required or in other words, we choose the constant to be zero.) This looks intimidating, but let us see whether it works.

Example (No.3 in Exercise 63).

$$x\frac{dy}{dx} + 3y = \frac{\sin x}{x^2}$$

$$\therefore \quad \frac{dy}{dx} + \frac{3}{x}.y = \frac{\sin x}{x^3} \qquad \text{... [1]}$$

$$P = \frac{3}{x}, \qquad Q = \frac{\sin x}{x^3}$$

$$\therefore \quad \int P\,dx = \int \frac{3}{x}\,dx$$

$$= 3\log_e x$$

$$= \log_e x^3 \quad \text{(theory of logs)}$$

$$\therefore \quad u = e^{\int P dx} = e^{\log_e x^3}$$

$$\therefore \quad u = x^3$$

$$(e^{\log_e A} = A \text{ by definition of logs})$$

Multiply [1] by x^3 :

$$x^3\frac{dy}{dx} + 3x^2 y = \sin x \qquad \text{... [2]}$$

The L.H.S. should be the differential of $x^3 y$ (i.e. u y).
Is it?

Check: $\frac{d}{dx}(x^3 y) = 3x^2 y + x^3\frac{dy}{dx}$ (correct)

$\therefore$ Integrating both sides of [2] :

$$x^3 y = -\cos x + c$$

$x^3 y = c - \cos x$ is the required general solution.

Summary of steps used to solve linear differential equations.

1. Write the equation in the form $\frac{dy}{dx} + Py = Q$ ... [1]

2. Pick out P and find $\int Pdx$ (no arbitrary constant needed here)

3. Find $u = e^{\int Pdx}$, remembering that if $\int Pdx$ is a log function $e^{\log_e A} = A$.

4. Multiply equation [1] by u, the integrating factor.

5. Check that L.H.S. is $\frac{d}{dx}$ (uy) and integrate.

Exercise 64.

I Solve the other linear equations in Exercise 63.

II Solve by this method the equation

$L\frac{di}{dt} + Ri = E_0$ given that i = 0 when t = 0

This has already been solved by 'separating the variables'. It is also linear.

Type IV. Exact differential equations

(May be omitted at first reading.)

A first order D.E. of the form

$$P(x,y)dx + Q(x,y)dy = 0$$

is said to be *exact* if the L.H.S. is the differential of some other function u (x,y) say.

i.e. $du = Pdx + Qdy = \text{L.H.S.}$

But L.H.S. $= 0$

$du = 0$

$u = \text{constant}$ is the required solution.

Let us consider the process in reverse.

Example. Suppose $x^2\ y^3 = A$ ... [1]

Then differentiating

$$y^3 \cdot 2x\ dx + x^2 \cdot 3y^2\ dy = 0 \qquad \text{... [2]}$$

This corresponds to our theory

$$P\ dx + Q\ dy = 0 \qquad \text{... [3]}$$

where P and Q are functions of x and y.

Conversely if we are given [2], then we can integrate and get back to [1] which is our solution.

We need to recognise a D.E. in the form [2] for what it is, i.e. the exact differential of [1]. How do we do this?

Test for exact Differential Equations

We illustrate the method by *partial differentiation.*

$$2xy^3\ dx + 3x^2y^2\ dy = 0 \qquad [2]$$

or $\quad P\ dx + Q dy = 0$

where $\quad P = 2xy^3, \quad Q = 3x^2y^2$

Differentiating partially:

Keeping x constant: $\dfrac{\partial P}{\partial y} = 6xy^2$

Keeping y constant: $\dfrac{\partial Q}{\partial x} = 6xy^2$

These results illustrate the fact that

for an exact differential, $\dfrac{\partial P}{\partial y} = \dfrac{\partial Q}{\partial x}$

No formal proof is given here, but it is not difficult to prove.

Exercise 65. Use the above test to check which of the following are exact:

1. $(x + y)\ dx + (x + y^2)\ dy = 0$
2. $y^2\ dx + \dfrac{x}{y}\ dy = 0$

3. $(2x\, e^y + e^x)\, dx + (x^2 + 1)\, e^y\, dy = 0$

4. $3x^2 y^2 dx + 2x^3 y dy = 0$

5. $(3x^2 + y + 1)\, dx + (3y^2 + x + 1)\, dy = 0$

Note 1: The function u which we require is a function of x and y such that $du = Pdx + Qdy$

If such a function exists the D.E. becomes

$du = 0$ from [3], p. 284

which gives on integration

$u = \text{constant}$

Note 2: We also need to know that:

$$du = \frac{\partial u}{\partial x}.\, dx + \frac{\partial u}{\partial y}.\, dy \qquad \text{i.e. } P = \frac{\partial u}{\partial x} \text{ and } Q = \frac{\partial u}{\partial y}$$

This result is too difficult to prove formally within the scope of this book, but two simple illustrations of this are given in Appendix 5.

Technique for solution

We illustrate this by taking a slightly more difficult example:

Example 1.

$$(x + \frac{1}{y})\, dx - \frac{x}{y^2}\, dy = 0 \qquad \text{is in the form}$$

$$P\, dx + Q\, dy = 0$$

where $$P = x + \frac{1}{y},\ Q = -\frac{x}{y^2}$$

(i) Now $$\frac{\partial P}{\partial y} = 0 - \frac{1}{y^2}, \qquad \frac{\partial Q}{\partial x} = -\frac{1}{y^2}$$

$$\therefore \frac{\partial P}{\partial y} = \frac{\partial Q}{\partial x} \qquad \therefore$$ Equation is exact. (Test for exactness)

(ii) Now consider again

$$P = x + \frac{1}{y} \qquad Q = -\frac{x}{y^2} \quad \ldots [1]$$

From Note 2

$$u = \int P\,dx = \frac{x^2}{2} + \frac{1}{y} \cdot x + \text{a constant}$$ (which may or may not contain y since we are keeping y constant)

$$\therefore \quad u = \frac{x^2}{2} + \frac{x}{y} + f(y) \text{ (say)} \qquad \ldots [2]$$

We now use [1] to find this f(y).

Differentiate [2] w.r.t. y keeping x constant

$$\frac{\partial u}{\partial y} = 0 - \frac{x}{y^2} + \frac{d\,f(y)}{dy}$$ (We can use this form instead of $\frac{\partial f}{\partial y}$ since only y is involved anyway)

This must equal Q (see Note 2 above).

$$\therefore \quad -\frac{x}{y^2} = -\frac{x}{y^2} + \frac{d\,f(y)}{dy} \text{ from [1]}$$

i.e. $\frac{d\,f(y)}{dy} = 0 \qquad \therefore f(y) = \text{constant in this case} = c \text{ (say)}$

$\therefore$ from [2] $\quad u = \frac{x^2}{2} + \frac{x}{y} + c^1 = 0$ is the solution required, where c^1 is the combined constant.

Check: Differentiating :

$$\frac{2x\,dx}{2} + \frac{1}{y}dx - x \cdot \frac{1}{y^2}\,dy = 0$$

$$\therefore \quad \left(x + \frac{1}{y}\right)dx - \frac{x}{y^2}\,dy = 0 \qquad \text{Correct.}$$

Example 2. Suppose $(1 + 4xy + 2y^2)\,dx + (1 + 4xy + 2x^2)\,dy = 0$

(i) Test whether exact

$$P = 1 + 4xy + 2y^2 \qquad Q = 1 + 4xy + 2x^2$$

$$\therefore \frac{\partial P}{\partial y} = 4x + 4y \qquad \frac{\partial Q}{\partial x} = 4y + 4x$$

$$\therefore \frac{\partial P}{\partial y} = \frac{\partial Q}{\partial x} \qquad \therefore \text{ exact.}$$

(ii) Integrate P w.r.t. x keeping y constant

$$\int P\,dx = x + 4y \cdot \frac{x^2}{2} + 2y^2 \cdot x + f(y)$$

$$= x + 2x^2y + 2xy^2 + f(y) = u \text{ (say)} \quad \ldots [1]$$

(iii) Differentiate [1] w.r.t. y keeping x constant

$$\frac{\partial u}{\partial y} = 0 + 2x^2 + 2x \cdot 2y + \frac{df(y)}{dy}$$

This must equal Q, i.e. $1 + 4xy + 2x^2$

$$\therefore \frac{df(y)}{dy} = 1$$

$\therefore f(y) = y$ (Remember f(y) is a function of y only)

But from [1] $u = x + 2x^2y + 2xy^2 + y = C$ is required solution.

Check: Differentiating :

$$dx + 2y \cdot 2x\,dx + 2x^2\,dy + 2y^2\,dx + 2x \cdot 2y\,dy + dy = 0$$

$\therefore (1 + 4xy + 2y^2)\,dx + (1 + 4xy + 2x^2)\,dy = 0$ Correct.

Summary.

1. Write equation in form $P\,dx + Q\,dy = 0$
2. If $\frac{\partial P}{\partial y} = \frac{\partial Q}{\partial x}$ then equation is exact.
3. Integrate P w.r.t. x keeping y constant giving $u = \int P\,dx + f(y)$
4. Differentiate the result (u) w.r.t. y keeping x constant. Compare with Q to find df(y)/dy. Then integrate this to find f(y).
5. The solution is $u = \int P\,dx + f(y) = C$
6. Check by differentiating.

Exercise 66. Use this method to solve the exact D.E.'s in Exercise 65.

SECOND-ORDER DIFFERENTIAL EQUATIONS

Introduction

A full study of the methods of solution of second-order D.E.'s requires more space than we are able to give in a text-book of this type. We therefore confine our attention to the group of equations called second-order D.E.'s with constant coefficients.

This sounds very formidable, but since this type of equation occurs most frequently in engineering and science it is a necessary study. We use two methods initially to try to solve this type of equation, namely equations of the type

$$a\frac{d^2y}{dx^2} + b\frac{dy}{dx} + cy = P(x)$$

where a, b, c are constants and P is a function of x only.

Methods of solution

1. By trial and error (if this is not too tedious).
2. By D-operator methods.

Examples from engineering and science

Many students will have met D.E.'s of which the following are only a few examples.

1. The equation of motion for a particle moving under the action of a force or forces such that the acceleration at time t towards a fixed point in its path is proportional to its distance x from the fixed point is

$$\frac{d^2x}{dt^2} + w^2x = 0 \quad \text{where } w \text{ is a constant.}$$

2. In an electric circuit consisting of a generator supplying an e.m.f. of E volts which may vary with time, a capacitor of capacitance C farads, an inductance of L henrys and a resistance R ohms, the equation

$$L\frac{d^2q}{dt^2} + R\frac{dq}{dt} + \frac{q}{C} = E$$

specifies the charge q on the capacitor at time t.

3.

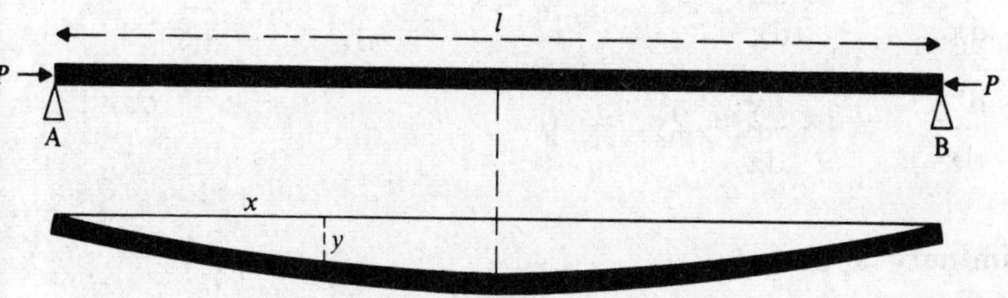

Fig.19.6.

In Fig.19.6 AB is a uniform beam of length l and weight w per unit length. It is supported freely at its ends, in a horizontal position and is under the action of compressive forces P acting at its ends. The displacement y at a position x from either end is given by the D.E.

$$E\,I\frac{d^2y}{dx^2} + Py = \tfrac{1}{2}\,w\,x^2 - \tfrac{1}{2}\,w\,l\,x$$

where E is Young's modulus and I is the second moment of area round the neutral axis and w is a constant.

4. $$\frac{d^2x}{dt^2} + 2k\frac{dx}{dt} + w^2x = 0$$

is similar to 1, above but also includes a resistance to motion of $2k\frac{dx}{dt}$ where k is a constant

We need, therefore, to find a method of solving such equations.

The standard form for this type is:

$$a\frac{d^2y}{dx^2} + b\frac{dy}{dx} + c\,y = P(x)$$ where a, b, c are constants, and P is a function of x.

Exercise 67. Pick out which of the following are equations of this type:

1. $3\dfrac{d^2y}{dx^2} + 2\dfrac{dy}{dx} - y = 3e^{2x}$
2. $\dfrac{d^2y}{dx^2} - 6\dfrac{dy}{dx} + 9y = 0$
3. $\dfrac{d^2y}{dx^2} - 2x\dfrac{dy}{dx} + 2y = 0$
4. $\dfrac{d^2y}{dx^2} = -w^2y$
5. $\dfrac{d^2x}{dt^2} - 4\dfrac{dx}{dt} + 3x = e^{-t}\cos t.$

Preliminary approach

If we consider the simpler equation, called the *reduced equation*

$$a\frac{d^2y}{dx^2} + b\frac{dy}{dx} + cy = 0 \qquad \text{.... [1]}$$

we can see that it is a similar type (though more difficult) to the equation we have already solved:

$$\frac{dy}{dx} = ky$$ which expresses the law of natural growth (cf. pages 185 - 186).

The solution of this D.E. is

$$y = Ae^{kx}$$ where A is a constant

This type of solution seems a logical one since the exponential function is the only function whose differential coefficient is a constant multiplied by itself.

i.e. $\dfrac{d}{dx}(e^{ax}) = ae^{ax}$

This suggests that perhaps a possible solution of [1] could be of this form too.
Let us try this.

Let us try $y = e^{mx}$ as a solution, where m is some constant which we do not know yet.

Then $\dfrac{dy}{dx} = m\,e^{mx}$

$$\frac{d^2y}{dx^2} = m^2e^{mx}$$

Hence, if this is a solution, substituting in [1]

$$a\,m^2\,e^{mx} + b\,m\,e^{mx} + c\,e^{mx} \quad \text{must equal } 0.$$

Dividing by e^{mx} (which cannot be zero):

$$a\,m^2 + b\,m + c = 0$$ our old friend the quadratic equation.

This equation, derived from the differential equation, is called the *auxiliary equation (A.E.)*

Example. Let us try No. 1 in Exercise 67.

$$3\frac{d^2y}{dx^2} + 2\frac{dy}{dx} - y = 0 \qquad \text{.... [1]}$$

(This is the reduced equation.)

Try $y = e^{mx}$

$$3m^2 + 2m - 1 = 0$$

$$(3m - 1)(m + 1) = 0$$

$$\therefore m = \frac{1}{3} \text{ or } -1.$$

Possible solutions are

$$e^{\frac{1}{3}x} \quad \underline{\text{or}} \quad e^{-x}$$

Check these. Yes, they each satisfy the D.E.
Now can we go any further?

Questions:

(1) Would the sum of these satisfy equation [1]? Try it.

(2) Would a combination such as

$$A\,e^{\frac{1}{3}x} + B\,e^{-x}$$ also satisfy equation [1]?

(3) Would we expect two constants of integration?

Let us try this together

Hence:

$$\text{If } y = A\,e^{\frac{1}{3}x} + B\,e^{-x} \qquad -y = -A\,e^{\frac{1}{3}x} - B\,e^{-x}$$

$$\frac{dy}{dx} = \frac{1}{3}A\,e^{\frac{1}{3}x} - B\,e^{-x} \qquad 2\frac{dy}{dx} = \frac{2}{3}A\,e^{\frac{1}{3}x} - 2B\,e^{-x}$$

$$\frac{d^2y}{dx^2} = \frac{1}{9}A\,e^{\frac{1}{3}x} + B\,e^{-x} \qquad 3\frac{d^2y}{dx^2} = \frac{1}{3}A\,e^{\frac{1}{3}x} + 3B\,e^{-x}$$

Adding: L.H.S. of [1] = 0 + 0 = 0

Therefore $y = A\,e^{\frac{1}{3}x} + B\,e^{-x}$ is a solution of [1].

This is called the complementary function (C.F.)
Note: The C.F. contains the required two arbitrary constants for a second order D.E. These require two sets of initial or boundary conditions for their evaluation.

Summary so far

1. Find the reduced equation in the form

$$a\frac{d^2y}{dx^2} + b\frac{dy}{dx} + cy = 0$$

2. Find the auxiliary equation in the form

$$am^2 + bm + c = 0 \text{ where } y = e^{mx} \text{ is a solution.}$$

3. Solve for m to give m_1 and m_2 and the *complementary function* (C.F.) in the form

$$y = A\,e^{m_1x} + B\,e^{m_2x} \quad \text{where A and B are constants.}$$

Exercise 68. Write down the auxiliary equation to each of the following and obtain the corresponding C.F.'s.

y' is another form of $\frac{dy}{dx}$

y'' is another form of $\frac{d^2y}{dx^2}$

1. $\frac{d^2y}{dx^2} + 2\frac{dy}{dx} = 0$ (remember $e^0 = 1$)

2. $\frac{d^2y}{dx^2} + 5\frac{dy}{dx} + 6y = 0$

3. $\frac{d^2y}{dx^2} + 6\frac{dy}{dx} + 5y = 0$

4. $2\frac{d^2y}{dx^2} + 5\frac{dy}{dx} - 3y = 0$

5. $\frac{d^2x}{dt^2} - 4\frac{dx}{dt} + 3x = 0$

6. $y'' - 6y' - 16y = 0$

7. $2y'' + 3y' = 0$

8. $y'' - 4y = 0$

Example. Now let us complete the solution of

$$3\frac{d^2y}{dx^2} + 2\frac{dy}{dx} - y = 3e^{2x} \quad \text{.... [2]}$$

We have found that the solution which satisfies the reduced equation, i.e. where the L.H.S. = 0, is given by

$$y = A\,e^{\frac{1}{3}x} + B\,e^{-x}$$

We obviously need an additional term in our solution to balance the $3e^{2x}$ on the R.H.S. of our D.E.

What kind of function can be differentiated twice, and combined so that multiples of $\frac{d^2y}{dx^2}$, $\frac{dy}{dx}$ and y can be collected up to make $3e^{2x}$?

Surely, only some multiple of e^{2x} can be considered since **an exponential function is the only function whose differential coefficient is a multiple of itself.**

Hence we try $y = \alpha\,e^{2x}$ where α is some constant to be determined.

$$\frac{dy}{dx} = 2\alpha e^{2x}$$

$$\frac{d^2y}{dx^2} = 4\alpha e^{2x}$$

Substituting these values in [2] :

$$12\alpha e^{2x} + 4\alpha e^{2x} - \alpha e^{2x} = 3e^{2x}$$

Therefore $15\alpha = 3$ since $e^{2x} \neq 0$

$$\alpha = \frac{1}{5}$$

Hence $y = \frac{1}{5}e^{2x}$ is a solution of [2]

This is called the *particular integral (P.I.)*
Hence a possible solution of our equation is $\frac{1}{5}e^{2x}$

Now let us try the complete solution

$$y = A e^{\frac{1}{3}x} + B e^{-x} + \frac{1}{5}e^{2x}$$

and see if it satisfies our D.E..

$$\frac{dy}{dx} = \frac{1}{3}A e^{\frac{1}{3}x} - B e^{-x} + \frac{2}{5}e^{2x}$$

$$\frac{d^2y}{dx^2} = \frac{1}{9}A e^{\frac{1}{3}x} + B e^{-x} + \frac{4}{5}e^{2x}$$

$$\therefore \text{L.H.S. of [2]} = 3\frac{d^2y}{dx^2} + 2\frac{dy}{dx} - y$$

$$= \frac{1}{3}A e^{\frac{1}{3}x} + 3B e^{-x} + \frac{12}{5}e^{2x} +$$

$$\frac{2}{3}A e^{\frac{1}{3}x} - 2B e^{-x} + \frac{4}{5}e^{2x}$$

$$- A e^{\frac{1}{3}x} - B e^{-x} - \frac{1}{5}e^{2x}$$

$$= 3\, e^{2x}$$

$\therefore$ L.H.S. = R.H.S. Correct.

We see that this method works in this case and our result

$$y = A e^{\frac{1}{3}x} + B e^{-x} + \frac{1}{5}e^{2x}$$

is called the general solution (G.S.) of the D.E. Hence
G.S. = C.F. + P.I.

Exercise 69. Find the general solutions for the following, by first finding the auxiliary equations, solving to find the C.F.'s and then find the P.I.'s in the form $a\,e^{kx}$ (see solutions to Exercise 68). [$\dot{x}$ means $\frac{dx}{dt}$, $\ddot{x}$ means $\frac{d^2x}{dt^2}$]

1. $y'' + 2y' = 3\,e^{2x}$
2. $y'' + 5y' + 6y = 2\,e^{x}$
3. $y'' + 6y' + 5y = 16\,e^{3x}$
4. $2y'' + 5y' - 3y = 3\,e^{2x}$
5. $\ddot{x} - 4\dot{x} + 3x = 2\,e^{-t}$
6. $y'' - 6y' - 16y = 9\,e^{-x}$
7. $2y'' + 3y' = 3\,e^{\frac{3}{2}x}$
8. $y'' - 4y = e^{3x}$

Perhaps you have asked yourself the following questions:

1. What happens if the auxiliary equation has equal roots?
2. What happens if the function on the R.H.S. (P(x) in the general equation) is not exponential?

Let us tackle the first of these. An example will suffice.

Equal roots of the auxiliary equation

Example.

Suppose the A.E. is $m^2 + 4m + 4 = 0$

from $y'' + 4y' + 4y = 0$ .... [1]

i.e. $(m + 2)^2 = 0$

$m = -2$ (twice)

Shall we write the C.F. as $A\,e^{-2x} + B\,e^{-2x}$?

This seems a little stupid as this is $(A + B)\,e^{-2x}$ i.e. $C\,e^{-2x}$ (where $A + B = C$)

Therefore we seem to have lost one of our constants. We can show, however, that $(A + Bx)\,e^{-2x}$ is a solution of our equation. This has two constants and if it satisfies [1] is our C.F.

Let $y = (A + Bx)\,e^{-2x}$

$$y' = -2(A + Bx)\,e^{-2x} + e^{-2x}(B)$$

$$= e^{-2x}(-2A + B - 2Bx)$$

$$\therefore\ y'' = (-2A + B - 2Bx)(-2\,e^{-2x}) + e^{-2x}(-2B)$$

$$= e^{-2x}(+4A - 4B) + 4Bxe^{-2x}$$

Substituting in the L.H.S. of [1] :

$$\text{L.H.S.} = e^{-2x}(4A - 4B + 4Bx - 8A + 4B - 8Bx + 4A + 4Bx)\text{-}$$

$$= 0 = \text{R.H.S.}$$

Hence a C.F. of the form $(A + Bx)\,e^{-2x}$ satisfies the D.E.[1]

A formal proof that

For equal roots of the auxiliary equation

C.F. = $(A + Bx)\,e^{mx}$ is similar to the above.

Exercise 70. Find the solutions of the following:

1. $y'' - 8y' + 16y = 0$
2. $9y'' - 12y' + 4y = 0$
3. $y'' + 6y' + 9y = 0$

Imaginary roots of the auxiliary equation (May be omitted on first reading).

The roots of $am^2 + bm + c = 0$ are

$$m = \frac{-b \pm \sqrt{b^2 - 4ac}}{2a}$$

If $b^2 < 4ac$ the roots are imaginary, say $p \pm jq$ where p and q are real.

Then we can show by De Moivre's theorem (see page 247) that the C.F. can be written most neatly in the form:

C.F. = $e^{px}\ (A \cos qx + B \sin qx)$.

Exercise 71. (May be omitted on first reading).

Solve the D.E.'s using the above method.

1. $\dfrac{d^2x}{dt^2} + w^2x = 0$
2. $\dfrac{d^2y}{dx^2} - 8\dfrac{dy}{dx} + 25y = 0$
3. $y'' + y' + y = 0$

Summary

The Complementary Function

Case 1 : If the A.E. has real unequal roots m_1, m_2 then the C.F. is

$$A e^{m_1 x} + B e^{m_2 x} \qquad \text{(A, B constants)}$$

Case II : If the A.E. has real but equal roots, both m, then the C.F. is $(A + Bx)\ e^{mx}$

Case III : If the A.E. has complex roots $p \pm\ jq$ then the C.F. is e^{px} (A cos qx + B sin qx)

We look again at the general second-order D.E.

$a \dfrac{d^2y}{dx^2} + b \dfrac{dy}{dx} + cy = P(x)$, and return to the second of the two questions asked earlier: what happens if P(x) is not exponential?

To find the particular integral when P(x) is a polynomial in x

Example. Solve the D.E.

$$\frac{d^2y}{dx^2} - 4\frac{dy}{dx} + 4y = x^2 + 2x \qquad .... [1]$$

Hence the A.E. is $m^2 - 4m + 4 = 0$

$$\therefore \quad m = 2 \quad \text{(twice)}$$

$$\therefore \text{The C.F. is } y = (A + Bx)\ e^{2x}$$

For the P.I. try $y = ax^2 + bx + c$ *since a polynomial (and its differentials) is the only function which can balance a polynomial.

then $\dfrac{dy}{dx} = 2ax + b$

and $\dfrac{d^2y}{dx^2} = 2a$

Substituting in [1] :

$$2a - 4\ (2ax + b) + 4\ (ax^2 + bx + c) \equiv x^2 + 2x$$

Equating coefficients of x^2 :

$$4a = 1 \qquad\qquad \therefore a = ¼$$

Equating coefficients of x :

$$-8a + 4b = 2 \qquad \text{But } a = \tfrac{1}{4}$$

$$\therefore -2 + 4b = 2 \qquad \therefore b = 1$$

Equating constant terms :

$$2a - 4b + 4c = 0$$

$$\tfrac{1}{2} - 4 + 4c = 0 \qquad \therefore c = \frac{7}{8}$$

$$\therefore \text{The P.I.} = \frac{1}{4}x^2 + x + \frac{7}{8}$$

*Note: If x^3 or higher powers of x were included, by equating their coefficients, these would vanish, since there are no terms in x^3 or higher powers on the R.H.S.

Check for P.I. :

$$y = \frac{1}{4}x^2 + x + \frac{7}{8}, \quad \frac{dy}{dx} = \frac{1}{2}x + 1, \quad \frac{d^2y}{dx^2} = \frac{1}{2}$$

Substituting in [1] :

$$\therefore \text{L.H.S.} = \frac{1}{2} - 2x - 4 + x^2 + 4x + \frac{7}{2}$$

$$= x^2 + 2x$$

$$\therefore \text{L.H.S.} = \text{R.H.S. Correct.}$$

Hence G.S. of [1] is given by :

$$y = (A + Bx)\, e^{2x} + \frac{1}{4}x^2 + x + \frac{7}{8}$$

To find the particular integral when P(x) is a function of sin μ x or cos μ x (or both).

In all cases try $y = \alpha \cos \mu x + \beta \sin \mu x$ where α and β are constants.

Note: $\sin \mu x$ or $\cos \mu x$ can arise only from differentials of $\sin \mu x$ and/or $\cos \mu x$. Both the sine and the cosine must be included in any trial solution as differentiation could bring in either of these. It is possible that α or β may work out to be zero but we must not assume this.

Example. Solve the D.E.

$$\frac{d^2y}{dx^2} + \frac{dy}{dx} = 2 \cos 3x \qquad \text{.... [1]}$$

Hence the A.E. is $\quad m^2 + m = 0$

$$\therefore m = 0 \text{ or } -1$$

$\therefore$ The C.F. is $\quad y = A + Be^{-x}$

For the P.I. try $\quad y = \alpha \cos 3x + \beta \sin 3x$

then $\quad \dfrac{dy}{dx} = -3\alpha \sin 3x + 3\beta \cos 3x$

and $\quad \dfrac{d^2y}{dx^2} = -9\alpha \cos 3x - 9\beta \sin 3x$

Substituting in [1]

$-9\alpha \cos 3x - 9\beta \sin 3x - 3\alpha \sin 3x + 3\beta \cos 3x = 2 \cos 3x$

$\therefore \cos 3x\,(-9\alpha + 3\beta) + \sin 3x\,(-9\alpha - 3\beta) = 2 \cos 3x$

Equating coefficients of sin 3x :

$9\alpha + 3\beta = 0 \qquad \therefore \alpha = -3\beta$

Equating coefficients of cos 3x:

$-9\alpha + 3\beta = 2$

$\therefore \quad 27\beta + 3\beta = 2 \qquad \therefore \beta = \frac{1}{15},\ \alpha = -\frac{3}{15} = -\frac{1}{5}$

Hence the P.I. is $y = -\frac{1}{5} \cos 3x + \frac{1}{15} \sin 3x$

Check for P.I. :

$y = -\frac{1}{5} \cos 3x + \frac{1}{15} \sin 3x, \quad \dfrac{dy}{dx} = \frac{3}{5} \sin 3x + \frac{1}{5} \cos 3x$

$\dfrac{d^2y}{dx^2} = \frac{9}{5} \cos 3x - \frac{3}{5} \sin 3x$

Substituting in [1] :

L.H.S. $= \frac{9}{5} \cos 3x - \frac{3}{5} \sin 3x + \frac{3}{5} \sin 3x + \frac{1}{5} \cos 3x$

$\therefore$ L.H.S. = 2 cos 3x = R.H.S. $\qquad$ Correct.

Hence the complete solution is :

$y = A + B e^{-x} - \frac{1}{5} \cos 3x + \frac{1}{15} \sin 3x$

Summary - the particular integral

If the function P(x) is on the R.H.S. of the D.E., we obtain the P.I. as follows :

Form of P(x)	Trial solution
(i) $ke^{\lambda x}$	(i) $y = \alpha e^{\lambda x}$
(ii) $ax^2 + bx + c$	(ii) $y = \alpha x^2 + \beta x + \gamma$ equate coefficients
(iii) $k \cos \mu x$ or $k \sin \mu x$	(iii) $y = a e^{j\alpha x}$ and compare real and imaginary parts or $y = \alpha \cos \mu x + \beta \sin \mu x$

Exercise 72. Miscellaneous.

Solve the following equations:

1. $\frac{d^2y}{dx^2} + \frac{dy}{dx} = x$

2. $\frac{d^2y}{dx^2} + y = \sin x$

3. $\frac{d^2y}{dx^2} + 2\frac{dy}{dx} + y = e^x$

4. $\frac{d^2y}{dx^2} - 2\frac{dy}{dx} + y = e^{-x}$

5. $\frac{d^2y}{dx^2} - y = x + 3$

6. $\frac{d^2y}{dx^2} + \frac{dy}{dx} = e^x$

7. $\frac{d^2y}{dx^2} - y = \sin x$

8. $\frac{d^2y}{dx^2} + 4\frac{dy}{dx} + 5y = 10$
   (Remember $10 = 10\,e^0$)

9. $\frac{d^2y}{dx^2} + 4\frac{dy}{dx} + 5y = x + 2$

D-OPERATOR METHODS

Introduction

We are now familiar with the method of finding the complementary function (C.F.) which has two arbitrary constants. So far we have formed the Particular Integral (P.I.) by trial. This method can be tedious, and the following methods in certain cases are more satisfactory.

Definition. The symbol D is used to replace the operator $\frac{d}{dx}$ so that

$$Dy = \frac{dy}{dx}$$

$$D^2y = \frac{d}{dx}\left(\frac{dy}{dx}\right) = \frac{d^2y}{dx^2}$$

$$D^3y = \frac{d}{dx}\left(\frac{d^2y}{dx^2}\right) = \frac{d^3y}{dx^3} \quad \text{etc.}$$

Query: What are $\frac{d^5y}{dx^5}$ and $\frac{d^ny}{dx^n}$ in D-operator form?

(D^5y, D^ny)

Laws of the D-operator

We have used the formula $d(u + v) = du + dv$

This becomes : $D(u + v) = Du + Dv$

and conversely $Du + Dv = D(u + v)$

Since $Du + Dv = D(u + v)$

Differentiating: $D^2u + D^2v = D^2(u + v)$

Also $$\frac{d}{dx}\left(\frac{du}{dx} + v\right) = \frac{d^2u}{dx^2} + \frac{dv}{dx}$$

i.e. $D(Du + v) = D^2u + Dv$

In other words, the operator D obeys the normal rules of algebra.

Examples. Write the expressions:

(i) $\dfrac{d^2y}{dx^2} + 3y$;

(ii) $\dfrac{d^2y}{dx^2} + 9\dfrac{dy}{dx} + 4y$ in D-form.

(i) is $(D^2 + 3)y$ where $(D^2 + 3)$ operates on y

(ii) is $(D^2 + 9D + 4)y$ where $(D^2 + 9D + 4)$ operates on y

Exercise 73. Write the following in D-form and 'factorise' the expressions. The order of the factors (operators) does not matter. We shall need to do this in order to use this method to find particular integrals for some types of D.E.'s.

1. $\dfrac{d^2y}{dx^2} + 3\dfrac{dy}{dx} - 4y$
2. $\dfrac{d^2y}{dx^2} - k^2y$
3. $\dfrac{d^4y}{dx^4} + 3\dfrac{d^2y}{dx^2} + 2y$

(Example: $(D^2 + 5D - 6)y = (D + 6)(D - 1)y$.)

Functions of D as operators

We think of such expressions as the one in the last example $(D^2 + 5D - 6)$ or $(D + 6)(D - 1)$ as an operator, i.e. something which operates on y and produces a certain result. For example, if $(D + 6)(D - 1)y = e^{3x}$ then $(D + 6)(D - 1)$ operates on y so that the result is e^{3x}.

In general we talk about an operator f(D).

The Inverse Operator

In the same way that integration is the reverse of differentiation, we have an inverse operator D^{-1} which is such that

$$D^{-1}(Dy) = y \text{ and } D(D^{-1}y) = y$$

in other words $D^{-1}y$ means $\int y\,dx$ - a very useful concept.

Example. Find:

$$(D^{-2} + D - 1)\,x^2 \qquad \text{.... [1]}$$

$$D^{-1}(x^2) = \int x^2\,dx = \frac{x^3}{3}$$

$$\therefore D^{-2}(x^2) = \int \frac{x^3}{3}\,dx = \frac{x^4}{12}$$

note no constant of integration needed*.

and $D(x^2) = 2x$

$$(-1)(x^2) = -x^2$$

$$\therefore \quad [1] = \frac{x^4}{12} + 2x - x^2$$

* We shall use this method for finding the particular integral. ∴ No arbitrary constants need to be included.

Exercise 74. Find:

(1) $(D^{-1} + 2 + \frac{2}{3}D)\,x^3$

(2) $\frac{1}{D^2}\,e^{2x}$

Note: We use this method for finding P.I.'s more easily than by trial and error. We find the C.F. as previously. But first we must see very clearly the effect of the D-operator on certain functions. At this stage, we restrict our study to: (i) $e^{\alpha x}$; and (ii) $\sin\alpha x$ ($\cos\alpha x$ is similar).

Effect of D-operator on $e^{\alpha x}$

$$D(e^{\alpha x}) = \alpha e^{\alpha x} \quad \text{where } \alpha \text{ is a constant}$$

$$(D + a)\,e^{\alpha x} = D(e^{\alpha x}) + a\,e^{\alpha x}$$

$$= (\alpha + a)\,e^{\alpha x} \quad \text{Note the pattern}$$

Find answers to the following:

$D^2(e^{\alpha x})$, $D^3(e^{\alpha x})$, $D^4(e^{\alpha x})$, $(D^2 + b^2)e^{\alpha x}$, $(D^2 + 3D - 4)e^{\alpha x}$

Did you get:

$\alpha^2 e^{\alpha x}$, $\alpha^3 e^{\alpha x}$, $\alpha^4 e^{\alpha x}$, $(\alpha^2 + b^2) e^{\alpha x}$, $(\alpha^2 + 3\alpha - 4) e^{\alpha x}$?

We need these results to develop our method further. We notice that in the case of $e^{\alpha x}$ the D-operator is replaced by α.

Using this we get

$$(D^3 + 2D - 1)e^{-x} = [(-1)^3 + 2(-1) - 1]e^{-x}$$
$$= -4e^{-x}$$

Check this by straight-forward differentiation.

Exercise 75. Find the following:

$(D + 1)e^{-3x}$; $(D + 1)^2 e^{-3x}$; $(D - 2)(D - 1)e^{4x}$;
$(D - 2)(D + 1)e^{2x}$.

Effect of D-operator on $\sin\alpha x$ and $\cos\alpha x$

$D(\sin\alpha x) = \alpha\cos\alpha x$ $\qquad$ $D(\cos\alpha x) = -\alpha\sin\alpha x$

$\therefore D^2(\sin\alpha x) = -\alpha^2 \sin\alpha x$ $\qquad$ $\therefore D^2(\cos\alpha x) = -\alpha^2\cos\alpha x$

and so on. $\qquad$ and so on.

Hence, we see that we get a multiple of the original function every time the function is differentiated an <u>even</u> number of times, i.e. D^2 is replaced by $-\alpha^2$.

Example. $(D^4 - D^2 + 2)\sin\alpha x$ can be written down at once as

$$[(-\alpha^2)^2 + \alpha^2 + 2]\sin\alpha x = (\alpha^4 + \alpha^2 + 2)\sin\alpha x$$

and $(D^2 - \beta^2)^2\cos\alpha x = (-\alpha^2 - \beta^2)^2\cos\alpha x$

So $(D^2 + 2)\cos 3x = (-9 + 2)\cos 3x$

(D^2 is replaced by -9)

$$= -7\cos 3x.$$

This is very simple.

Exercise 76. Write down:

1. $(D^4 - 3D^2 + 3)\cos 2x$
2. $(D^2 + 3)\sin 4x$
3. $(D^4 + 1)(e^{2x} + \sin 3x)$ (Hint: treat e^{2x} and $\sin 3x$ separately.)

The second order D.E. (see page 288) can now be written in the form:

$$(aD^2 + bD + c)y = P(x)$$

Finding the particular integral when P(x) is an exponential function.

Example. $(3D^2 - 5D - 4)\,y = e^{2x}$ .... [1]

Does $y = \dfrac{1}{3D^2 - 5D - 4}e^{2x}$ give us the P.I.?

(We can try this since $3D^2 - 5D - 4$ is not zero when $\alpha = 2 = D$).

Let us see if it works. Using the method we have tried for $D(e^{2x})$, i.e. putting $D = 2\ (=\alpha)$,

$$y = \frac{1}{3.2^2 - 5.2 - 4}e^{2x} \quad \text{should be the P.I.}$$

$$= \frac{1}{-2}e^{2x}$$

$\therefore$ **Try** $y = -\frac{1}{2}e^{2x}$ **as the P.I.**

Check: $D(y) = -e^{2x}$, $D^2(y) = -2e^{2x}$, $-4y = +2e^{2x}$

$\therefore$ L.H.S. $= (-6 + 5 + 2)\,e^{2x} = e^{2x} =$ R.H.S. Correct.

Hence this method seems to give the P.I. quite easily.

Use this method to find the P.I.'s for the following D.E.'s :

1. $(D + 1)\,y = e^{3x}$; 2. $(D^2 - 2D - 3)\,y = 3e^{-2x}$

Did you get: 1. $\frac{1}{4}e^{3x}$; 2. $\frac{3}{5}e^{-2x}$?

Finding the particular integral when P(x) is $\sin\alpha x$ or $\cos\alpha x$.

Example. The fact that $D^2 \begin{pmatrix}\sin\alpha x\\ \cos\alpha x\end{pmatrix} = -\alpha^2 \begin{pmatrix}\sin\alpha x\\ \cos\alpha x\end{pmatrix}$ seems to suggest that in certain cases we can use a similar method to the above when the function of the R.H.S. involves sines and cosines and the operator occurs with *even powers.*

Suppose $(D^2 - 1)\,y = 5 \sin 3x$

$\therefore$ Try $y = \dfrac{1}{D^2 - 1} \cdot 5 \sin 3x$ as P.I.

[put $D^2 = -\alpha^2 = -9$] $= \dfrac{1}{-9-1} \cdot 5 \sin 3x$

$\therefore$ Try $y = -\dfrac{1}{2} \sin 3x$ as the P.I.

Check: $D^2\,(y) = \dfrac{9}{2} \sin 3x$

L.H.S. $= (D^2 - 1)y = \left(\dfrac{9}{2} + \dfrac{1}{2}\right) \sin 3x = 5 \sin 3x =$ R.H.S.

$\therefore$ This gives the particular integral.

Use this method to find P.I.'s for:

1. $(2D^2 + 1)\,y = 7 \cos 2x$; 2. $(D^4 + D^2)\,y = 12 \sin 3x$

Did you get: 1. $-\cos 2x$; 2. $\dfrac{1}{6} \sin 3x$?

Exercise 77. Use the above methods to find:

1. $\dfrac{1}{D+2}\, e^{3x}$
2. $\dfrac{1}{D^2 - 1}\, e^{2x}$
3. $\dfrac{1}{D^2 + 6} \sin 2x$
4. $\dfrac{1}{D^2 - 4}(2e^{-x} + \sin 3x)$

Exercise 78. Solve completely :

1. $(D^2 - 5D + 6)\,y = 4$ (remember $4 = 4e^0$)
2. $(D^2 + D - 2)\,y = 12e^{2x}$
3. $(4D^2 + 1)\,y = 6 \sin x$
4. $(D^2 + 1)\,y = \cos 2x$
5. $(D^2 + 4D + 4)\,y = 16e^{2x}$ given that $y = 0$ and $y' = 0$ when $x = 0$.

Another helpful trick

Let us try an example where $\sin \alpha x$ occurs on the R.H.S. but the function of D contains odd powers.

Example. Suppose: $(D^2 + 2D + 5)\,y = 17 \sin 2x$

Putting $D^2 = -(2)^2 = -4$

we get $y = \dfrac{1}{-4 + 2D + 5} 17 \sin 2x$ for the P.I

$$= \frac{1}{2D + 1} 17 \sin 2x$$

Using a method similar to that used in complex numbers (see p. 236, Example 1) to simplify the denominator, multiply numerator and denominator by $(2D - 1)$

$$y = \frac{2D - 1}{4D^2 - 1} 17 \sin 2x$$

Put $D^2 = -4$: $y = \dfrac{2D - 1}{-16 - 1} 17 \sin 2x$

$$= -(2D - 1) \sin 2x$$

$$= -2 \cdot 2 \cos 2x + \sin 2x$$

$$[D (\sin 2x) = 2 \cos 2x]$$

$\therefore$ $y = -4 \cos 2x + \sin 2x$ is the P.I.

Check: $D(y) = 8 \sin 2x + 2 \cos 2x$

$$D^2 (y) = 16 \cos 2x - 4 \sin 2x$$

$$\text{L.H.S.} = (D^2 + 2D + 5)y = (16 \cos 2x - 4 \sin 2x) + (16 \sin 2x + 4 \cos 2x)$$

$$- 20 \cos 2x + 5 \sin 2x$$

$$= 17 \sin 2x = \text{R.H.S.}$$ Correct.

Case of failure

If $f(D) = 0$ for some value of D, then this treatment fails.

For example $\frac{1}{D-2}e^{2x}$

Putting $D = 2$ we get $\frac{1}{0}\,e^{2x}$, which is valueless.

There is a special technique for dealing with these cases, but it is too long for an elementary treatment of the subject.

Exercise 79. Find the P.I.'s given by the following :

1. $y = \frac{1}{D^2 + 3D + 2}\,40\sin 2x$
2. $y = \frac{1}{D^2 - 3D + 2}\,5\cos x$
3. $y = \frac{1}{2D^2 + 5D + 3}\,25\cos 2x$

Exercise 80. Using the results of the last exercise, solve completely the following D.E.'s. Check your solutions by differentiation.

1. $\frac{d^2y}{dx^2} + 3\frac{dy}{dx} + 2y = 40\sin 2x$
2. $\frac{d^2y}{dx^2} - 3\frac{dy}{dx} + 2y = 5\cos x$
3. $2\frac{d^2y}{dx^2} + 5\frac{dy}{dx} + 3y = 25\cos 2x$

Finding the Particular Integral when P(x) is a polynomial expression

We illustrate the method by means of an example.

Example. Find the P.I. for the D.E.

$$(D^2 - 3D + 2)\ y = x^2 + 2x$$

$$\therefore\quad (D-2)(D-1)\ y = x^2 + 2x$$

$$y = \frac{1}{(D-2)(D-1)}(x^2 + 2x)\ \ldots\ [1]$$

When the operator can be factorised in this way the simplest method is to express the inverse operator in partial fractions in order to expand by the binomial theorem.

$$f(D) \equiv \frac{1}{(D-2)(D-1)} \equiv \frac{1}{(1-D)(2-D)}$$

$$\equiv \frac{1}{(1-D)} - \frac{1}{(2-D)}$$

$$\equiv (1-D)^{-1} - \tfrac{1}{2}(1-\tfrac{D}{2})^{-1}$$

Expanding by the binomial theorem :

$$f(D) \equiv (1 + D + D^2 \quad \ldots) - \tfrac{1}{2}(1 + \frac{D}{2} + \frac{D^2}{4} + \quad \ldots)$$

$$\equiv \tfrac{1}{2} + \tfrac{3}{4} D + \tfrac{7}{8} D^2 + \ldots$$

From [1] $y = (\tfrac{1}{2} + \tfrac{3}{4} D + \tfrac{7}{8} D^2 + \ldots)(x^2 + 2x)$

Note: The expansion is only required as far as the term in D^2 since further differentiation of $(x^2 + 2x)$ will merely give zero results.

Hence the P.I. is given by

$$y = \tfrac{1}{2}(x^2 + 2x) + \tfrac{3}{4}(2x + 2) + \tfrac{7}{8} \cdot 2$$

$$y = \tfrac{1}{2} x^2 + \frac{5}{2} x + \frac{13}{4}$$

Exercise 81. Find the particular integrals for the D.E.'s : *

1. $(D^2 - 1)\, y = 3x^2$
2. $(D^2 - D)\, y = -3x^2$ (Remember $D^{-1} y = \int y\, dx$)
3. $(D^2 - 6D + 8)\, y = 8x^2 + 16x$

* Use the binomial expansions

$$(1 \pm x)^{-1} = 1 \mp x + x^2 \mp x^3 + \ldots$$

Summary of D-Operator methods for obtaining the P.I.'s for second-order differential equations.

We are considering D.E's. of type $a\frac{d^2 y}{dx^2} + b\frac{dy}{dx} + cy = P(x)$

$$\text{i.e.} \qquad (a D^2 + bD + c)\, y = P(x)$$

(i) P(x) an exponential function $e^{\alpha x}$:

$$y = \frac{1}{aD^2 + bD + c}.\, P(x) \qquad \text{where } D = \alpha$$

(ii) P(x) a function $\sin \alpha x$ or $\cos \alpha x$:

$$y = \frac{1}{aD^2 + bD + c}.P(x) \qquad \text{where } D^2 = -\alpha^2$$

(iii) P(x) a polynomial expression in x :

Expand $\dfrac{1}{aD^2 + bD + c}$

by the binomial theorem, using partial fractions where applicable, and operate on P(x) to give y.

Chapter 20
A first look at statistics

We shall not attempt a formal definition of statistics. It is sufficient to say that we are bombarded with statistics, and mankind has been familiar with them at least since the Domesday Book was written, and probably much earlier than that. We meet them under the headings of cricket averages, average earnings, inflation rates, through advertising such as 'nine people out of ten buy our margarine' and so on.

Statistics seem to give a guide, however rough, to what is happening in society. It can be a very useful tool, but we need to know something about the good and the not-so-good uses to which it can be put. Scientists and technologists need this tool in their everyday work.

Therefore, we must attempt to put statistics on a rational basis, and have a look at some of the tools the statistician has forged for himself. We cannot do more than this in the present book.

ON THE AVERAGE

We are all familiar with batting averages, bowling averages, average rainfall, etc. We recognise this as a quick way of conveying an understanding of what a batsman or bowler or Nature has done, and it conveys the information much more clearly than a whole set of figures. This common *average* is called *the mean* of the set of figures.

But the arithmetic average has to be treated very carefully. It can convey the wrong idea.

An example will illustrate this.

Example 1. An aeroplane flies in a straight line from A to B, and from B to C. His speed from A to B is 400 km/h. and from B to C is 450 km/h. If AB = 200 km and BC = 150 km what is his average speed?

A ——— 200 km ——— B ——— 150 km ——— C

400 km/h. 450 km/h.

We could say: Average speed = the average of the two speeds

$$= \frac{400 + 450}{2}$$

= 425 km/h. But is it?

What do we mean by 'average speed'? When we make a long journey by car and compliment ourselves on 'averaging' 60 km/h in spite of 'hitting the rush hour' in a certain town, stopping for meals or refuelling, don't we mean that if we had been able to travel straight through without let or hindrance at the speed of 60 km/h we would have taken the same time for the journey as that actually taken? In other words:

Average speed = (total distance) / (total time)

In this case: time from A to B $= \frac{200}{400}$ hours $= \frac{1}{2}$ hour

time from B to C $= \frac{150}{450}$ hours $= \frac{1}{3}$ hour

$\therefore$ Total time $= \frac{5}{6}$ hour

$\therefore$ Average speed = total distance/total time

$$= 350 \div \frac{5}{6}$$

= **420 km/h**

This is the correct answer. We must treat averages with caution. We fell into a trap here because speed is a combination of distance and time, i.e. kilometres per hour.

It is permissible to consider an average of quantities such as pounds or runs or ages, since these consist of simple units.

THE MEAN

Mathematically we define the mean as

$$\overline{x} = \frac{x_1 + x_2 + x_3 + \ldots + x_n}{n}$$

where $x_1, x_2, x_3 \ldots\ldots x_n$ are a set of n numbers.

or using our 'sigma' notation (see page 101)

The mean, $\overline{x} = \frac{1}{n}\Sigma x_i$ where i takes the values 1 to n.

This is what is normally understood as the 'average': we add up all the figures and divide by the number of them.

Example 2. The following table gives the lifetime x in years of six washing machines. Calculate the mean lifetime.

x = 14, 6, 11, 7½, 4, 9½ years
(n = 6)

$$\overline{x} = \frac{1}{n}\Sigma x = \frac{1}{6}(14 + 6 + 11 + 7\tfrac{1}{2} + 4 + 9\tfrac{1}{2})$$

$$= \frac{52}{6}$$

∴ **The mean = $8^2/_3$ years.**

CODING

This method is quite laborious if the numbers involved are large. There are two methods which help to simplify the arithmetic:

1. We can work with the smallest number as a base as in Example 3 below.

2. We can make a rough guess at the mean and then work as in Example 3 below.

These methods are called CODING METHODS.

Example 3. Find the mean of the following numbers.

453, 475, 450, 461, 492, 450, 455, 485, 470, 481.
(10 numbers, i.e. n = 10).

We notice that $\alpha = 450$ is the least of these. We use this as a base for calculating and arrange the work as follows:

x	α	$(x - \alpha)$
453	450	3
475		25
450		0
461		11
492		42
450		0
455		5
485		35
470		20
481		31

$\Sigma(x - \alpha) = 172$

$\Sigma(x - \alpha) = 172$, $n = 10$.

$\therefore$ Average of $(x - \alpha) = \frac{172}{10} = 17.2$

But this is over and above the base 450

$\therefore$ Average $= 450 + 17.2$
$= 467.2$

or We can make a rough guess at the mean. We notice the numbers range from 450 to 492, so we might take $\alpha = 470$ as a rough estimate, and set out the work as follows:

x	α	(x − α)
453	470	−17
475		+ 5
450		−20
461		− 9
492		+ 22
450		−20
455		−15
485		+ 15
470		0
481		+ 11

$\Sigma(x - \alpha) = -81 + 53$

$$\Sigma(x - \alpha) = -81 + 53\,, \quad n = 10$$
$$= -28$$
$$\therefore \frac{1}{n}\Sigma(x - \alpha) = -\frac{28}{10}$$
$$= -2.8$$

This is the error from the guessed mean 470.

$$\therefore \text{True mean} = 470 - 2.8$$
$$= 467.2 \text{ as before.}$$

Exercise 82.

1. Calculate the mean of the following percentages (20 in all) gained by a set of students in an examination.

   45, 71, 64, 32, 37, 48, 25, 62, 54, 60,
   58, 29, 36, 42, 38, 43, 65, 72, 15, 46.

2. (a) Do the same for the following:

   45, 61, 64, 32, 37, 48, 25, 62, 54, 60,
   58, 29, 36, 42, 38, 43, 65, 62, 35, 46.

   (b) Can you account for these answers noting that the highest and lowest marks in the two cases (i.e. the ranges of marks) are quite different?

Note: In the above examples, although the *mean* gives part of the picture, there could be many sets of numbers having the same mean. We therefore need another indicator to give us some idea of the *spread* of the values. We shall see later how this is done.

SAMPLING

Suppose the government is interested in finding out something about the incomes of families in the U.K. week by week, how they spend their incomes, how the incomes are grouped, what kind of houses they live in, how many children there are in each income group, etc. It would obviously be an impossible task to ask every household in the country every week about this. Therefore, they make a limited survey, or in other words, they take a *sample* of the population. For example, in 1972 the total number of households surveyed was 7017 and these were taken as a random sample. The results were as follows:

Average Weekly expenditure in 1972 of households grouped according to gross income of household.

	Under £10	£10 and under £15	£15 and under £20	£20 and under £25	£25 and under £30	£30 and under £35
Total No. of H'holds	442	605	423	476	513	553
Total No. of Persons	468	978	892	1,214	1,417	1,679
Av. No. Persons per H'hold	1.06	1.61	2.11	2.55	2.76	3.04

	£35 and under £40	£40 and under £45	£45 and under £50	£50* and under £60	£60* and under £80	£80* and over
Total No.of H'holds	630	565	530	833	880	567
Total No.of Persons	2,010	1,883	1,756	2,866	3,068	2,241
Av. No. Persons per H'hold	3.19	3.33	3.31	3.44	3.95	2.91

The average income per head of population in the various groups is also found. Expenditures are also taken under various headings such as food (split up into sections, e.g. bread, milk, meat, etc.), rent and rates, clothing, etc. This does not give the whole picture of what is happening to the incomes and expenditures in the U.K. but it gives some idea of the standard of living of the various groups in a much clearer way than if we just worked out (total income/total population), taken over the whole country.

*(Note the larger income ranges for the higher income groups).

We are only too aware these days, of the phenomenon of 'opinion polls', whether they concern elections or how much marmalade people buy per week. These are 'sampling processes' and the samples are taken in a random way from the whole 'population'. This meaning of population is not confined to people. We can talk about the population of all the cars in this country or the population of trees in a park.

FREQUENCY DISTRIBUTIONS

We notice that when taking the results of a large sample, the same numbers may occur several times. For example in Example 3 the number 450 occurred twice, i.e. with a *frequency* of two. When this occurs we arrange our work in tabular form as in the following example:

Example 4. When a die is thrown 100 times the scores 1 to 6 turn up with the following frequencies. Find the mean score.

Score (x)	1	2	3	4	5	6
Frequency (f)	16	20	9	14	21	20

Total throws, $n = \Sigma f = 100$

$$\text{Total Score} = 1 \times 16 + 2 \times 20 + 3 \times 9 + 4 \times 14 + 5 \times 21 + 6 \times 20$$

$$= \Sigma \text{ frequency } \times \text{ score}$$

$$= \Sigma f \, . \, x$$

$$\therefore \textbf{ Average or mean} = \frac{1}{n} \Sigma f.x$$

We take a guessed mean, α, of 3.

Score x	α	$u = (x - \alpha)$	f	fu
1	3	−2	16	−32
2		−1	20	−20
3		0	9	0
4		1	14	+14
5		2	21	+42
6		3	20	+60
			$\Sigma f = 100$	$-52 + 116 = 64$ $= \Sigma fu$

$n = \Sigma f \quad = 100$

$\Sigma fu \quad = 64$

$\frac{1}{n} \Sigma fu \quad = 0.64$

above the guessed mean 3

$\therefore$ True Mean $= 3.64$

In the above, the possible scores, 1 to 6, are *discrete values*, i.e. they are definite exact numbers. Other examples are the number of children in a family, or the marks scored in an examination, or the number of cars completed in a day at a particular factory.

But we can think of examples where the measurements are not discrete but *vary continuously*, e.g. the time taken by various workers to perform a specific task, or the heights of children of school age. These variables are called *continuous random variables*, and we may be able to measure them only approximately. The heights of children may be given to the nearest centimetre for convenience. Thus a child given as 145 cm may be anything between 144.5 cm and 145.5 cm, but would be classed as 145 cm. When we do this, we are grouping a set of values within a range into one group or class, e.g. the '145 cm class.' This is called *a grouped frequency distribution,* and the *class* is distinguished by the *midpoint of the range.*

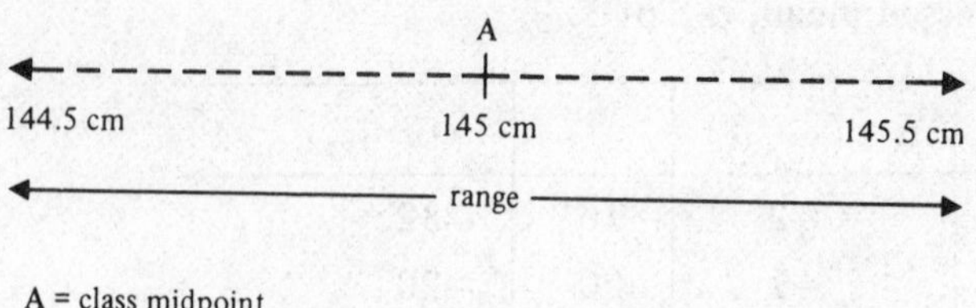

Note: We must always make it perfectly clear what we intend to do if a measurement falls on exactly one or other of the boundaries. i.e. we could say 144.5 cm (exactly) falls into the 145 cm class, but 145.5 cm falls into the class above, i.e. the 146 cm class.

TALLY MARKS

When a sample has a large number of values the work in calculating the mean may be simplified as in the following example by using tally marks. Here the results are grouped and the mean found by grouping may be slightly different from that of the original data, (but only slightly).

Example 5. An efficiency expert takes a sample of 100 'breakdown' times in minutes of the machines in his factory. (Breakdown time is the length of time during which a machine is out of action either awaiting repair or being repaired or replaced). The results are as follows. Find the mean breakdown time.

21	23	19	27	43	24	20	45	22	22
21	38	36	49	23	20	18	22	17	35
38	24	11	22	45	21	9	29	21	41
59	27	12	23	27	10	7	34	22	33
36	32	24	44	16	13	27	23	33	37
22	42	19	47	29	31	10	48	15	21
40	13	24	25	22	23	19	20	34	39
25	37	16	52	17	28	24	18	23	53
35	20	31	28	25	44	30	32	29	30
27	28	21	23	12	17	24	40	14	15

We organise the work as follows:

1. Pick out the least and greatest readings; here 7 and 59.
2. Decide the total range. Here we take 5 to 60, i.e. a range of 55.
3. This suggests 11 classes of 5. We choose 5–9, 10–14, 15–19 etc. inclusive.
4. Corresponding to each value in the table we put a stroke in the appropriate range, and to help counting we make 'gates' of five, ~~1111~~ .
5. We find the class midpoint, e.g. for numbers 5, 6, 7, 8, 9, the class midpoint is 7.
6. We calculate the mean as before. (We use $\alpha = 22$ as a guessed mean).
7. We avoid any confusion about the class in which a value should be placed by taking the boundaries as shown.

Class Values	Class boundaries	Class Midpoint x	Tally Marks	Frequency f
5– 9	4.5– 9.5	7	11	2
10–14	9.5–14.5	12	~~1111~~ 111	8
15–19	14.5–19.5	17	~~1111~~ ~~1111~~ 11	12
20–24	19.5–24.5	22	~~1111~~ ~~1111~~ ~~1111~~ ~~1111~~ ~~1111~~ ~~1111~~	30
25–29	24.5–29.5	27	~~1111~~ ~~1111~~ 1111	14
30–34	29.5–34.5	32	~~1111~~ ~~1111~~	10
35–39	34.5–39.5	37	~~1111~~ 1111	9
40–44	39.5–44.5	42	~~1111~~ 11	7
45–49	44.5–49.5	47	~~1111~~	5
50–54	49.5–54.5	52	11	2
55–59	54.3–59.5	57	1	1

To calculate the mean, we take a guessed mean, α. of 22.

x	α	$(x-\alpha)$	factor*	$\frac{x-\alpha}{5}$	[1] f	[2] $f\cdot(x-\alpha)/5$
7	22	−15	5	−3	2	− 6
12		−10		−2	8	−16
17		− 5		−1	12	−12
22		0		0	30	0
27		5		1	14	14
32		10		2	10	20
37		15		3	9	27
42		20		4	7	28
47		25		5	5	25
52		30		6	2	12
57		35		7	1	7
					$n = \Sigma f = 100$	$133-34 = 99 = \frac{\Sigma f\,(x-\alpha)}{5}$

Note: Taking out the common factor 5 eases the arithmetic considerably.

From column [1] $n = \Sigma f \quad = 100$

From column [2] $\frac{\Sigma f(x-\alpha)}{5} = 99$

$$\therefore \Sigma f(x-\alpha) = 99 \times 5 = 495$$

$$\therefore \frac{\Sigma f(x-\alpha)}{n} = 4.95$$

This is above the guessed mean of 22.

Hence the true mean, $\bar{x} = 26.95$

Note: If all the results are added separately, instead of taking for example 30 samples with class midpoint 22, and treating the whole of this class together as a total of 30 x 22, we would find the result to be 27.06. A pocket calculator is an invaluable ally here.

Exercise 83.

1. (a) Calculate the mean of the distribution

x	1	2	3	4	5	6
f	1	3	5	8	2	1

using $\left[\begin{array}{l}\bar{x} = \frac{1}{n}\Sigma fx \\ n = \Sigma f.\end{array}\right.$

(b) What difference would it make to $\bar{x}$ if the first and last frequencies were both increased by: (i) 5; (ii) 10? Account for this.

2. Using a guessed mean $\alpha = 5$, calculate the mean score of the following results:

Score x	0	1	2	3	4	5	6	7	8	9	10
Frequency f	7	3	1	12	16	37	14	4	3	2	1

3. Check the result $\bar{x} = 26.95$ for Example 5 taking x as the class midpoint, frequency f as shown, and $\alpha = 32$. (See answers for complete solution.)

GRAPHICAL REPRESENTATION OF FREQUENCY DISTRIBUTIONS

The Histogram

We represent each class by means of a rectangle whose width is the class width and whose height is the frequency.

Example 6. In a certain city there is a 'population' of milk delivery vans. The ages of these vans are as follows:

No. of vans	26	39	52	61	31	20	6	frequency
Age in years	0–1	1–2	2–3	3–4	4–5	5–6	6–7	classes

The age is a continuous variable but we have grouped these as shown. Plotting frequency against age (Figure 20.1) we obtain:

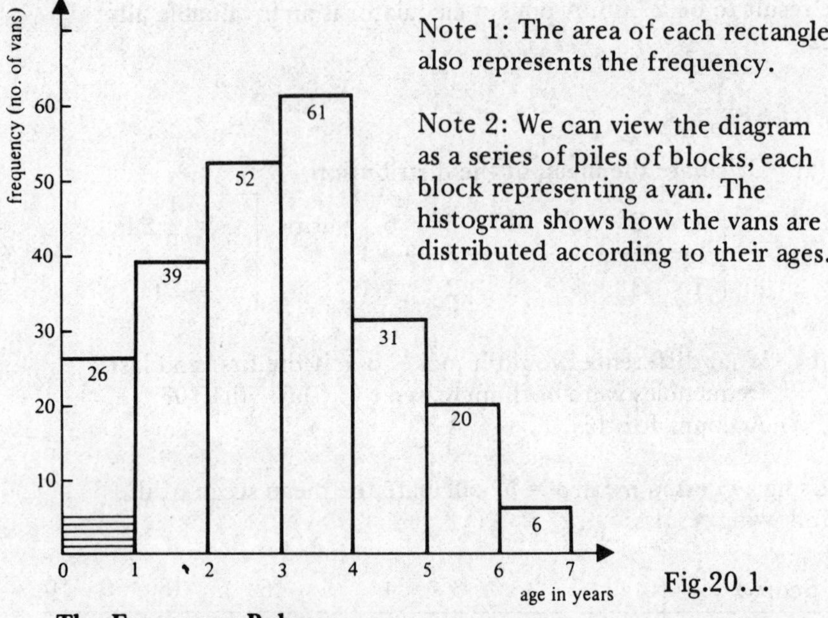

Note 1: The area of each rectangle also represents the frequency.

Note 2: We can view the diagram as a series of piles of blocks, each block representing a van. The histogram shows how the vans are distributed according to their ages.

Fig.20.1.

The Frequency Polygon.

If we plot the frequency against the *class midpoint* (Figure 20.2) we obtain the frequency polygon of the distribution. This correspond to joining the midpoints of the tops of the rectangles in the histogram

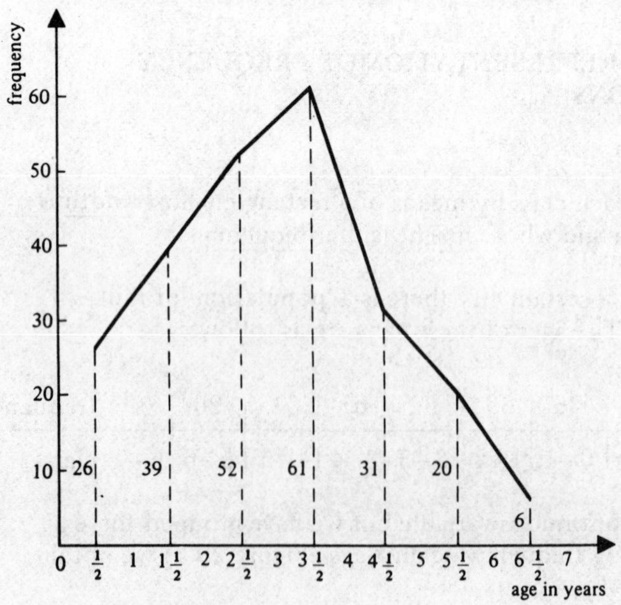

Fig.20.2.

The Main Features of Histograms

A comparison of histograms is often useful in giving a clear picture when we wish to convey information quickly. Below we see the results of two examination papers set to the same group of 70 students.

Exam A

Marks	20 – 30	30 – 40	40 – 50	50 – 60	60 – 70	70 –80
No. of students	3	4	20	27	12	4

Exam B

Marks	10 – 20	20 – 30	30 – 40	40 – 50	50 – 60	60 – 70
No. of students	2	7	15	24	16	6

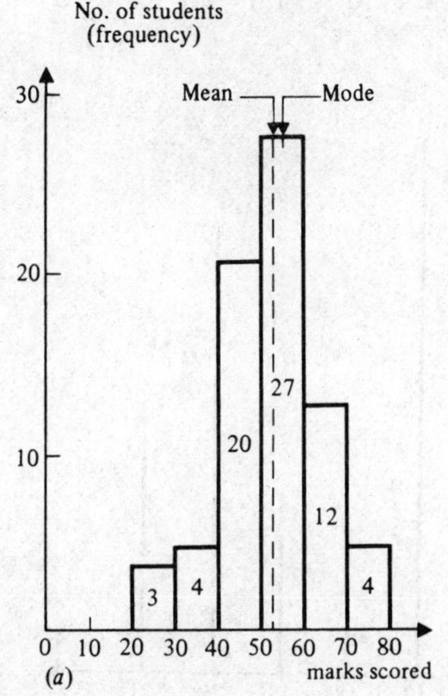

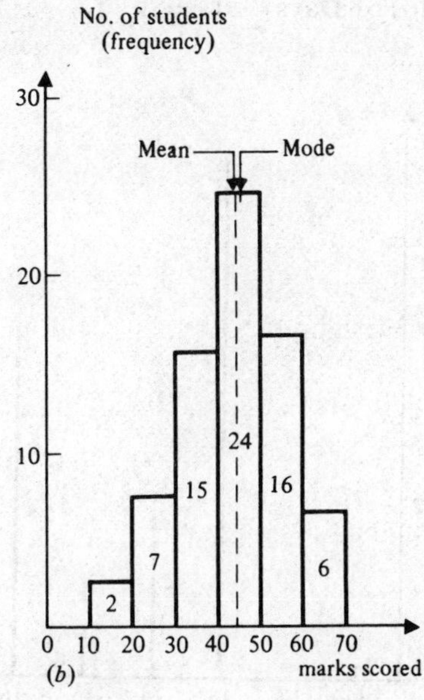

Fig. 20.3

If the histograms (Fig.20.3) were drawn on transparent paper, by superimposing one on the other it would be obvious that in exam. A there is a very definite shift to the right compared with exam. B. In other words a higher standard of performance was achieved in exam. A.

Mean of A marks = 52.6 Mean of B marks = 44.0

Mode of A marks = 55 Mode of B marks = 45.0

The *centre values* of the *tallest blocks* are the *modes.*

The Mean and the Mode can be very different.

The Bar Chart.

In the month of September, temperatures were taken at 12 noon each day and frequencies given as below:

Temperature at 12 noon (^{o}C)	13	14	15	16	17	18	19	20	21
Frequency (No. of Days)	6	2	1	4	6	1	2	5	3

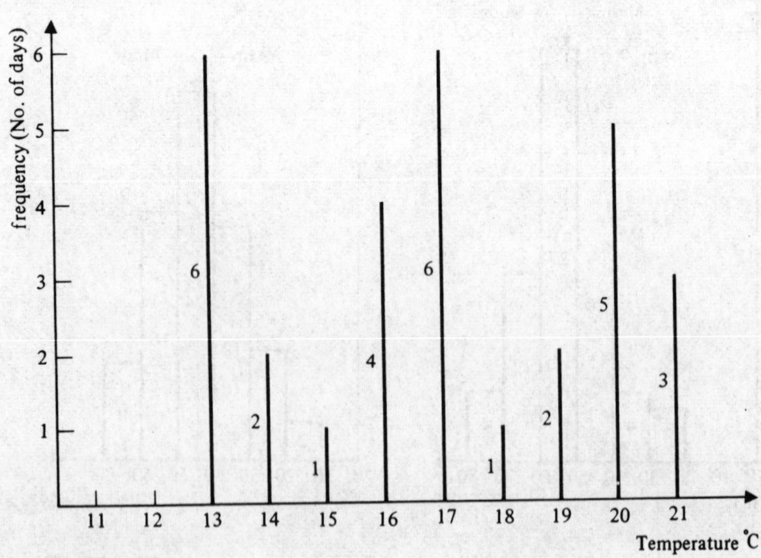

Fig. 20.4

For *ungrouped frequency distributions* we can use the *bar chart* as in Fig. 20.4.

Note 1. On a **histogram** it is the **area of the block** which represents **frequency**.

On a **bar chart** it is the **length of the bar** which represents **frequency**.

Note 2: The fact that in the histogram it is the area which represents frequency is useful as we do not necessarily have to have all the blocks of the same width, i.e. the class width may vary.

Exercise 84. Draw the bar chart for No.2 in Exercise 83.

THE STANDARD DEVIATION (S) of a SAMPLE.

If we regard the *mean* as the *centre* of calculations the left-hand side would balance the right, i.e. it resembles the vertical line through the centre of gravity of the area under the histogram. Therefore we need another measure to indicate how the various values are distributed around the mean. This new indicator of spread is called the *standard deviation,* s, of the sample.

If we are talking about a whole 'population' we use σ (this is 'small sigma' just as Σ is 'capital sigma')

VARIANCE AND STANDARD DEVIATION

Let $\overline{x}$ be the mean of n observations $x_1, x_2, \ldots, x_n$
Then $(x_1 - \overline{x})^2 + (x_2 - \overline{x})^2 + \ldots + (x_n - \overline{x})^2$ is called the sum of the squares of the deviations from the mean.

The average of these, i.e. $\frac{1}{n}[(x_1 - \overline{x})^2 + (x_2 - \overline{x})^2 + \ldots +$ $(x_n - \overline{x})^2]$ is called the variance, s^2, of the n observations.

$$\text{i.e. } s^2 = \frac{1}{n}\Sigma(x - \overline{x})^2$$

The square root of this is called the standard deviation, s, from the mean

i.e. $s = \sqrt{\frac{\Sigma(x-\overline{x})^2}{n}}$ and x takes the values $x_1, x_2, \ldots x_n$

With frequency data, if the observations $x_1, x_2, \ldots x_n$ occur with frequency $f_1, f_2, \ldots f_n$ respectively, then the variance,

$$s^2 = \frac{f_1(x_1-\overline{x})^2 + f_2(x_2-\overline{x})^2 + \ldots + f_n(x_n-\overline{x})^2}{f_1 + f_2 + f_3 + \ldots + f_n}$$

i.e. $s^2 = \frac{1}{N}\Sigma f(x-\overline{x})^2$ where $N = \Sigma f$

and x takes the values $x_1, x_2, \ldots, x_n$

Similarly the standard deviation, s, is given by

$$s = \sqrt{\frac{\Sigma f(x-\overline{x})^2}{\Sigma f}} \quad \text{or} \quad \sqrt{\frac{\Sigma f(x-\overline{x})^2}{N}}$$

This is not a very easy expression to use for calculations in practice and alternative forms can be proved to be

$$s_x{}^2 = \frac{1}{N}\Sigma fx^2 - \overline{x}^2 \quad \text{or} \quad \frac{1}{N}\Sigma fu^2 - \overline{u}^2 = s_u{}^2$$

and $s_x = s_u$*

where $\overline{x}$ = the mean and where $\overline{u}$ = the mean of data measured from the working mean α.

This is much easier to use, especially if coding is used. An example will illustrate the method.

*Since $u = x - \alpha$ then $x - \overline{x} = u - \overline{u}$

and $\overline{u} = \overline{x} - \alpha$ $\therefore$ $\Sigma f(x-\overline{x})^2 = \Sigma f(u-\overline{u})^2$

$\therefore$ $s_x{}^2 = s_u{}^2$

Example 7. A hundred children were examined in school and their heights noted to the nearest inch. Calculate the mean and standard deviation of the distribution. What is the mode of the distribution?

x = Height to nearest inch	60	61	62	63	64	65	66	67	68
f = Frequency	2	0	15	29	25	12	10	4	3

We arrange the calculation as follows:

Working Mean $= \alpha = 64$

x	α	u $=(x-\alpha)$	f	fu	u^2	fu^2
60	64	−4	2	− 8	16	32
61		−3	0	0	9	0
62		−2	15	−30	4	60
63		−1	29	−29	1	29
64		0	25	+ 0	0	0
65		1	12	+12	1	12
66		2	10	+20	4	40
67		3	4	+12	9	36
68		4	3	+12	16	48
			100 = N	−67 +56 = Σ fu		257 = Σ fu^2

From the table: $\Sigma fu = -11$, $N = 100$

$$\therefore \bar{u} = \frac{\Sigma fu}{N} = -\frac{11}{100} = -0.11$$

This is measured from the working mean 64.

$\therefore$ True Mean $= 64 - 0.11$

$\bar{x}$ **= 63.89 inches.**

$$\Sigma fu^2 = 257$$

$$\therefore \frac{\Sigma fu^2}{N} = 2.57$$

$$\text{But } s_x^2 = s_u^2 = \frac{\Sigma fu^2}{N} - \bar{u}^2$$

$$= 2.57 - (-0.11)^2$$

$$= 2.57 - 0.0121$$

$$= 2.5579$$

$$\therefore s_x = s_u \triangleq 1.6$$

From the table the height occurring most frequently is 63 inches
∴ The class midpoint is 63 inches, i.e. the **Mode = 63 inches.**

Exercise 85.

1. Calculate the mean and standard deviation of the following set of results.

x	30	31	32	33	34	35	36	37	38	39
f	4	8	23	35	62	44	18	4	1	1

2. The weights of 50 men to the nearest 10-lb. are measured and grouped as follows:

x	115	125	135	145	155	165	175	185	195	205	215
f	2	3	3	6	9	8	7	8	1	1	2

Where x = the class midpoint in lb.
Calculate the mean and standard deviation of the grouped frequency distribution.

From the Histogram to the CONTINUOUS DISTRIBUTION.

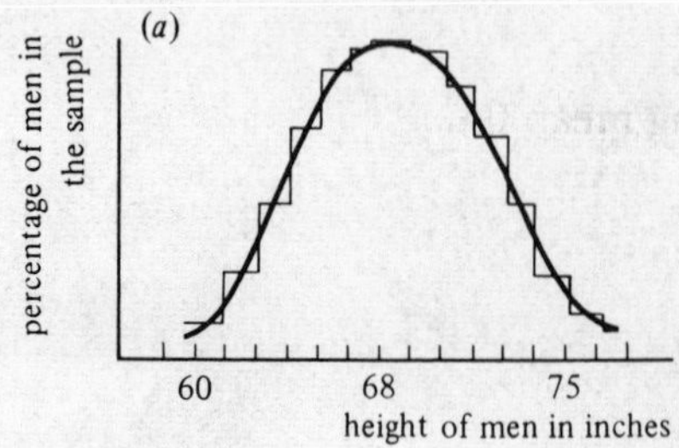

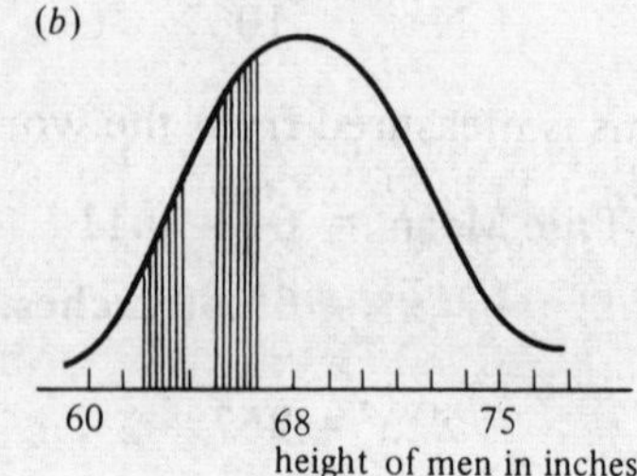

Fig. 20.5.

If we take a sample of men, say 1000, and measure their heights to the nearest inch, we should probably obtain a histogram similar to the one in Fig.20.5(a) in which only the tops of the columns are indicated. We could sketch a reasonably smooth curve through the midpoints of the tops of the columns as shown in Fig.20.5(b).

If we take a larger sample of men, say 10000, we could take more accurage measurements, say to the nearest 1/10″, and obtain ten times as many columns and get an even more accurate picture of what is happening in the whole population of men. The 'zig-zags' would be much finer. In this way, by taking larger and larger samples and narrower and narrower ranges we would eventually build up a picture which would be entirely made up of lines of which we have shown only a few in Fig.20.5(b). The shape of the curve would alter slightly from our original small sample curve but it would be of the same type. This type of graph is called a *continuous distribution* for obvious reasons. The height of the curve at any point gives the proportion of people of that height, and more important **the area under the curve** between given limits represents the proportion of the population having heights within those limits.

We have already said (p. 322) that the histogram may be considered as columns of blocks, each block representing one member of the 'population' in the distribution. In the same way, it may help the student to view the continuous distribution as a heap of dots, like a heap of sand, each dot representing one member of the very large population being studied. The dots are piled highest in the centre where the frequency is greatest.

Many 'populations' have a distribution pattern of this type with a single 'bulge' and fading away towards zero on either side. Mathematicians have fitted several useful equations to this type of curve and we shall mention some of these when we have discussed the question of probability. Meanwhile, it is worthwhile here to say what the indicator 'standard deviation' means for the normal curve (see p. 351).

USEFULNESS OF THE STANDARD DEVIATION.

We have calculated the mean and standard deviation from the mean. What use is this? We anticipate here what we shall later see in more detail. If we take a distribution such as the one discussed, which is reasonably symmetrical about the mean and is 'unimodal' i.e. has one maximum point as illustrated in Fig.20.6, we have a good guide as to what proportion of the distribution falls within certain areas.

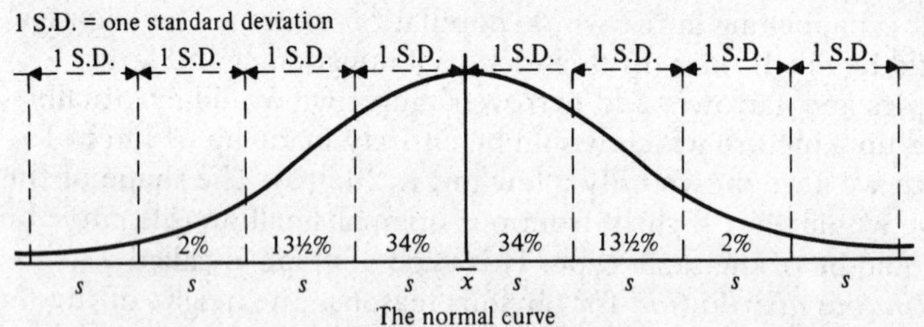

Fig. 20.6.

A rough guide to the distribution is given by dividing the area under the curve by standard deviations from the mean. It can be shown that:

(a) Within 1 standard deviation lies 68 per cent of the distribution (i.e. 34 per cent on either side of the mean).

(b) Within 2 standard deviations lies 95 per cent of the distribution.

(c) Within 3 standard deviations lies 99 per cent of the distribution.

This is a very useful guide when estimating what proportion of manufactured items may be rejected when certain limits are set to variation from some standard of measurement of the dimension concerned. This assumes that the dimension has a distribution of the above type.

CHANCE, PROBABILITY AND POSSIBILITY.

(a) When we throw a die there is an equal chance of any of the six faces finishing uppermost. We say that there is a 'one in six' chance of scoring any of the numbers on the faces. What do we mean by a 'one in six' chance?

(b) When we say that if we smoke 24 cigarettes a day we have a 1 in 9 chance of contracting lung cancer, what are we implying?

In the first case (a) we *do not mean* that if we throw a die six times we shall throw one of each of a one, a two, a three, a four, a five and a six. We could score any combination of these.

In the second case (b) we *do not mean* that if nine people each smoke at least 24 cigarettes a day one of them will eventually contract lung cancer and the others will escape.

We do mean that:

(a) If we throw a die a great number of times (say 2400) then for about one-sixth of the throws, i.e. 400 times, we should throw a six or a five etc., that is about 400 of each. It could be 398 or 403 but it would be in the region of one-sixth of the total. We say, therefore, that the **probability** of throwing any particular number is 1/6, meaning 'in the long run.' (We note that the sum of all the probabilities of all the outcomes when throwing a die is 1/6 + 1/6 + 1/6 + 1/6 + 1/6 + 1/6 = 1).

(b) If a large number of people all smoke at least 24 cigarettes a day about one-ninth of them will get lung cancer, and eight-ninths will escape. We say:

The probability of getting lung cancer = 1/9
The probability of not getting lung cancer = 8/9
(Total = 1)

Mathematically we state:
The probability of an event E occurring is given by

$$p(E) = \lim_{n \to \infty} \frac{n_E}{n} \quad \text{(Definition of Probability)}$$

where n_E = the number of times E occurs in a sequence of n trials.

Note: What we are saying here is that when we make a succession of trials the fraction $\frac{n_E}{n}$ can be almost any faction less than 1 for small trials but the more trials we make, the nearer it gets to some definite fraction which we call p(E). This is represented diagramatically in Fig.20.7.

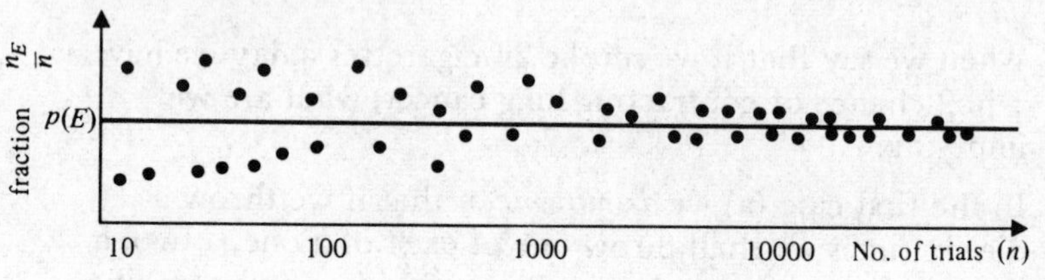

Fig.20.7.

The dots represent the value of $\frac{n_E}{n}$ after n trials.

POSSIBILITY

'Possibility' is a different thing from 'probability'. It is possible that all the people in a certain country will commit suicide on the same day at the same time, but it isn't probable. It is possible that all the cars in Yorkshire could try to travel along the M1 on a Wednesday. But that isn't probable either. It is possible that all the air molecules which are bouncing about in a room could all finish up just under the ceiling, but it isn't probable.

A physicist has to deal with very large numbers of molecules, atoms etc. He cannot deal with each molecule separately, not only because they are so small, but because each one has an effect on others by collisions, attractions, bouncing off the walls and so on. Calculations, therefore, when dealing with such a large number of individuals would be impossible even with a computer. The scientist does not know which particular atom of radio-active substance is going to disintegrate next, but he does know how many will probably disintegrate within a given period of time. This he has found by observation. Therefore, he has to deal with probabilities and work with these. Hence the necessity for trying to understand *the laws of probability*, which are quite simple and quite mathematical.

Causal laws, that is, laws which say 'to every effect there is a precise cause', have their uses in large-scale effects, but are severely limited at the atomic level. For example, if a few atoms are moving about in a given space, it is impossible to calculate what is going to happen to them, even if we send them off in given directions. Owing to the limited accuracy when dealing with such microscopically small objects, we don't know whether they will collide or not. If however we are dealing with a large number of atoms we could perhaps expect some of them to collide and in such a case predict the outcome. This is where probability is useful.

Probability theory is used extensively in work concerned with the reliability of aircraft, atomic power stations, chemical plant and other complex systems.

In order to clarify the laws of probability we must discuss what seems at first some very elementary and perhaps pointless problems. Here is one.

Example. What are the probabilities that, when 3 coins are thrown, we shall turn up: (a) 3 heads; (b) 2 heads, 1 tail; (c) 1 head, 2 tails; (d) 3 tails?

First let us find out how many different outcomes are possible.

When tossing 1 coin there are 2 possible outcomes, either a head or a tail, i.e. H or T.

We have to assume here that these are *equiprobable,* i.e. there is a long-run expectancy that equal numbers of each would turn up

$$\left.\begin{aligned} \therefore\ p(H) &= \tfrac{1}{2} \\ p(T) &= \tfrac{1}{2} \end{aligned}\right] \text{Total} = 1$$

(We read this as 'The probability of a head = ½', etc.)

When tossing 2 coins, for each outcome of the first toss there are 2 outcomes for the second, HH, HT, TH, TT.
∴ There are 4 outcomes altogether, or 2^2 outcomes.

When tossing 3 coins, for each outcome of the first two there are 2 outcomes for the third.
∴ There are 8 outcomes altogether, or 2^3 outcomes.

Let us write these down.

[1]	[2]	[3]	
H	H	H	Notice the quick way of writing these down.
H	H	T	Column [1] goes in groups of 4
H	T	H	Column [2] goes in groups of 2
H	T	T	Column [3] goes in groups of 1 i.e. H and T alternately.
			We note:
T	H	H	p (throwing 3H) = 1 out of 8 = $\frac{1}{8}$
T	H	T	p (throwing 2H, 1T) = 3 out of 8 = $\frac{3}{8}$
T	T	H	p (throwing 1H,2T) = 3 out of 8 = $\frac{3}{8}$
T	T	T	p (throwing 3T) = 1 out of 8 = $\frac{1}{8}$
			Total = 1

This last result is a particular case of the binomial expansion.

$$(a+b)^n = a^n + na^{n-1}\,b + \frac{n(n-1)}{2!}\,a^{n-2}\,b^2 + \ldots + b^n$$

e.g. $(a+b)^3 = a^3 + 3a^2b + 3ab^2 + b^3$ (cf. Chapter 12).

If $a = \frac{1}{2}$, $b = \frac{1}{2}$

$$(\tfrac{1}{2}+\tfrac{1}{2})^3 = (\tfrac{1}{2})^3 + 3(\tfrac{1}{2})^2(\tfrac{1}{2}) + 3(\tfrac{1}{2})(\tfrac{1}{2})^2 + (\tfrac{1}{2})^3$$
$$= p(3H) + p(2H, 1T) + p(1H, 2T) + p(3T)$$

Notice these terms are exactly the probabilities we have found for 3 heads; 2 heads, 1 tail; 1 head, 2 tails; and 3 tails.

This is a particular case of the general binomial probability distribution.

Note: The binomial distribution is only useful when **two mutually exclusive outcomes** are involved, e.g. right or wrong, black or white, heads or tails, win or lose, a success or a failure, a good product or a defective product - the two out-comes cannot both occur together.

Exercise 86.

1. How many different outcomes are there when 4 coins are tossed? Is this the same as when the same coin is tossed 4 times?

2. Write down these outcomes using the pattern given in the last example and then say what the probabilities are of throwing:

   (a) 4 heads; (b) 3 heads, 1 tail; (c) 2 heads, 2 tails;
   (d) one head, 3 tails; (e) 4 tails.

3. Expand the binomial $(\frac{1}{2} + \frac{1}{2})^4$. Does this give the same terms as you have just obtained in No.2 ?

4. There are 10 balls in a bag, 9 white balls and 1 black ball. What is the probability of drawing a black ball from the bag? A white ball? Call these p(B), p(W) respectively. If a ball is taken at random from the bag and then replaced and a second one taken and replaced, what are the probabilities of getting:
   (a) Two white balls in succession?
   (b) One white and one black?
   (c) The black ball twice?

5. If there are a very large number of articles in a batch of which it is known 10 per cent are defective, what is the probability that if two articles are picked at random; (a) both will be good; (b) one will be good and one defective;
   (c) both will be defective?
   (The answer should be as in No.4 since the probabilities are not substantially affected when drawing from a large number).

THE BINOMIAL PROBABILITY DISTRIBUTION

This distribution is useful when 'fault-finding' in industry, cutting down faulty batches to the minimum. Industry tries to do this by 'sampling.' The reasons for sampling and testing these samples are fairly obvious.

1. It may be impossible to check every item produced (e.g. every tiny screw) or it may be too expensive.

2. It may be impossible for various other reasons. For example, testing the life of a piece of electrical equipment may mean running it until it breaks, which of course one cannot do with every item. However, taking a sample need not be too expens but is certainly necessary in order to build up the firm's repu tion for reliability, and to give an indication for what length time a guarantee should be given.

Therefore sampling and testing are really necessary.

Example on the binomial probability distribution

Suppose that in a certain locality records indicate that in a particular month it will probably be fine 3 days out of 4, i.e.

p = probability that it will be fine = ¾

$\therefore q$ = probability that it will rain = ¼

on any one day.

Find (a) the probability that in a 5-day period it will stay fine on all 5 days;

(b) the probability that it will be fine at least 4 days out of the 5;

(c) the probability that it will be fine on 3 days and rain on 2;

(d) the probability that it will be fine on 2 days and rain on 3;

(e) the probability that it will be fine on at least 1 day.

We use $(p + q)^n$ where $p = \frac{3}{4}$, $q = \frac{1}{4}$, $n = 5$.

$$(\tfrac{3}{4} + \tfrac{1}{4})^5 = (\tfrac{3}{4})^5 + 5\,(\tfrac{3}{4})^4(\tfrac{1}{4}) + \frac{5\cdot 4}{2\cdot 1}(\tfrac{3}{4})^3(\tfrac{1}{4})^2 + \frac{5\cdot 4\cdot 3}{3\cdot 2\cdot 1}(\tfrac{3}{4})^2(\tfrac{1}{4})^3 \text{; et}$$

(a) is the first term $= (\frac{3}{4})^5 =$ **0.2373**

(b) is the first term + second term = 0.2373 + 0.3955 = **0.6328**

(c) is the third term = **0.2637**

(d) is the fourth term = **0.0879**

(e) is found by calculating the probability of 5 wet days

i.e. $(\frac{1}{4})^5 = 9.7656 \times 10^{-4}$) and subtracting from 1.

This gives **0.9990** to 4 d.p.

(Here, a pocket calculator is invaluable).

Problem. What is the probability that it will rain on at least 1 day? (Hint: use one of the above probabilities.)

Did you get 0.7627?

EQUIPROBABILITY

In the examples of tossing a coin or throwing a die we are making a very fundamental assumption that any outcome is equally likely. This is a big assumption, but we have to make it in the first instance. In other words, we are assuming that the tosses or throws are made in an identical manner and that the coin or die is equally balanced, i.e. is symmetrical.

If on the other hand, these conditions are *not* satisfied we have a *weighted* probability.

When two results A and B are unpredictable and when all the known factors which could influence the result are *symmetrical* between A and B we say that the two results are *equiprobable.*

It is only possible to assess this symmetry by means of past trials, i.e. by experience. If for example, **over a long period**, the number of times A has occurred is twice that of B occurring, this shows conclusively that the factors influencing the outcome are not symmetrical. We would have expected that, if the results were equiprobable, the more trials that were taken the nearer the results would be to a 50-50 division.

Choosing at random

We can obtain equiprobable results by choosing at random provided there are equal numbers of the different kinds of objects.

Example. A man puts two tickets labelled 6, three tickets labelled 5, one ticket labelled 4, and one of each of 3, 2 and 1 into a bag, shakes them up and draws one. Would it be equally likely that a 5 or a 3 would be drawn? Of course not. The fact that there are three 5s and only one 3 destroys symmetry.

Probability Law 1.

If the probability of an event occurring is p, then the probability of it not occurring is $(1 - p)$

We have illustrated this by throwing a die.
The probability of getting any one of the numbers 1, 2, 3, 4, 5 or 6 is $\frac{1}{6}$

The probability of not getting that number, i.e. the probability of throwing any of the other five numbers, is $\frac{5}{6}$.

Example 1. If a coin is tossed 3 times there are 8 possible outcomes, i.e. 2^3.

∴ The probability of getting a head each time = $p(3H) = \frac{1}{8}$

The probability of getting at least 1 tail not getting 3 heads = the probability of

$$= 1 - \frac{1}{8}$$

$$= \frac{7}{8}$$

Exercise 87.

1. If I toss a coin 10 times, what is the probability: (a) of getting a head each time; (b) of getting at least one head?
2. If I throw 3 dice, what is the probability of throwing 3 sixes? What is the probability of throwing any other combination of 1, 2, 3, 4, 5 or 6?

Example 2. The probability of picking an ace from an ordinary pack of 52 cards is 4 out of 52, i.e. $\frac{4}{52}$. Therefore, the probability

of picking any other type of card is $1 - \frac{4}{52}$ or $\frac{48}{52}$.

This checks since there are 48 cards in the pack which are not aces.

Probability Law II Addition of probabilities

If A and B are mutually exclusive events, i.e. they cannot both occur simultaneously, then $P(A \text{ or } B) = p(A) + p(B)$

Example 1. What is the probability of picking a 'picture card' or an ace from a pack of cards?

The probability of picking an ace $= \frac{4}{52}$ since there are 4 aces.

The probability of picking a picture $= \frac{12}{52}$ since there are 12 pictures.

∴ The probability of picking an ace or a picture $= \frac{4}{52} + \frac{12}{52} = \frac{16}{52}$

Check: There are 16 aces and picture cards altogether in the pack.

∴ p (ace or picture) $= \frac{16}{52}$

Exercise 88.

1. The probability that an athlete will win a race is $\frac{1}{10}$
   The probability that he will be second is $\frac{1}{20}$
   The probability that he will be third is $\frac{1}{25}$
   What is the probability that he: (a) will be, (b) will not be in the first three places?
2. The probability that a book may be published by a certain publisher is $\frac{1}{6}$, and by another $\frac{1}{4}$. What is the probability that it will be published by one of these two?
3. An insurance company considers that the probabilities of rain, hail, snow, fog at a fete on a certain day are $\frac{1}{4}, \frac{1}{12}, \frac{1}{480}, \frac{1}{16}$ respectively. Assuming only one of these could happen: (a) What is the probability that one will happen? (b) What is the probability that it will be fine?
4. The probabilities that a sealed envelope contains 1, 2, 3, 4 or 5 tickets are $\frac{1}{2}, \frac{1}{4}, \frac{1}{8}, \frac{1}{16}, \frac{1}{32}$;
   Find the probability that it contains either more than 5 tickets or no tickets at all.

Probability Law III. Multiplication

If A and B are two events and the probility of A occurring affects the probability of B occurring or vice versa, then the two events are *dependent*. If one event does *not* affect the other they are said to be independent.

Here we shall only consider independent probabilities and we wish to find out the probability of both A and B occurring.

Example 1. What is the probability of picking a black ace from a pack of playing cards?

There are two black aces in the pack. Therefore, the probability of picking one of them is $\frac{2}{52}$

We could answer the question another way, by asking what is the probability of picking an ace which is also black?

The probability of picking an ace $= \frac{4}{52}$

The probability of picking a black card $= \frac{1}{2}$ since half of the cards are black cards.

Hence the probability of picking a card which is an ace AND black is given by:

$$\text{p (black ace)} = \text{p(ace)} \times \text{p (black card)}$$

$$= \frac{4}{52} \times \frac{1}{2}$$

$$= \frac{2}{52} \text{ which we know is correct.}$$

Example 2. A farmer takes a horse and a cow to market. He reckon[s] he has a 50-50 chance of selling the horse but only a 25-75 chance of selling the cow from previous experience.
What is the probability that he will sell: (i) both; (ii) one or the other; (iii) neither?

(i) Let selling the horse be represented by H_s
Let not selling the horse be represented by H_{ns}
Let selling the cow be represented by C_s
Let not selling the cow be represented by C_{ns}

Then the probabilities of H_s and H_{ns} occurring are equal, i.e. 1:1.
But the probabilities of C_s and C_{ns} occurring are in the ratio of 1 : 3.
In other words $p(H_s) = \frac{1}{2}$ and $p(C_s) = \frac{1}{4}$
If H_s occurs C_s can occur. But C_{ns} is 3 times more likely than C_s.
A representation of this is as in Fig. 20.8(a)

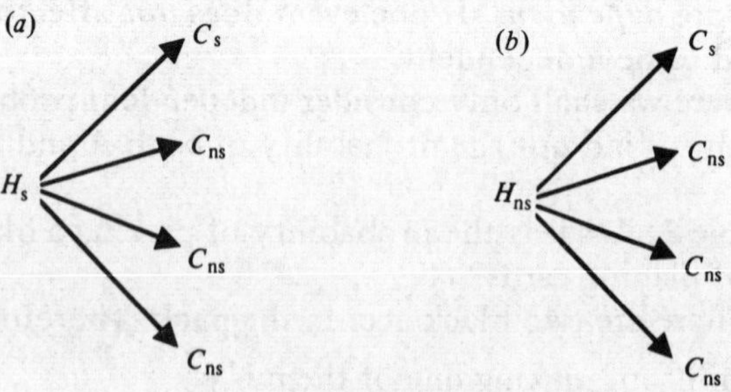

Figure 20.8

Similarly if H_{ns} occurs then C_s can occur or C_{ns} can occur.
But again C_{ns} is 3 times more likely than C_s.
This can be represented as in Figure 20.8(b).
These diagrams illustrate the probable outcomes in the correct ratios.
Hence the combined outcomes are as follows:

$H_s\,C_s$	$H_{ns}\,C_s$
$H_s\,C_{ns}$	$H_{ns}\,C_{ns}$
$H_s\,C_{ns}$	$H_{ns}\,C_{ns}$
$H_s\,C_{ns}$	$H_{ns}\,C_{ns}$

We see that the probability of $H_s\,C_s$ occurring is 1 out of 8, i.e. $\frac{1}{8}$.
This is obtained another way by using:

(i) $p(H_s \text{ and } C_s) = p\,(H_s) \times p\,(C_s) = \frac{1}{2} \times \frac{1}{4} = \frac{1}{8}$.

(ii) $p(H_s \text{ or } C_s \text{ but not both}) = p\,(H_s) \times p\,(C_{ns}) + p\,(H_{ns}) \times p\,(C_s)$

$$= \frac{1}{2} \times \frac{3}{4} + \frac{1}{2} \times \frac{1}{4} = \frac{3}{8} + \frac{1}{8} = \frac{1}{2}$$

(iii) $p(H_{ns} \text{ and } C_{ns}) = 1 - \text{(i)} - \text{(ii)} = 1 - \frac{1}{8} - \frac{1}{2} = \frac{3}{8}$

Exercise 89. Repeat example 2 with $P\,(H_s) = \frac{1}{2}$, $P\,(C_s) = \frac{1}{3}$.

This example is illustrated in Fig. 20.9.

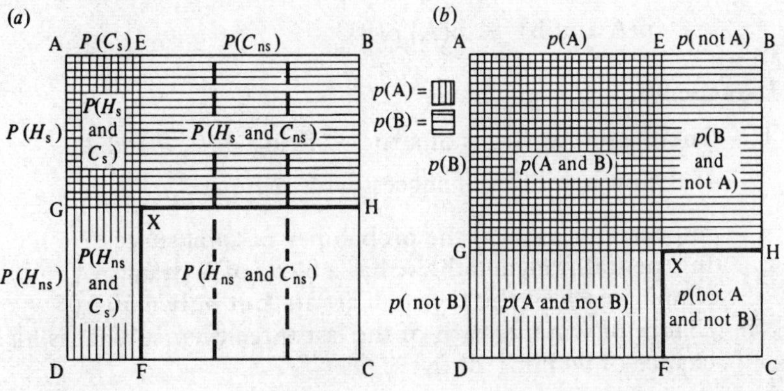

The representation of probabilities of independent outcomes.

Figure 20.9

In Fig. 20.9(a) a square ABCD of unit side is shown. It therefore has unit area.

A horizontal line GH is drawn dividing the square into two equal areas. Hence the rectangle ABHG and the rectangle GHCD are each of area ½ square unit. These two areas can be said to represent the equal probabilities H_s and H_{ns} in Example 2.
Similarly if a vertical line EF is drawn at a distance ¼ unit from AD then the areas AEFD and EBCF can be said to represent the probabilities of C_s and C_{ns}.

Hence the events H_s and C_s occurring simultaneously is represented by the area AEXG (EF cuts GH at X).
i.e. p (H_s and C_s) = $\frac{1}{8}$ since the whole area is one unit.
Similarly in Fig. 20.9 (b):
if AEFD represents the probability of event A occurring, p(A)
EBCF represents the probability of event A not occurring, p(not

ABHG represents the probability of event B occurring, p(B)
GHCD represents the probability of event B not occurring, p(not B)
then AEXG represents the event of both A and B occurring, i.e. p(A and B)

Hence p (A and B) = p(A) × p(B)

Probability Law III may be stated as:

If A and B are independent events then

$$p(A \text{ and } B) = p(A).p(B)$$

Exercise 90.

1. There are four stages of a rocket firing, 1, 2, 3 and 4. If the probabilities of success with these are $\frac{4}{5}, \frac{5}{6}, \frac{6}{7}, \frac{7}{8}$, respectively, what is the probability of total success?
2. In a pentathlon, an athlete has a 3 our of 5 chance of winning each of the first two events, but only a 50-50 chance of winning each of the last three events. What is his chance of winning all five?

PROBABILITY TREES.

In a complicated probability problem it is often useful to draw a diagram illustrating the various outcomes, which can then be seen at a glance. Such a diagram is called a probability tree.
We start with a very simple example.

Example 1. A man tosses a coin. If it is a head he draws a card from a pack. If it is a tail he tosses the coin again. Illustrate the various outcomes and find the probabilities of getting an ace, a picture, any other card, a head or a tail.

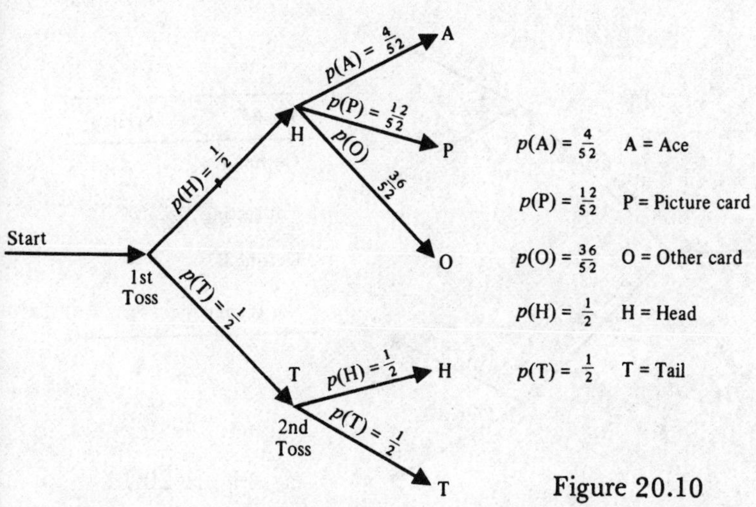

Figure 20.10

Hence:

p (H followed by A) $= \frac{1}{2} \times \frac{4}{52} = \frac{2}{52}$

p (H followed by P) $= \frac{1}{2} \times \frac{12}{52} = \frac{6}{52}$

p (H followed by O) $= \frac{1}{2} \times \frac{36}{52} = \frac{18}{52}$

p (T followed by a card) $= 0$

p (T followed by H) $= \frac{1}{2} \times \frac{1}{2} = \frac{1}{4}$

p (T followed by T) $= \frac{1}{2} \times \frac{1}{2} = \frac{1}{4}$

TOTAL $= \frac{2 + 6 + 18 + 13 + 13}{52}$

$= \frac{52}{52}$

$= 1$

as expected.

Example 2. A company bids for two contracts, A and B. The probability of getting A is 0.7. The probability of getting B depends on whether or not they get A, and is 0.8 if they get A, but only 0.4 if they do not get A. Draw a tree diagram to illustrate the probabilities of the outcomes. (a) What is the probability that they get both contracts? (b) What is the probability of getting A but not B? (c) What is the probability of getting B but not A? (d) What is the probability of getting neither contract? (e) What is the probability of getting exactly one contract? (f) What is the probability of getting at least one contract?

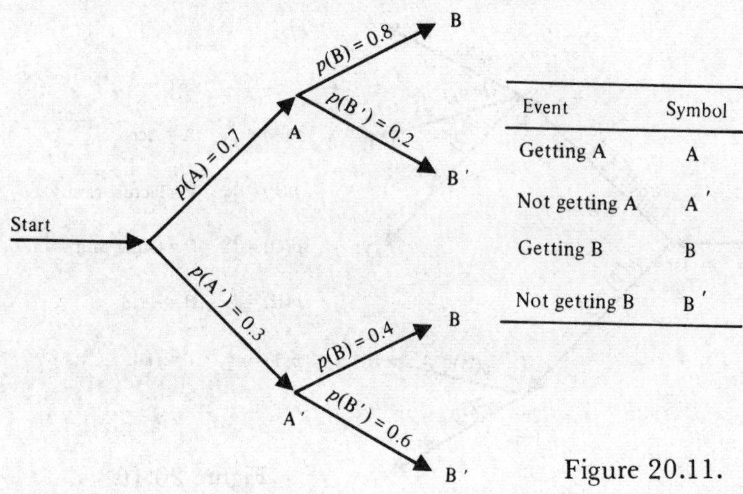

Event	Symbol
Getting A	A
Not getting A	A '
Getting B	B
Not getting B	B '

Figure 20.11.

(a) the probability of getting A and B $= 0.7 \times 0.8 =$ **0.56**
(b) the probability of getting A but not B $= 0.7 \times 0.2 =$ **0.14**
(c) the probability of not getting A but getting B $= 0.3 \times 0.4 =$ **0.12**
(d) the probability of not getting A nor B $= 0.3 \times 0.6 =$ **0.18**
Total $=$ **1.00**

(e) the probability of getting exactly one contract
= the probability of getting either A or B but not both
= 0.14 + 0.12 [(b) + (c)]
= 0.26

(f) the probability of getting at least one contract
= the probability of getting either A or B or both
= 0.14 + 0.12 + 0.56 [(b) + (c) + (a)]
= 0.82 which of course is the same as (1 – (d)).

Exercise 91.

1. A die is thrown and if the result is an odd number a coin is tossed. If it is an even number no further action is taken. Draw a diagram showing the nine possible outcomes and calculate the probability of each.
2. A candidate has a 95 per cent probability of passing exam A. If he fails the first time he is allowed to take it again, but not a third time. If he passes, he sits for exam B, which he can only take once. He has a 90 per cent chance of passing B if he takes it. Draw a probability diagram showing the possibilities, and calculate the probability that he will pass both exams: (a) the first time; (b) eventually.

PROBABILITY DISTRIBUTIONS

We discussed on pages 328, 329 the way in which a histogram becomes a continuous curve when the numbers in the sample are increased and the class widths are decreased. Consider another example. Suppose records have been kept, over a long period, of the daily rainfall in centimetres at a certain place. The distribution of days when a certain rainfall was registered would probably look like Fig. 20.12.

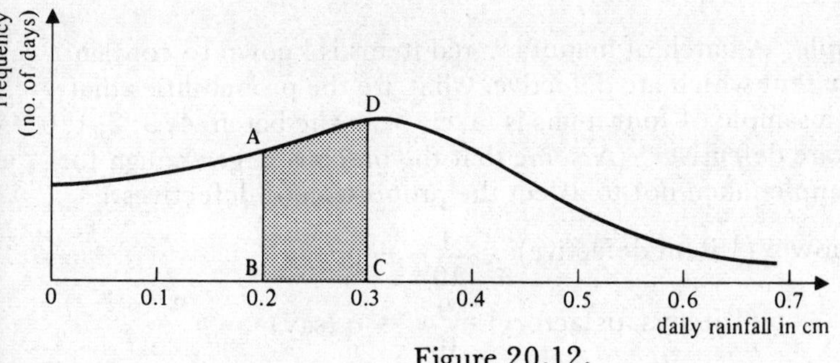

Figure 20.12.

This is a typical continuous distribution. In the example given the total number of days on which the rainfall was between 0.2 and 0.3 cm. (say) is represented by the area ABCD. This area is the sum of a very large number of very narrow columns of a histogram. Hence, the proportion of the total number of days on which the rainfall was in this range is given by:
(Area ABCD) ÷ (total area under curve)
This is the probability that a day selected at random will have a rainfall in the range 0.2 to 0.3 cm. The vertical scale is chosen so that the **total area under the curve is 1 unit.** In this case, the required probability is simply given by the area under the curve between AB and CD, since dividing by unity makes no difference. We call this a *probability distribution.*
Note: The total area under the curve must be 1 unit for a probability distribution.

TYPES OF PROBABILITY DISTRIBUTIONS.

We now take a look at three different probability distributions:
1. The binomial distribution;
2. The Poisson distribution;
3. The normal or Gaussian distribution.

1. The Binomial Distribution

We have used this before, but another example will refresh our memories.

Example. A batch of manufactured items is known to contain 10 per cent which are defective. What are the probabilities that, when a sample of four items is taken from the batch, 4, 3, 2, 1, 0 items are defective? (Assume that the batch is large enough for the sample taken not to affect the proportion of defectives.)

We know p (1 item defective) $= \frac{1}{10} = p$ (say)

p (1 item satisfactory) $= \frac{9}{10} = q$ (say) $\qquad n = 4$

$$(p + q)^4 = p^4 + 4p^3q + 6p^2q^2 + 4pq^3 + q^4$$

$\therefore$ p (all defective) $= p^4 = \frac{1}{10^4} = \mathbf{0.0001}$

$\therefore$ p (3 defective) $= 4p^3q = \frac{4.9}{10^4} = \mathbf{0.0036}$

p (2 defective) $= 6p^2q^2 = \frac{6.81}{10^4} = \mathbf{0.0486}$

$$p\ (1\ \text{defective}) = 4pq^3 = \frac{4.729}{10^4} = 0.2916$$

$$p\ (0\ \text{defective}) = q^4 = \frac{9^4}{10^4} = 0.6561$$

$$\text{Total of all probabilities} = 1.0000$$

A histogram of these results is shown in Fig. 20.13.

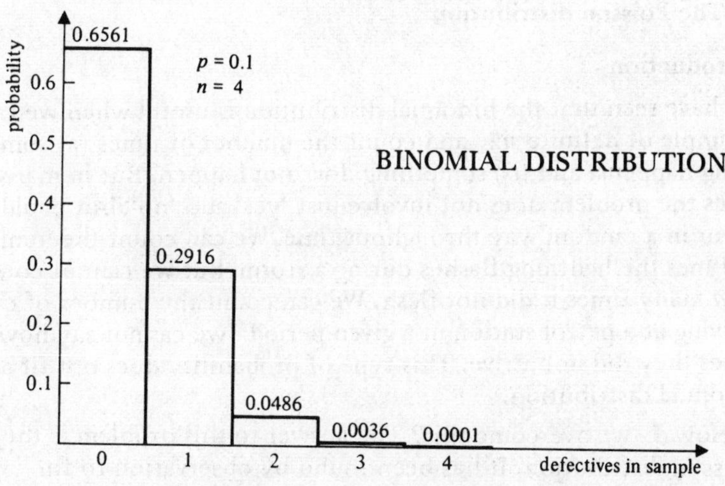

Figure 20.13

Notes on the histogram of the binomial distribution

1. If the width of the column is 1 unit, **the area of the column represents the probabilities** of 0, 1, 2, 3, 4, defectives.
2. **The total area of the graph is unit area;** this will always be so if we include all possible outcomes.
3. This distribution is useful in such cases as the one quoted but its use is limited.
4. We can extend the idea to the case when a large sample is taken from a very large batch. The graph will approximate to a continuous curve as the width of the column decreases, but the **area under the curve** will still represent **the total probability of all outcomes** and will still be **unit area.**

5. **The mean = np** (Proof of this is given in appendix 7.)
6. **The variance = npq**
7. **The standard deviation = $\sqrt{npq}$** (For proof of 6 and 7, see any textbook on Mathematical statistics).
8. In practice binomial probabilities are rarely calculated directly. These probabilities have been tabulated for n = 2 to n = 49 by the National Bureau of Standards and can be read off directly.

2. The Poisson distribution

Introduction

We have seen that the binomial distribution is useful when we take a sample of definite size and count the number of times (a) something happens, and (b) something does not happen. But in many cases the problem does not involve just 'yes' and 'no', but could occur in a random way throughout time. We can count the number of times the lightning flashes during a storm, but we cannot count how many times it did not flash. We can count the number of cars arriving at a petrol station in a given period - we cannot say how mar times they did not arrive. This type of probability does not fit a binomial distribution.

How do we overcome this? The answer to this problem is the Poisson distribution. It has been found by observation to fit cases such as the above with remarkable accuracy.

We know that the definition of e^x is given by

$$e^x = \lim_{n\to\infty} \left(1 + \frac{x}{n}\right)^n = 1 + x + \frac{x^2}{2!} + \frac{x^3}{3!} + \ldots$$

(see page 171)

Can we use this fact? The answer is 'yes'.

Imagine a time axis extending to infinity and divided up into small elements of time, δt (Fig.20.14.)

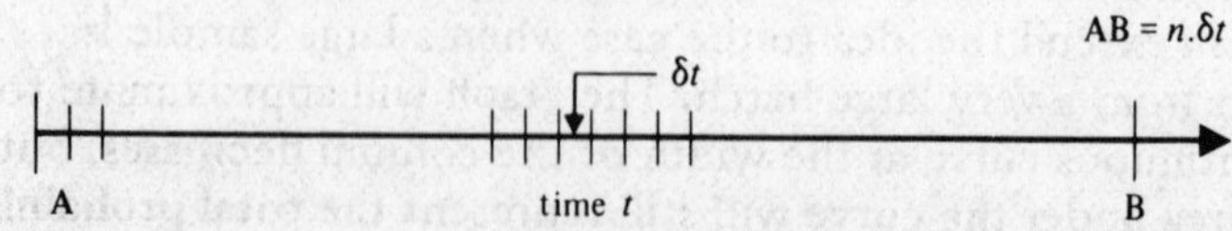

Figure 20.14.

We can imagine our 'lightning flashes' slotting into some of these tiny elements of time of which there are n (say) where $n \to \infty$, but where $n.\delta t$ is still finite. Since the exponential expansion is an extension of the binomial expansion where $n \to \infty$, the exponential expansion can be adapted for use as a probability distribution in cases like the above where there are a large number of very small time slots in which to fit random events.

In order for this expansion to be used as a probability distribution the sum of all the terms must equal unity, the total of all possible probabilities.

We derive the Poisson distribution as follows:

We have used p as the probability of success and q (= 1 – p) as the probability of failure in discussing the Binomial distribution, and n as the number of trials. The Poisson distribution is the form assumed by the distribution when p is small and n is large (i.e. $p \to 0$ and $n \to \infty$) but the mean number of successes np is a constant and equal to λ which is finite. In $(p + q)^n$ let $p = \frac{\lambda}{n}$

The probabilities of 0, 1, 2, 3, ... successes are

$$q^n, nq^{n-1}p; \frac{n(n-1)}{2!} q^{n-2}p^2; \frac{n(n-1)(n-2)}{3!} q^{n-3}p^3; ....$$

by expanding $(q + p)^n$. Put $np = \lambda$.

These become:

$$q^n; \lambda q^{n-1}; \frac{1 - \frac{1}{n}\lambda 2 q^{n-2}}{2!}; \frac{(1-\frac{1}{n})(1-\frac{2}{n})\lambda^3 .q^{n-3}}{3!}; ....$$

When $p \to 0$ and $n \to \infty$, $q \to 1$. These terms then become proportional to

$$1, \lambda, \frac{\lambda^2}{2!}, \frac{\lambda^3}{3!}, ...$$

This is the exponential series whose sum is e^{λ}.
However, the sum of the actual probabilities must be unity, since it is the limit of $(p + q)^n$ and $p + q = 1$.
Hence we obtain the actual probabilities by dividing by e^{λ}.
i.e. multiplying by $e^{-\lambda}$.
Thus the actual probabilities of 0, 1, 2, 3, ... successes are

$$e^{-\lambda}, \lambda e^{-\lambda}, \frac{\lambda^2}{2!} e^{-\lambda}, \frac{\lambda^3}{3!} e^{-\lambda}; .... \text{ respectively.}$$

(A proof of this is set out more formally in Appendix 8.)

Note: λ **is the long-run average** number of occurrences of the event in a given period.

λ is also called the *expectation* (or expected number) of the occurrence of an event. It is found by observation over a long period.

Definition of the Poisson distribution

$$p(X = r) = e^{-\lambda} . \frac{\lambda^r}{r!}$$

which we read as 'the probability of an event X occurring r times is given by $e^{-\lambda} . \frac{\lambda^r}{r!}$, where r = 0, 1, 2 ....

(0! = 1 by definition.)

Example. Radio-active particles randomly strike an apparatus at a rate of 0.01 per second. Calculate the probabilities that 0, 1, 2, 3 or 4 particles will strike the apparatus in any one minute.

Expected rate of striking = 0.01 per second,
= 0.6 per minute

This is the long-run average striking rate and must have been observed during thousands of hours of experimentation. i.e. $\lambda = 0.6$. ∴ Probabilities of 0, 1, 2, 3 or 4 particles striking in 1 minute are the terms

$$e^{-0.6}, 0.6e^{-0.6}, \frac{(0.6)^2}{2!} e^{-0.6}, \frac{(0.6)^3}{3!} e^{-0.6} \text{ and } \frac{(0.6)^4}{4!} e^{-0.6}$$

∴ $p_0 = 0.5488$, $p_1 = 0.3293$, $p_2 = 0.0988$, $p_3 = 0.0198$, $p_4 = 0.0030$.

For the Poisson distribution:

the mean (μ) = λ; the variance (σ^2) = λ; the standard deviation (σ) = $\sqrt{\lambda}$

(The proof of this needs a more formal approach than is possible in a book of this type, but is quite straight-forward. See any text-book on mathematical statistics.)

Exercise 92. (Binomial distribution)

1. Calculate correct to 3 d.p. the binomial probabilities for p = ¾, n = 8.
   Calculate the mean and variance, i.e. np and npq.

2. A pack of cards is shuffled and cut 5 times in succession. What are the probabilities of getting an ace: (i) 4 times; (ii) 3 times, [Leave answer in factor form.]
3. If 2/5 of the voters in a certain constituency favour Mr. A, what is the probability that, of 5 voters interviewed at random, the majority will favour Mr. B, assuming a 'straight' fight.
4. In the manufacture of screws, it is found that in the long term 1 in 20 are rejected as defective. Calculate the probability that 12 screws chosen at random will contain: (i) 2 rejects; (ii) not more than 2 rejects; (iii) at least 3 rejects.

Exercise 93. (Poisson distribution)

1. In a book of 400 pages, there are 40 errors. Find the probabilities of 0, 1, 2, or 3 errors per page.
2. With the information of No. 1, in a similar book of 500 pages, how many pages approximately would you expect to contain: (i) 2 errors or less; (ii) 3 errors or more?
3. In a certain area, the number of violent storms occurring each year is a random variable whose probability distribution can be approximated closely with a Poisson distribution having a parameter $\lambda = 8$. Find the probability that in a given year fewer than 6 storms hit the area.

3. The normal distribution or Gaussian distribution

Introduction.

We have discussed the binomial distribution and the Poisson distribution, which enable us to deal with the occurrence of distinct events, e.g. the number of defective items in a sample of known size, or the probability of breakdown or accidents in a factory in a given time. We now need a distribution pattern which will deal with quantities that are not whole numbers of items, but are variable. For example, how do we estimate the probability of the length of a bar of steel (which should be 10 cm. long) being more than or less than 0.001 cm out?

The distribution required here is the normal distribution, so called because it is a distribution which occurs frequently. The normal curve (Fig. 20.15) is bell-shaped and symmetrical about the mean μ.

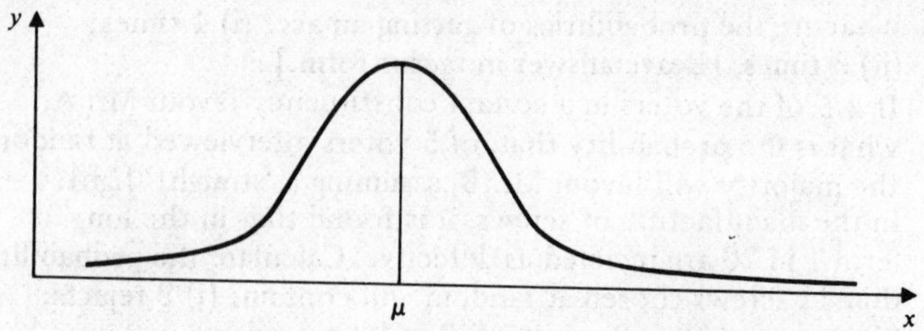

Figure 20.15.

For example, if we take the heights of a large number of children and take very small class widths, the frequency distribution (i.e. the histogram) evens out to form a smooth curve, the most frequent height being, of course, μ the mean value, tailing off on either side.

Mathematicians have worked on this type of curve for over 200 years and have shown that its equation is:

$$y = \frac{1}{\sigma\sqrt{2\pi}} e^{-(x-\mu)^2/2\sigma^2} \quad \left[\begin{array}{l}\mu = \text{mean value} \\ \sigma = \text{standard deviation}\end{array}\right.$$

Several people worked on this and it is sometimes attributed to Gauss, De Moivre, or Laplace.

The equation $y = \frac{1}{\sigma\sqrt{2\pi}} e^{-(x-\mu)^2/2\sigma^2}$ is very formidable, and difficult to deal with. It can easily be transformed into a simpler form by moving the axes and changing the scale, as we shall see later. When this has been done it is said to be in *standard form*, for which we have tables enabling us to read off the facts we need, given the mean μ and the standard deviation σ, of our particular distribution.

What do we mean by 'standardising'?

As an example consider the general parabola

$$y = ax^2 + bx + c.$$

All parabolas are fundamentally the same. The difference between them is due to: (a) their position relative to the axes;
(b) the scales used on the axes.

By suitable substitutions for x and y, and by changing the scale, the equation of the curve can be converted to the simple form $y = x^2$, which is much simpler to handle.

In the same way we can convert any normal curve to standard form by:

1. Moving the y axis so that it is at the centre of symmetry.
2. Increasing or decreasing the scale so that **the area under the curve is unit area.**

When this has been done, we can say the curve represents a probability distribution. Tables can then be used to give the probability of a quantity lying between given limits. This is represented by the area under the standard normal curve between these limits.

THE STANDARD NORMAL DISTRIBUTION

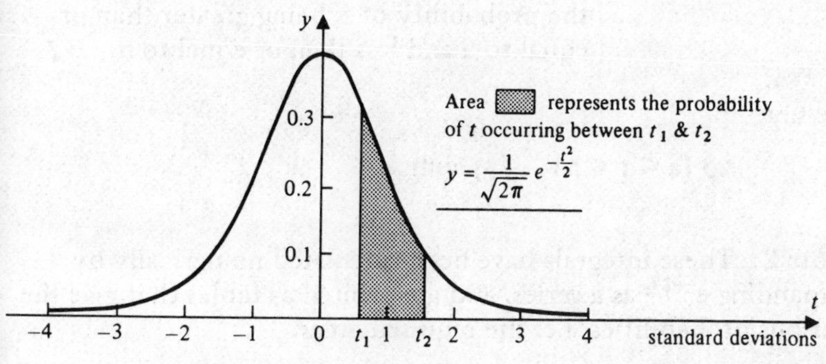

Figure 20.16

Note 1: **The total area** under the curve between $-\infty$ and $+\infty$ is **unit area,** i.e. represents all the probabilities of t occurring.

Note 2: **The probability** of an event occurring between t_1 and t_2 is given by the **area under the curve** between t_1 and t_2.

Note 3: **The scale on the t axis is in standard deviations.**

To convert the normal distribution to standard form.

The equation is $y = \frac{1}{\sigma\sqrt{2\pi}} e^{-(x-\mu)^2/2\sigma^2}$

Take the units on the t axis as in units of standard deviation, i.e. we are making $\sigma = 1$ unit.

Also put $\frac{x-\mu}{\sigma} = t$ in order to make the curve symmetrical about the y axis.

Then $y = \frac{1}{\sqrt{2\pi}} e^{\frac{-t^2}{2}}$ which is more manageable.

Why the $\frac{1}{\sqrt{2\pi}}$ factor? Because without this the area under the curve would not be unity. It can be shown that with y defined as above:

$$\int_{-\infty}^{+\infty} y \, dt = 1$$

(The proof of this is too difficult at this stage.)

Note 1: $\int_a^b y \, dt$, i.e. the area under the curve between a and b, is the probability of t, being greater than or equal to a and less than or equal to b.

We say:

$$p\,(a \leqslant t \leqslant b) = \int_a^b y \, dt.$$

Note 2: These integrals have been calculated numerically by expanding $e^{-t^2/2}$ as a series, and are printed as tables that give the various probabilities, i.e. the required areas.

Note 3: Sometimes the tables give the values of the areas to the left and right of the y axis, i.e. the area is 0 when t = 0 and 0.5 when t = ∞ (Fig. 20.17(a)). Sometimes the tables give the area from −∞ to the value of t required, giving area 0.5 when t = 0 and 1 when t = ∞ (Fig. 20.17(b)), but in both cases common sense gives the value of the area between two given t values.

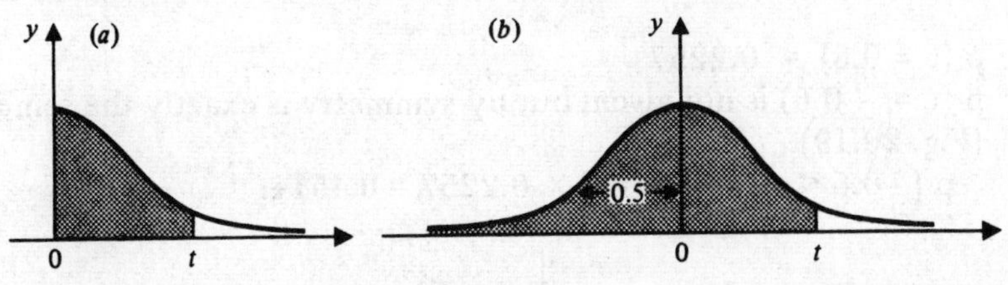

Figure 20.17

Example. From the tables evaluate the following: (for $\mu = 0, \sigma = 1$)
(i) p $(0.7 \leqslant t \leqslant 0.9)$; (ii) p $(|t| \leqslant 0.6$; (iii) p $(-0.7 \leqslant t \nleqslant 0.9)$
(Use the table (appendix 9) at the end of the book.)

(i) From table:
p (t = 0.7) = 0.2580 .... (1)
p (t = 0.9) = 0.3159 .... (2)

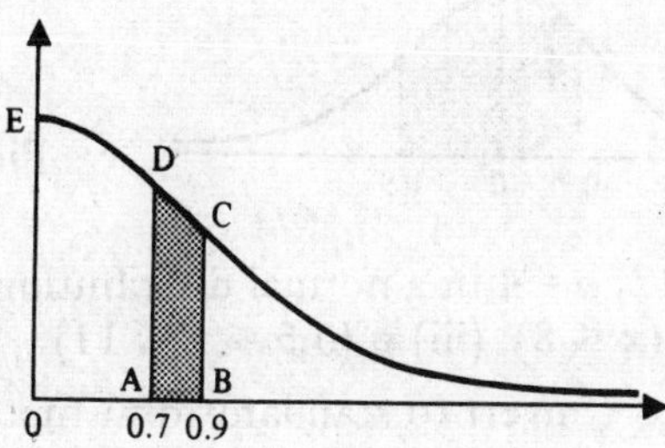

Figure 20.18

This means on the half-probability curve that (1) represents the area OADE, (2) represents the area OBCE (Fig. 20.18).

∴ Area required, i.e. shaded area ABCD = (2) – (1) = 0.0579.

∴ p $(0.7 \leqslant t \leqslant 0.9)$ = 0.0579

(ii) Read p $(|t| \leqslant 0.6)$ as the 'probability that mod t is less than or equal to 0.6'. This is the same as saying the 'numerical value of t is less than or equal to 0.6'.
or $-0.6 \leqslant t \leqslant +0.6$ or 't lies between –0.6 and + 0.6 and includes –0.6 and + 0.6'.

From tables

p (t = 0.6) = 0.2257
p (t = − 0.6) is not given, but by symmetry is exactly the same (Fig. 20.19).
∴ p (−0.6 ⩽ t ⩽ +0.6) = 2 × 0.2257 = **0.4514.**

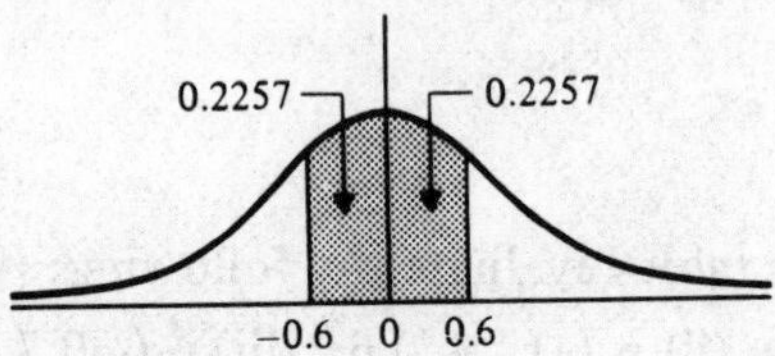

Figure 20.19.

(iii) p (−0.7 ⩽ t ⩽ 0.9) is represented by the shaded area (Fig 20.20)
p (t = −0.7) = p (t = +0.7) = 0.2580
p (t = 0.9) = 0.3159
∴ p (−0.7 ⩽ t ⩽ 0.9) = 0.2580 + 0.3159 = **0.5739**

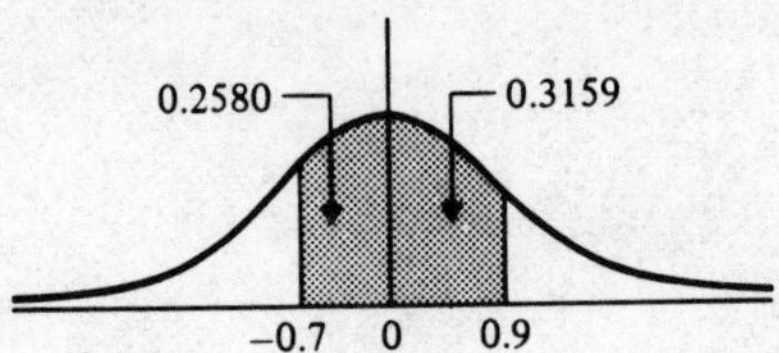

Figure 20.20.

Example 2. For μ = 12, σ = 4 in a normal distribution, find:
(i) p (x ⩽ 14) (ii) p (x ⩽ 8) (iii) p (5.5 ⩽ x ⩽ 11)

In this case we have to convert to standard form first by putting

$$t = \frac{x - \mu}{\sigma} = \frac{x - 12}{4}$$

(i) When x = 14, $t = \frac{14 - 12}{4} = \frac{1}{2}$

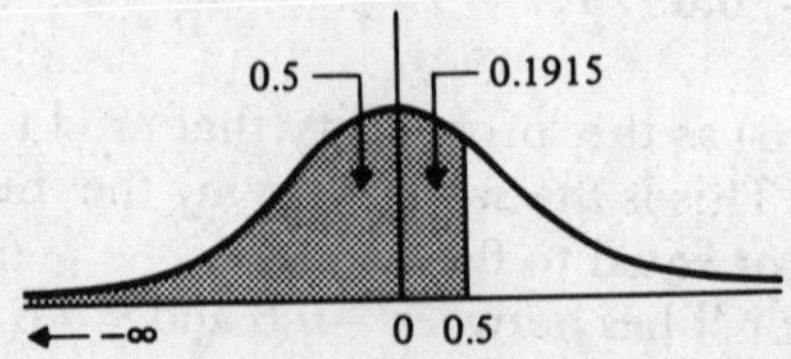

Figure 20.21.

$\therefore$ p (x ⩽ 14) = p (t ⩽ 0.5) in standard tables (Fig. 20.21).

= (probability from −∞ to 0) + (probability from 0 to 0.5)

= 0.5 + 0.1915 = **0.6915**

(ii) When x = 8, $t = \frac{8-12}{4} = -1$

$\therefore$ p (x ⩽ 8) = p(t ⩽ −1)

i.e. represented by area from −∞ to −1

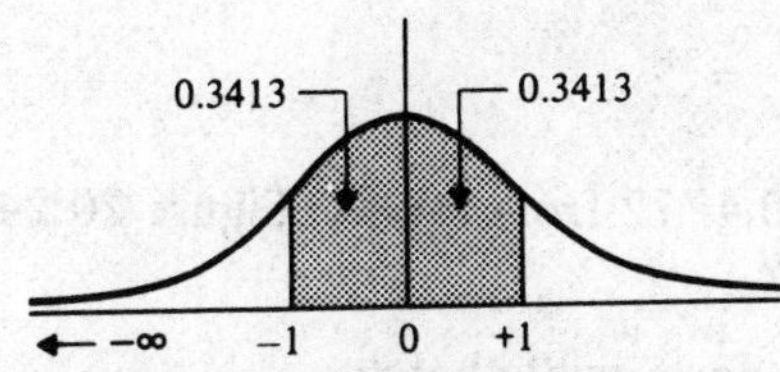

Figure 20.22.

p (t = −1) = p (t = + 1) = 0.3413

$\therefore$ p (t ⩽ −1) = 0.5 − 0.3413

= **0.1587**

(iii) When x = 5.5, $t = \frac{5.5-12}{4} = -1.625$

x = 11, $t = \frac{11-12}{4} = -0.25$

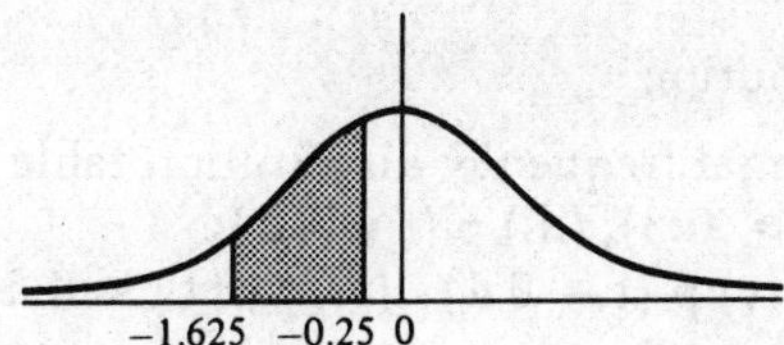

Figure 20.23

Required probability = p (t ⩽ 1.625) − p (t ⩽ 0.25)

= 0.4479* − 0.0987 *(by interpolation)

= **0.3492**

Example 3. The amount of permissible impurity in a certain chemical is 3 per cent. When batches of the chemical are tested it is found that the impurity varies and is normally distributed about a mean of 2 per cent with standard deviation of ½ per cent.

(i) What is the probability of getting a permissible batch?

(ii) What percentage of batches are accepted in the long run?

Here μ = 2 per cent = 0.02] We require the probability of
σ = ½ per cent = 0.005] impurity to be less than or equal to 3 per cent i.e. $\leqslant 0.03$

$\therefore p(x \leqslant 0.03)$ is the required probability.

Standardise:

$$\text{Put } t = \frac{x-\mu}{\sigma} = \frac{x-0.02}{0.005}$$

$$\text{When } x = 0.03 \quad t = \frac{0.03-0.02}{0.005}$$

$$= \frac{0.01}{0.005} = 2$$

$$p(t \leqslant 2) = 0.5 + 0.4772 \text{ from tables (Figure 20.24)}$$
$$= 0.9772$$

This is the probability of a permissible batch.
∴ Thus nearly 98 per cent of all batches are acceptable in the long run.

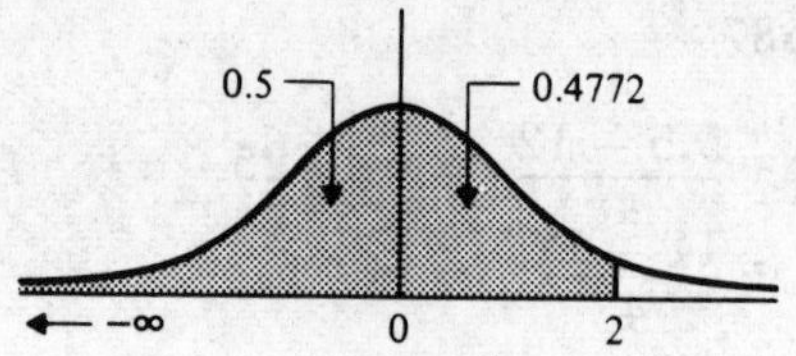

Figure 20.24

Exercise 94. Normal distribution

1. Using a cumulative normal frequency distribution table find: (i) $p(t \leqslant 0.3)$; (ii) $p(t \geqslant 0.3)$; (iii) $p(t \leqslant 0.1)$; (iv) $p(0.1 \leqslant t \leqslant 0.3)$; (v) $p(t \geqslant 0.1)$; (vi) $p(|t| \leqslant 0.1)$

2. In a factory electrical components are manufactured having a mean resistance of 50 ohms. The standard deviation is 2 ohms. If the distribution of the values of the product is known by past experience to be normal, find how many rejects per 1,000 there will be if a tolerance of ± 6.6 ohms. from the mean is allowable.

SAMPLING FROM NORMAL POPULATIONS

When we take a sample we are trying to learn something about the population from which it is drawn. If this sample is taken in an unbiased way, i.e. it is a random sample, we believe it gives a good idea of what is happening to the whole population, and the bigger the sample the truer the picture.

But these 'spokesmen' for the whole population do not all carry the same authority. We need to know how reliable they are, i.e. whether they are 'well informed', or 'usually well informed', or merely saying 'rumour has it that ...' to use the language of journalism.

Statisticians need to be discriminating about this. It is realised that tools such as the mean and standard deviation will vary with the different samples taken - only slightly, but we want to know how slightly. Thus we are using a tool which is a bit uncertain. In the same way when using a hammer we cannot be 100 per cent certain of hitting a nail in straight, so too we must realise the limitations of our sample calculations. What are we to do?

When an engineer has to decide on the basis of sampling whether the true average lifetime of a television tube is at least 1000 hours, he has to rely on statistics. When a pharmaceutical firm has to decide whether at least 95 per cent of the patients given a new drug will recover, he has to rely on the tests devised by statisticians.

This is why we have tried to distinguish between $\overline{x}$ (the sample mean) and μ(the true mean). We now take a look at confidence intervals.

CONFIDENCE INTERVALS AND SAMPLING

If we take several different samples of the same size, say 10 samples size 100, we shall get 10 different values for the mean $\overline{x}$. Let us call these $\overline{x}_1$, $\overline{x}_2$, $\overline{x}_3$, . . . $\overline{x}_{10}$. These vary slightly. Suppose $\overline{x}_1$ is the least and $\overline{x}_{10}$ is the greatest. The others lie somewhere in between (Fig. 20.25).

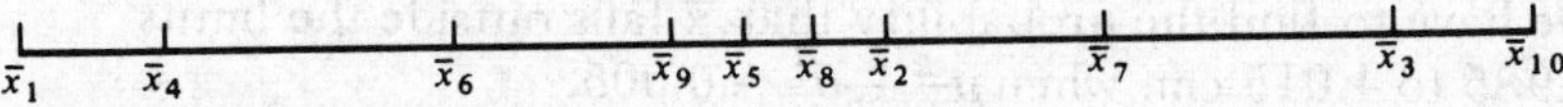

Figure 20.25.

Then we hope that the true mean μ will also lie somewhere in this range.

If we take many more samples we find that the $\overline{x}$'s tend to cluster round their own mean, i.e. they are themselves normally distributed and this distribution is related to the distribution of the original population in the following way:

The central limit theorem

If $\overline{x}$ is the mean of a random sample of size n from a normal population whose mean is μ and standard deviation is σ, then $\overline{x}$ itself is normally distributed with the same mean μ but with standard deviation $\frac{\sigma}{\sqrt{n}}$ $(=\hat{\sigma})$, pronounced 'sigma hat', and called the standard error of the mean.

Example. In a production process, wire is made into springs. The machine can accept the wire if the mean length (μ) is 4 cm. and the variance (σ^2) is 0.0050. A sample of 50 springs are taken from each day's production and the process is under control if their mean length $\overline{x}$, which is normally distributed, does not vary more than 0.015 cm. on either side of the mean value. We need to know the probability that the sample taken will fail this criterion even though the process is under control.

Let us illustrate this on the normal distribution curve (Fig. 20.26.)

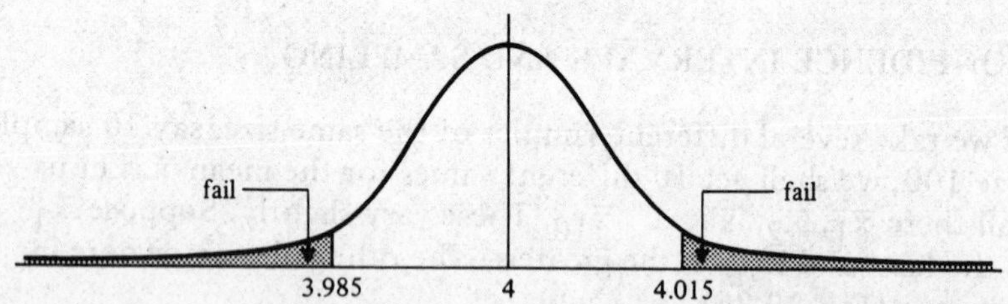

Figure 20.26.

We have to find the probability that $\overline{x}$ falls outside the limits 3.985 to 4.015 cm. when $\mu = 4, \sigma^2 = 0.005$.

$$\text{Now } \hat{\sigma}^2 = \frac{\sigma^2}{n} = \frac{0.005}{50} = 0.0001$$

Therefore $\hat{\sigma} = 0.01$

From previous work, to standardise the distribution put

$$t = \frac{\overline{x} - \mu}{\hat{\sigma}}$$

When $\overline{x} = 4.015$, $t = \dfrac{4.015 - 4}{0.01} = 1.5$

When $\overline{x} = 3.985$, $t = \dfrac{3.985 - 4}{0.01} = -1.5$

Hence if t lies outside the limits -1.5 to $+1.5$ the sample will fail. From the standardised curve using the table in Appendix 9, we see that the probability that the wire will fail the criterion (represented by the shaded areas) $= 2 \times 0.0668 = 0.1336$

$= 13.36$ **per cent**

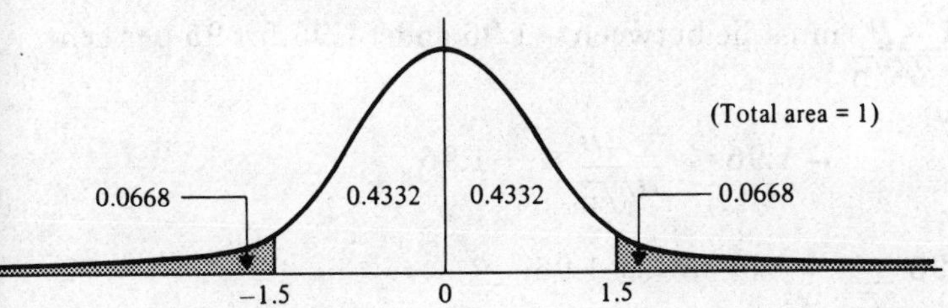

Figure 20.27.

Here we have a *confidence interval* of 86.64 per cent.

THE 95 PER CENT CONFIDENCE INTERVAL

Suppose we take random samples of size n (large) from a normally distributed population of mean μ and standard deviation σ. Suppose the mean of our samples is $\overline{x}$ and the standard deviation is $\hat{\sigma}$. Then we know that $\overline{x}$ is also normally distributed with mean μ and $\hat{\sigma} = \dfrac{\sigma}{\sqrt{n}}$. Then if we wish to investigate the range into which 95 per cent of our $\overline{x}$'s will fall we proceed as follows:

Required probability 95 per cent $= 0.95$
i.e. 0.475 on either side of the vertical axis in the standardised normal curve (Fig. 20.28).

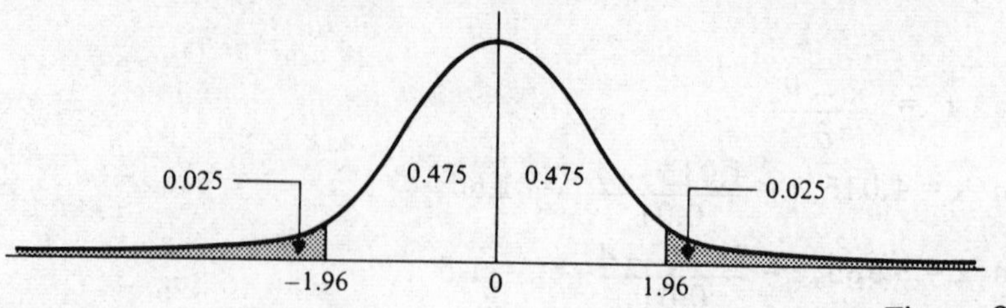

Figure 20.28

From the table in Appendix 9 :
$0.475 = p\,(t \leqslant 1.96)$

But the standardised tables apply only to $t = \dfrac{\bar{x}-\mu}{\hat{\sigma}} = \dfrac{\bar{x}-\mu}{\sigma/\sqrt{n}}$

Hence $\dfrac{\bar{x}-\mu}{\sigma/\sqrt{n}}$ must lie between -1.96 and $+1.96$ for 95 per cent certainty.

This gives $$-1.96 \leqslant \frac{\bar{x}-\mu}{\sigma/\sqrt{n}} \leqslant +1.96$$

i.e. $$-1.96\frac{\sigma}{\sqrt{n}} \leqslant \bar{x}-\mu \leqslant +1.96\frac{\sigma}{\sqrt{n}}$$

i.e. $$-1.96\frac{\sigma}{\sqrt{n}} + \mu \leqslant \bar{x} \leqslant \mu + 1.96\frac{\sigma}{\sqrt{n}}$$

or $$\bar{x} - 1.96\frac{\sigma}{\sqrt{n}} \leqslant \mu \leqslant \bar{x} + 1.96\frac{\sigma}{\sqrt{n}}$$

This interval $\left[\bar{x} - \dfrac{1.96\sigma}{\sqrt{n}},\ \bar{x} + \dfrac{1.96\sigma}{\sqrt{n}}\right]$ is called the 95 per cent confidence interval for μ.

What does this really mean? It is saying that if we take a lot of samples all of the same size n, work out the mean $\bar{x}$ for each sample and substitute in the given inequality, then in 95 per cent of the cases the true value μ will lie within the limits obtained.

We use the table (Appendix 9) to work out other confidence intervals in the same way. Diagrammatically, Fig. 20.29 is transformed into Fig. 20.30.

In general, in order to obtain a $(1 - \Theta)$ confidence interval for the true mean μ, where Θ is the probability of no confidence (5 per cent or 0.05 in the case of 95 per cent confidence), we organise the work as follows:

1. Express the confidence interval as a decimal (e.g. 99 per cent = 0.99).
2. Divide this by 2, since the table gives only half the picture (e.g. ½ × 0.99 = 0.4950).
3. Use this figure (0.4950) to find the corresponding value of t from the table (here, t = 2.575).
4. Substitute this value of t in the interval

$$\left[\bar{x} - t\frac{\sigma}{\sqrt{n}}, \ \bar{x} + t\frac{\sigma}{\sqrt{n}}\right]$$

5. When $\bar{x}$, σ and n are known, this gives the required confidence interval. To simplify problems we quote some of the values commonly used in the following table. (The values of t are obtained from the table of Appendix 9.)
6. For normal distributions (only), when σ is unknown it may be replaced by s, where s is the standard deviation of the *sample.*

Confidence interval reqd.	(1 – Θ)	p = ½(1 – Θ)	t
99.9%	0.999	0.4995	3.295
99%	0.990	0.4950	2.575
98%	0.980	0.4900	2.326
95%	0.950	0.4750	1.960
90%	0.900	0.4500	1.645

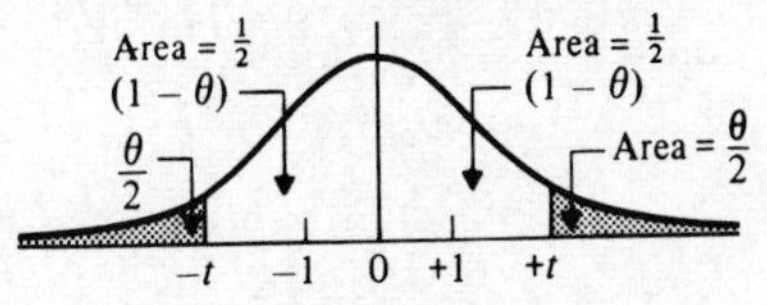

Figure 20.29

transforms into

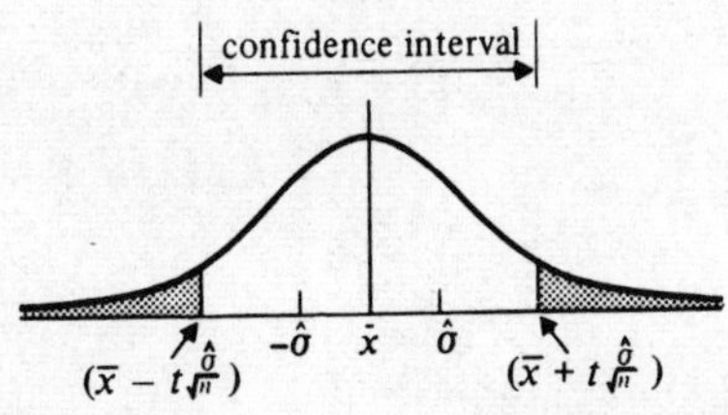

Figure 20.30

Exercise 95

1. Use the table of special confidence intervals just quoted to answer the following:

   (a) What is the 95 per cent confidence interval for $\overline{x} = 49.9$, $\sigma = 2.02$, $n = 100$?

   (b) What is the 99 per cent confidence interval for the same values of $\overline{x}, \sigma$, and n?

2. If in measuring the specific gravity of a substance a mean of 2.705 is found from 16 experiments, with standard deviation of 0.029, find a 95 per cent confidence interval for the actual specific gravity of the substance, assuming the sample is a random sample from a normal distribution.
3. At a local firm producing light bulbs, experiments were conducted to find the average lifetime of a certain type of bulb. Taking a random sample of 20 bulbs the average was 722 hours with standard deviation of 54 hours. Taking the lifetime of the population of lightbulbs as being normally distributed find a 98 per cent confidence interval for the true average lifetime of the bulbs.
4. At a certain large store a sample of 100 accounts outstanding was taken and the mean was found to be £58.14 with a standard deviation of £15.30. Find the 95 per cent confidence interval for the actual mean size of accounts outstanding at this store, assuming that these accounts are normally distributed around the mean.

APPENDIX 1. Orthogonal projection

Definition

The projection of a line AB on a given line OX is defined as that part of OX which is cut off between the feet of the perpendiculars drawn from A and B to OX (Fig. A1).

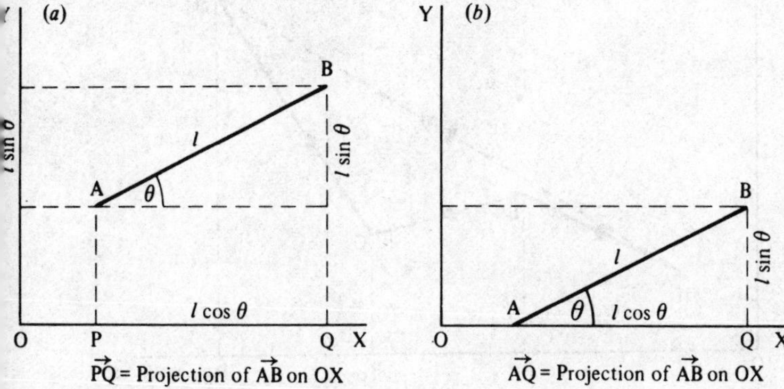

Figure A1.

Note: An easy way to think of this is that if the Sun is directly overhead, the projection on the horizontal is the shadow of the line on the horizontal ground.
Also, if AB = l and AB makes $\angle \Theta$ with OX, then projection AB = l cos Θ.

Similarly, projection of AB on the vertical axis = l sin Θ.

APPENDIX 2

Theorem to show that the projection on a given line of one side of a polygon is the algebraic sum of the projections of the other sides on the same line.

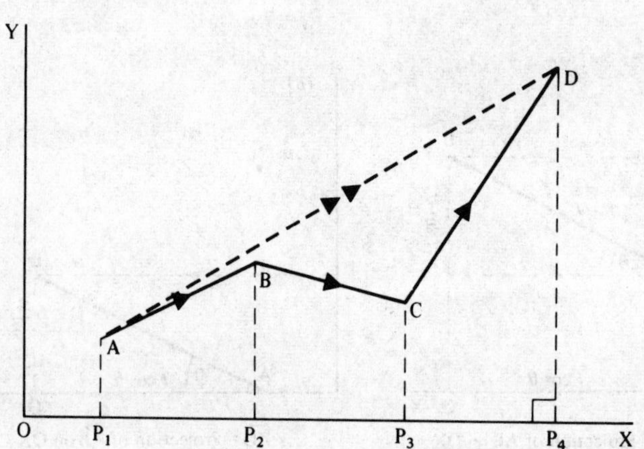

Figure A2

Take any 'chain' of lines, AB, BC, CD for example (Fig. A2). Then we can prove that:

projection $\vec{AD}$ = projection $\vec{AB}$ + projection $\vec{BC}$ + projection $\vec{CD}$

and similarly for any number of 'links' in the chain.

Draw AP_1, BP_2, CP_3, DP_4 perpendicular to OX

then projection of $\vec{AB} = \vec{P_1 P_2}$ by definition

projection of $\vec{BC} = \vec{P_2 P_3}$ and $\vec{P_1 P_4}$ = projection of AD

projection of $\vec{CD} = \vec{P_3 P_4}$

But $\vec{P_1 P_4} = \vec{P_1 P_2} + \vec{P_2 P_3} + \vec{P_3 P_4}$

i.e. projection AD = projection AB + projection BC + projection CD and similarly projecting on the y axis.

APPENDIX 3

To prove sin (A + B) = sin A cos B + cos A sin B.

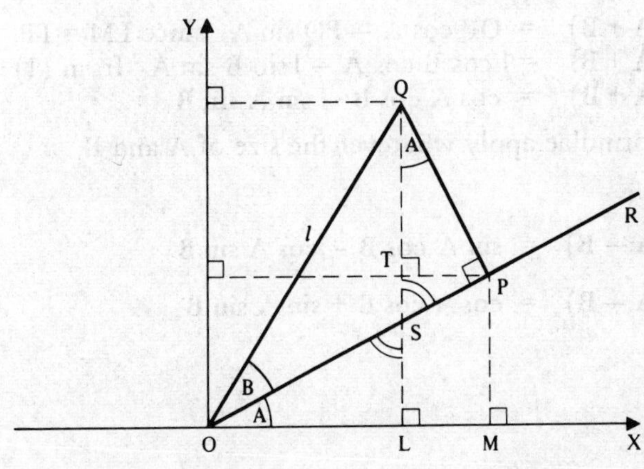

Figure A3

In Fig A3:

$$\left.\begin{array}{ll} \text{Let } \angle \text{ROX} & = \angle \text{A} \\ \text{Let } \angle \text{QOR} & = \angle \text{B} \\ \text{Let OQ} & = l \end{array}\right] \therefore \angle \text{QOX} = (\angle \text{A} + \angle \text{B})$$

Draw QP perpendicular to OR
and QSL perpendicular to OX, cutting
OP at S.

By simple geometry:
using the angles of Δ OLS and Δ SPQ (sum of angles of a triangle = 180°)

$\angle$ PQS = $\angle$ A QP = l sin B .... (1)
OP = l cos B

Projecting on the y axis:

$$\begin{aligned} \text{Projection of } \overrightarrow{OQ} &= \text{projection } \overrightarrow{OP} + \text{projection } \overrightarrow{PQ} \\ OQ \sin (A+B) &= OP \sin A + PQ \cos A \\ l \sin (A+B) &= l \cos B \sin A + l \sin B \cos A \text{ [from (1)]} \\ \mathbf{\sin (A+B)} &= \mathbf{\sin A \cos B + \cos A \sin B.} \end{aligned}$$

To prove cos (A + B) = cos A cos B − sin A sin B

Using Fig. A3 again and projecting on the x axis
Projection $\overrightarrow{OQ}$ = projection $\overrightarrow{OP}$ + projection $\overrightarrow{PQ}$
OL = OM − LM in magnitude since projection $\overleftarrow{PQ}$ is in negative direction

$$\begin{aligned} OQ \cos (A + B) &= OP \cos A - PQ \sin A \quad \text{since } LM = TP \\ l \cos (A + B) &= l \cos B \cos A - l \sin B \sin A \quad \text{from (1)} \\ \cos (A + B) &= \cos A \cos B - \sin A \sin B \end{aligned}$$

These two formulae apply whatever the size of A and B

Similarly:

$$\sin (A - B) = \sin A \cos B - \cos A \sin B$$

$$\cos (A - B) = \cos A \cos B + \sin A \sin B$$

APPENDIX 4. Solution of the simple harmonic equation $\ddot{x} + \omega^2 x = 0$

The simplest solution is found by writing the acceleration, $\ddot{x}$ in a different form.

$$\text{Acceleration} = \ddot{x} = \frac{dv}{dt} \quad \text{where } v = \text{velocity}$$

$$\text{But } \frac{dv}{dt} = \frac{dv}{dx} \cdot \frac{dx}{dt} \, .$$

$$= \frac{dv}{dx} \cdot v \quad \text{since } v = \frac{dx}{dt}$$

$$\therefore \text{ Acceleration} = v\frac{dv}{dx}$$

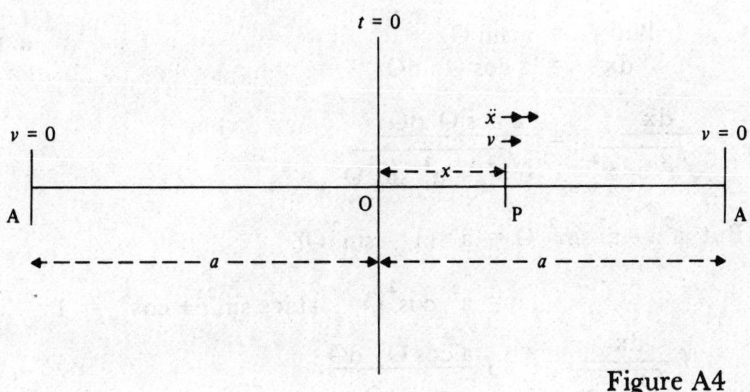

Figure A4

Putting this in the simple harmonic equation:

$$v\frac{dv}{dx} = -\omega^2 x$$

Now we can integrate both sides w.r.t. x :

$$\int v \, dv = -\omega^2 \int x \, dx$$

$$\frac{v^2}{2} = -\omega^2 \frac{x^2}{2} + \text{constant}$$

But v = 0 when x = a (See fig. A4).

$$\therefore 0 = -\frac{\omega^2 a^2}{2} + \text{constant}$$

$\therefore$ the constant $= \dfrac{\omega^2 a^2}{2}$

$$\therefore \frac{v^2}{2} = -\frac{\omega^2 x^2}{2} + \frac{\omega^2 a^2}{2}$$

i.e. $v^2 = \omega^2 (a^2 - x^2)$

or $v = \pm\omega\sqrt{a^2 - x^2}$ giving velocity at any point.

$$\therefore \frac{dx}{dt} = \pm\omega\sqrt{a^2 - x^2}$$

Separating the variables and integrating :

$$\int \frac{dx}{\sqrt{a^2 - x^2}} = \pm\int \omega dt \quad \text{... (1)}$$

$$\text{Put } x = a \sin \Theta \quad \text{... (2)}$$
$$\therefore dx = a \cos \Theta \,.\, d\Theta$$

$$\therefore \frac{dx}{\sqrt{a^2 - x^2}} = \frac{a \cos \Theta \; d\Theta}{\sqrt{a^2 - a^2 \sin^2 \Theta}}$$

But $a^2 - a^2 \sin^2 \Theta = a^2 (1 - \sin^2 \Theta)$

$= a^2 \cos^2 \Theta$ since $\sin^2 + \cos^2 = 1$

$$\therefore \int \frac{dx}{\sqrt{a^2 - x^2}} = \int \frac{a \cos \Theta \; d\Theta}{a \cos \Theta}$$

$$= \int d\Theta$$

$$= \Theta$$

$= \sin^{-1} \dfrac{x}{a}$ from (2)

$\therefore \sin^{-1} \dfrac{x}{a} = \pm\, \omega t + \epsilon$ from (1) where ϵ is a constant

But x = 0 when t = 0 $\quad \therefore \epsilon = 0$

$$\therefore \quad x = \pm\; a \sin \omega t$$

This is the solution to the simple harmonic equation.
Differentiating w.r.t. :

$$v = \pm a\omega\cos\omega t$$

Differentiating again w.r.t. t:

$$\text{Acceleration} = \ddot{x} = \mp a\omega^2 \sin\omega t$$

$$\therefore \ddot{x} = -\omega^2 x$$

This checks that our solution is a correct one and also gives the standard formula as previously.

APPENDIX 5

Two illustrations of the formula

$$du = \frac{\partial u}{\partial x} \cdot dx + \frac{\partial u}{\partial y} \cdot dy$$

1. We first consider the simple case of

$$u = xy$$

Then $\frac{\partial u}{\partial x} = y, \quad \frac{\partial u}{\partial y} = x$

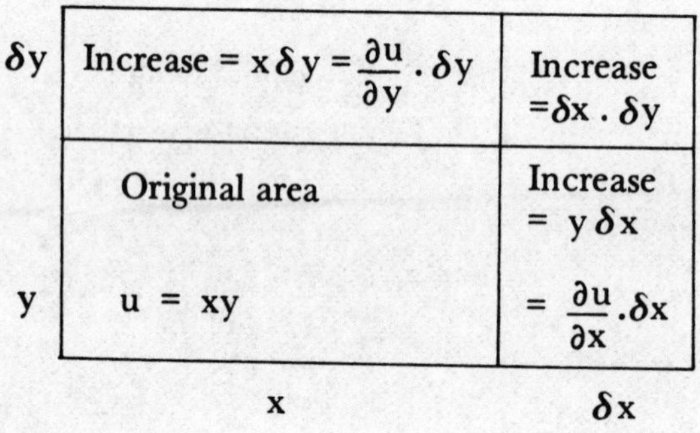

δy	Increase $= x\delta y = \frac{\partial u}{\partial y} . \delta y$	Increase $= \delta x . \delta y$
y	Original area $u = xy$	Increase $= y\delta x$ $= \frac{\partial u}{\partial x} . \delta x$
	x	δx

Figure A5.1

Let x, y be the sides of a rectangle (Fig. A5.1).

Let x increase by a small amount δx
Let y increase by a small amount δy
Let u increase by a small amount δu

Then δu is given by the sum of the three rectangles as shown

Hence $\delta u = \frac{\partial u}{\partial y} . \delta y + \frac{\partial u}{\partial x} . \delta x + \delta y . \delta x.$

or $\delta u = x\delta y + y\delta x + \delta y \delta x$

Dividing by δx:

$$\frac{\delta u}{\delta x} = x\frac{\delta y}{\delta x} + y + \delta y$$

Let $\delta x, \delta y, \delta u$ approach zero

$$\text{Then} \quad \frac{du}{dx} = x\frac{dy}{dx} + y$$

$$du = x\,dy + y\,dx$$

$$\text{i.e. } du = \frac{\partial u}{\partial x}\,.\,dx + \frac{\partial u}{\partial y}\,.\,dy$$

To illustrate that $du = \frac{\partial u}{\partial x}\,.\,dx + \frac{\partial u}{\partial y}\,.\,dy$ where $u = f(x, y)$

2. Consider an area on a hill which is sloping (say) towards the north-easterly direction, approximately. This is illustrated by the curved surface XYZW.

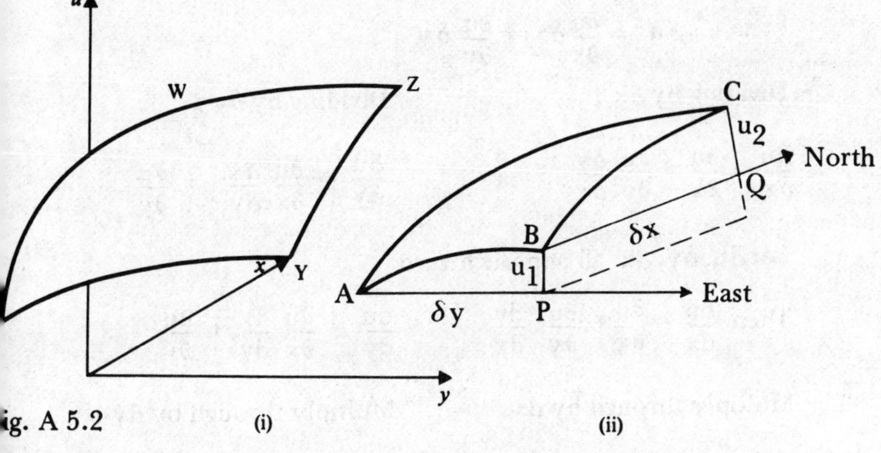

Fig. A 5.2 (i) (ii)

Take the x axis due north, the y axis due east, and the u axis vertically. Suppose one wishes to climb from the point A to the point C approximately N.E. of A. Then one would climb directly from A to C, or do it in two easier stages from A to B in an easterly direction and then from B to C in a northerly direction. NOW CONSIDER ALL DISTANCES VERY SMALL.

Let AP be the horizontal line through A, i.e. AP is due east.
Let BP be the vertical line through B (Fig. A 5.2 (ii))
Let BQ be the horizontal line through B due north
and CQ be the vertical line through C

Let u_1 = BP = increase in u due to climbing from A to B
and u_2 = CQ= increase in u due to climbing from B to C

∴ Total rise between A and C = $u_1 + u_2 = \delta u$ (say)

Then AP = δy (towards the east) and BQ = δx (towards the north
None of the sides of the area ABC are straight but

approximately the gradient of AB = $\frac{\partial u}{\partial y}$ since x is constant due eas

and the gradient of BC = $\frac{\partial u}{\partial x}$ since y is constant due nort

Hence $u_1 \triangleq \frac{\partial u}{\partial y} . \delta y$ $\quad u_2 \triangleq \frac{\partial u}{\partial x} \delta x$

$$\therefore \quad \delta u \triangleq \frac{\partial u}{\partial x} \delta x + \frac{\partial u}{\partial y} \delta y$$

Dividing by δx :

$$\frac{\delta u}{\delta x} \triangleq \frac{\partial u}{\partial x} + \frac{\partial u}{\partial y} \frac{\delta y}{\delta x}$$

Dividing by δy :

$$\frac{\delta u}{\delta y} \triangleq \frac{\partial u}{\partial x} \frac{\delta x}{\delta y} + \frac{\partial u}{\partial y}$$

Let $\delta u, \delta y, \delta x$ all approach zero

Then $\frac{du}{dx} = \frac{\partial u}{\partial x} + \frac{\partial u}{\partial y} \frac{dy}{dx}$ $\quad \frac{du}{dy} = \frac{\partial u}{\partial x} \frac{dx}{dy} + \frac{\partial u}{\partial y}$

Multiply through by dx : Multiply through by dy :

$$du = \frac{\partial u}{\partial x} dx + \frac{\partial u}{\partial y} dy \qquad \text{(in both cases).}$$

This method of illustration is called 'hill-climbing'.

APPENDIX 6. The mean of a discrete random variable.

On page 316 Example 4, we discussed the mean value of the score obtained in throwing a die 100 times, and we showed that the mean is given by:

$$\mu = \Sigma \frac{(\text{frequency} \times \text{score value})}{\text{total number of trials}}$$

If the score value r = 1, ... n

and f_r = frequency of getting score r

then N $= \Sigma f_r$ = total number of trials

$$\mu = \frac{\Sigma f_r \times r}{N} \quad \text{where } r = 1, ... n$$

From the definition on probability we have $P_r = \lim_{N \to \infty} \frac{f_r}{N}$

where r = 1, ... n

∴ When $N \to \infty$

The mean $\mu = \Sigma P_r \times r$ where r = 1, ... n

APPENDIX 7. The binomial distribution

To prove the mean = np

where p = the probability of the success of an outcome
q = the probability of the failure of an outcome
p + q = 1
n = the number of independent trials.

The probability P_r of r successes and (n – r) failures is given by the term of the binomial expansion,

$$\frac{n(n-1)(n-2)\ldots(n-r+1)\; p^r q^{n-r}}{r!} \text{ where } r = 0, 1, \ldots n.$$

The mean of this distribution is given by

$$\mu = \Sigma\, P_r \,.\, r \text{ where } r = 0, 1 \ldots\ldots n$$

But when r = 0, $P_o . 0 = 0$, i.e. the first term is zero.

∴ We can consider the range of values for r as 1, 2, ... n

$$\therefore \qquad \mu = \sum_{r=1}^{n} \frac{n(n-1)(n-2)\ldots(n-r+1)\, p^r q^{n-r} . r}{r!}$$

Cancelling by r :

$$\mu = \sum_{r=1}^{n} \frac{n(n-1)(n-2)\ldots(n-r+1)\, p^r q^{n-r}}{(r-1)!}$$

Put S = r – 1

i.e.r. = S + 1

$$\mu = \sum_{S=0}^{n-1} \frac{n(n-1)(n-2)\ldots(n-S)}{S!}\, p^{S+1} q^{n-S-1}$$

where S ranges from 0 to n – 1

Taking out the common factor np

$$\mu = np \sum_{S=0}^{n-1} \frac{(n-1)(n-2)\ldots(n-S)}{S!} p^S q^{n-S-1}$$

$$= np \, . \, (p+q)^{n-1}$$

But $p + q = 1$

$$\therefore \; \mu = np \, . \, 1 = np$$

APPENDIX 8. The conditions under which the binomial distribution can be converted to the Poisson distribution

The binomial distribution is given by the terms of the expansion of $(p + q)^n$ where
p = the probability that an event will occur,
q = the probability that an event will not occur,
n = the number of repeated trials.

$$(p + q)^n = (q + p)^n$$

$$= q^n + nq^{n-1} p + \frac{n(n-1)}{2!} q^{n-2} p^2 + \frac{n(n-1)(n-2)}{3!} q^{n-3} p^3 \ldots$$

The $(r + 1)^{th}$ term of this expansion gives the probability that an event X will occur r times.

$$\text{i.e. } p(X = r) = \frac{n(n-1)(n-2)\ldots(n-r+1)\,p^r q^{n-r}}{r!} \qquad \ldots (1)$$

But the sum of the probabilities of all possible outcomes must be 1

$$\therefore \quad p + q = 1$$

$$\therefore \quad q = 1 - p$$

Substituting for q in (1) :

$$p(X = r) = \frac{n(n-1)(n-2)\ldots(n-r+1)\,p^r (1-p)^{n-r}}{r!} \qquad \ldots (2)$$

Now suppose p becomes very small as n becomes very large, but that pn remains constant and equal to λ(say). This corresponds to a very small probability of the occurrence of an event such as a lightning flash within a small element of time δt, of which there are a large number n.

Now $pn = \lambda$ and $n \to \infty$, $p \to 0$

$$\therefore \quad p = \frac{\lambda}{n}$$

Substituting for p in [2] :

$$p(X=r) = \frac{n(n-1)(n-2)\ \dots\ (n-r+1)}{r!}\left(\frac{\lambda}{n}\right)^r\left(1-\frac{\lambda}{n}\right)^{n-r}$$

$$= \frac{n(n-1)(n-2)\ \dots\ (n-r+1)}{n^r}\frac{\lambda^r}{r!}\left(1-\frac{\lambda}{n}\right)^n\cdot\left(1-\frac{\lambda}{n}\right)^{-r}$$

interchanging r! and n^r and using $a^{m-n} = a^m \times a^{-n}$

Now split up n^r in the denominator into its r factors each n.

(Note: there are r factors in the numerator)

$$\therefore p(X=r) = \frac{n}{n}\left(\frac{n-1}{n}\right)\left(\frac{n-2}{n}\right)\dots\left(\frac{n-r+1}{n}\right)\frac{\lambda^r}{r!}\left(1-\frac{\lambda}{n}\right)^n\cdot\left(1-\frac{\lambda}{n}\right)^{-r}$$

$$= 1\left(1-\frac{1}{n}\right)\left(1-\frac{2}{n}\right)\dots\left(1-\frac{r-1}{n}\right)\frac{\lambda^r}{r!}\left(1-\frac{\lambda}{n}\right)^n\cdot\left(1-\frac{\lambda}{n}\right)^{-r}$$

Now let $n \to \infty$ while λ remains constant

$$p(X=r) = 1\cdot 1\cdot 1\ \dots\ 1\cdot\frac{\lambda^r}{r!}\ e^{-\lambda}\ 1^{-r} \qquad \dots [3]$$

[Since the definition of e^x is:

$$e^x = \lim_{n\to\infty}\left(1+\frac{x}{n}\right)^n$$

it follows that

$$\lim_{n\to\infty}\left(1-\frac{\lambda}{n}\right)^n = e^{-\lambda}$$]

$\therefore\ p(X=r) = \dfrac{\lambda^r}{r!}\cdot e^{-\lambda}$ from [3]

This is the Poisson distribution

Since the mean of a binomial distribution is np (See Appendix 7)

The mean $\mu = np = \lambda$

APPENDIX 9. The cumulative normal distribution function

$$y = p(t) = \frac{1}{\sqrt{(2)\pi}} \int_{o}^{t} e^{-\frac{1}{2}t^2}\, dt$$

t	**0.00**	**0.01**	**0.02**	**0.03**	**0.04**	**0.05**	**0.06**	**0.07**	**0.08**	**0.09**
0.0	.0000	.0040	.0080	.0120	.0160	.0199	.0239	.0279	.0319	.0359
0.1	.0398	.0438	.0478	.0517	.0557	.0596	.0636	.0675	.0714	.0753
0.2	.0793	.0832	.0871	.0910	.0948	.0987	.1026	.1064	.1103	.1141
0.3	.1179	.1217	.1255	.1293	.1331	.1368	.1406	.1443	.1480	.1517
0.4	.1554	.1591	.1628	.1664	.1700	.1736	.1772	.1808	.1844	.1879
0.5	.1915	.1950	.1985	.2019	.2054	.2088	.2123	.2157	.2190	.2224
0.6	.2257	.2291	.2324	.2357	.2389	.2422	.2454	.2486	.2517	.2549
0.7	.2580	.2611	.2642	.2673	.2704	.2734	.2764	.2794	.2823	.2852
0.8	.2881	.2910	.2939	.2967	.2995	.3023	.3051	.3078	.3106	.3133
0.9	.3159	.3186	.3212	.3238	.3264	.3289	.3315	.3340	.3365	.3389
1.0	.3413	.3438	.3461	.3485	.3508	.3531	.3554	.3577	.3599	.3621
1.1	.3643	.3665	.3686	.3708	.3729	.3749	.3770	.3790	.3810	.3830
1.2	.3849	.3869	.3888	.3907	.3925	.3944	.3962	.3980	.3997	.4015
1.3	.4032	.4049	.4066	.4082	.4099	.4115	.4131	.4147	.4162	.4177
1.4	.4192	.4207	.4222	.4236	.4251	.4265	.4279	.4292	.4306	.4319
1.5	.4332	.4345	.4357	.4370	.4382	.4394	.4406	.4418	.4429	.4441
1.6	.4452	.4463	.4474	.4484	.4495	.4505	.4515	.4525	.4535	.4545
1.7	.4554	.4564	.4573	.4582	.4591	.4599	.4608	.4616	.4625	.4633
1.8	.4641	.4649	.4656	.4664	.4671	.4678	.4686	.4693	.4699	.4706
1.9	.4713	.4719	.4726	.4732	.4738	.4744	.4750	.4756	.4761	.4767
2.0	.4773	.4778	.4783	.4788	.4793	.4798	.4803	.4808	.4812	.4817
2.1	.4821	.4826	.4830	.4834	.4838	.4842	.4846	.4850	.4854	.4857
2.2	.4861	.4864	.4868	.4871	.4875	.4878	.4881	.4884	.4887	.4890
2.3	.4893	.4896	.4898	.4901	.4904	.4906	.4909	.4911	.4913	.4916
2.4	.4918	.4920	.4922	.4925	.4927	.4929	.4931	.4932	.4934	.4936
2.5	.4938	.4940	.4941	.4943	.4945	.4946	.4948	.4949	.4951	.4952
2.6	.4953	.4955	.4956	.4957	.4959	.4960	.4961	.4962	.4963	.4964
2.7	.4965	.4966	.4967	.4968	.4969	.4970	.4971	.4972	.4973	.4974
2.8	.4974	.4975	.4976	.4977	.4977	.4978	.4979	.4979	.4980	.4981
2.9	.4981	.4982	.4983	.4983	.4984	.4984	.4985	.4985	.4986	.4986
3.0	.4987	.4987	.4987	.4988	.4988	.4989	.4989	.4989	.4989	.4990
3.1	.4990	.4991	.4991	.4991	.4992	.4992	.4992	.4992	.4993	.4993
3.2	.4993	.4993	.4994	.4994	.4994	.4994	.4994	.4995	.4995	.4995
3.3	.4995	.4995	.4996	.4996	.4996	.4996	.4996	.4996	.4996	.4997
3.4	.4997	.4997	.4997	.4997	.4997	.4997	.4997	.4997	.4997	.4998
3.5	.4998	.4998	.4998	.4998	.4998	.4998	.4998	.4998	.4998	.4998
3.6	.4998	.4998	.4999	.4999	.4999	.4999	.4999	.4999	.4999	.4999
3.7	.4999	.4999	.4999	.4999	.4999	.4999	.4999	.4999	.4999	.4999
3.8	.4999	.4999	.4999	.4999	.4999	.4999	.4999	.4999	.4999	.5000
3.9	.5000	.5000	.5000	.5000	.5000	.5000	.5000	.5000	.5000	.5000
t	**0.00**	**0.01**	**0.02**	**0.03**	**0.04**	**0.05**	**0.06**	**0.07**	**0.08**	**0.09**

Answers

Ex.1 (Page 2)

1. (i) a^4 (ii) 4a (iii) 2abc (iv) $3ab^2c^3$
2. (i) 4, 6 (ii) 9, 6 (iii) 6 (iv) 36
(v) 24 (vi) 13

Ex.2 (Page 3)

1. a^8 2. a^5 3. a^9 4. a^4 5. a^6 6. a^5 7. a^3b^6 8. a^3b^4

Ex.3 (Page 3)

1. $8a^3$ 2. $9a^2b^2$ 3. a^7b^5

Ex.4 (Page 4)

1. 9x 2. 3x 3. 3x 4. 10x 5. 10a 6. $10x^2y$

Ex.5 (Page 7)

1. $5a - 10b - 3c$ 2. $-2x - 3y + 3z$ 3. $-5x^2y$
4. 2pq 5. 0 6(a) $6x - 4y + 3z$ (b) $-6x^2 - 4x - 2$

Ex.6 (Page 9)

1. 30ab 2. 3 3. $\frac{4a}{b}$ 4. $\frac{4ac}{3b^2}$ 5. $\frac{225}{4b}$ 6. $\frac{8r^2}{p}$

Ex.7 (Page 12)

1. $23a + 7b$ 2. $11a + b$ 3. $7a + 11b - 5c$ 4. $7a - 7b$
5. $3a - 8b + c$ 6. $5a + 15b$ 7. $-pq + 4pr$ 8. $13ab + 17ac$
9. $a^2 - ac + b^2 - bc$ 10. 2ac

Ex.8 (Page 14)

1. $a + 2b$ 2. $-a - 2b - 2c$ 3. $4x - 5y + 4z$
4. $-7xy - 3yz + 10zx$ 5. $7x - 2y + z$ 6. $2a + 2b + c$

Ex.9 (Page 15)

1. -6 2. -12 3. $+10$ 4. $+9$ 5. -10 6. -1
7. $+12$ 8. $+12a^3$ 9. $-8x^2y$ 10. $+6abc$ 11. -3
12. $+4$ 13. -2 14. $-3\frac{1}{2}$ 15. $+1$ 16. -10

Ex.10 (Page 15)

1. $4x$ 2. $2a$ 3. $12a$ 4. $4a$ 5. $7p$ 6. $-7p$ 7. $-7p$
8. $+7p$ 9. $10x$ 10. $4x - 5y$ 11. $4e + f$
12. $x - 6y - 3z$ 13. $18a^3$ 14. $16b^2$ 15. $36x^2$
16. $10cd$ 17. $6k^2hm$ 18. $6x^2yz^2$ 19. 5 20. $\frac{3x}{2}$
21. $12y$ 22. xy 23. $\frac{1}{h}$ 24. $\frac{1}{y}$ 25. $\frac{p}{q}$ 26. $3x^2$
27. $4x^2 - 3x^2y - 3x^2z$

Ex.11 (Page 22)

1. $x = 3$ 2. $b = 3$ 3. $b = \frac{1}{5}$ 4. $x = 4$ 5. $x = 3$
6. $x = 0$ 7. $a = 2$ 8. $a = 3\frac{1}{2}$ 9. $x = 5$ 10. $a = 3$
11. $a = 11$ 12. $a = \frac{47}{10} = 4\frac{7}{10}$

Ex.12 (Page 25)

1. $r = 2$ 2. $x = 1\frac{1}{5}$ 3. $x = 11$ 4. $a = 3$ 5. $x = -17$
6. $p = 17$ 7. $y = -\frac{1}{5}$ 8. $x = -1$ 9. $x = 1\frac{1}{2}$ 10. $a = 17$

Ex.13 (Page 25)

1. $x = 1\frac{1}{5}$ 2. $x = \frac{2}{3}$ 3. $x = -7\frac{1}{3}$ 4. $a = \frac{7}{8}$ 5. $x = 1\frac{1}{2}$
6. $a = 6$

Ex.14 (Page 28)

1. Given 2. $6ab + x^2 + 2bx + 3ax$ 3. $6ax + by + bx + 6ay$
4. $10ac + 3bd + 2bc + 15ad$

Ex.15 (Page 29)

1. $6a^2 + 11a + 4$ 2. $a^2 + 13a + 42$ 3. $a^2 - a - 42$
4. $a^2 + a - 42$ 5. $a^2 - 13a + 42$ 6. $6a^2 - 5a - 4$
7. $6a^2 - 11a + 4$ 8. $6a^2 + 5a - 4$ 9. $1 - 2b + b^2$
10. $4 - 9b^2$ 11. $a^2 - b^2$ 12. $a^2 + 2ab + b^2$
13. $a^2 - 2ab + b^2$ 14. $4a^2 - 12ab + 9b^2$ 15. $9a^2 - 1$
16. $4a^2 - 9$ 17. $x^2 - 100$ 18. $a^2b^2 - 4$
19. $25a^2 - 4b^2$ 20. $4a^2 - 81$

N.B. (a) In each case, the inside pair and the outside pair give the same term but opposite in sign.
(b) The brackets are the same except for the sign in the middle.

Ex.16 (Page 30)

1. $(x + 2)(x + 2)$ 2. $(x - 2)(x - 2)$ 3. $(x + 4)(x + 1)$
4. $(x - 4)(x - 1)$, 5. $(x + 4)(x - 3)$ 6. $(x - 4)(x + 3)$
7. $(x + 4)(x + 2)$ 8. $(x - 4)(x - 2)$ 9. $(x - 4)(x + 2)$
10..$(x + 4)(x - 2)$ 11.$(x + 8)(x + 1)$ 12. $(x - 8)(x - 1)$
13.$(x - 8)(x + 1)$ 14.$(x + 8)(x - 1)$

Ex.17 (Page 31)

1. $(x - 3)(x + 3)$ 2. $(2x - 5)(2x + 5)$ 3. $(3x - 1)(3x + 1)$
4. $(10a - 3b)(10a + 3b)$ 5. $(4x - 11y)(4x + 11y)$
6. $(7 - y)(7 + y)$

Ex.18 (Page 33)

1. $x^3 - x^2 - 13x + 4$ 2. $a^3 + b^3$ 3. $6x^3 - 5x^2 + 9x - 4$
4. $x^2 - x - 3$ 5. $x^2 + 3x + 1$
6. $x + 4$. Remainder: $15x - 18$ 7. $3x^3 - 4x^2 - 13x + 14$

Ex.19 (Page 38)

1. $x = -5$ or $+2$ 2. $x = 6$ or 1 3. $x = 3$ or 2
4. $x = +4$ or -4 5. $x = 0$ or 16 6. $x = 10$ or -10

Ex.20 (Page 39)

1. 3 or $-\frac{1}{2}$ 2. 3.64 or −0.14 3. 1.79 or −1.12
4. $-1, \frac{1}{3}$ 5. −1.57 or 0.32 6. −1.65 or 0.15
7. 2.28 or 0.22 8. −2.39 or −0.28 9. 1.31 or 0.19
10. −1.29 or −0.31 11. 2.37 or 0.63 12. 1.36 or 0.44

Ex.21 (Page 41)

1. a^5 2. a^5 3. (i) a^3 (ii) $a^{\frac{5}{2}}$ (iii) $a^{\frac{7}{3}}$ 4. a^{12} 5. a^8
6. (i) 1 (ii) 1 (iii) 1 7. (i) a^{-9} or $\frac{1}{a^9}$ (ii) a^{-1} or $\frac{1}{a}$
(iii) $a^{\frac{1}{2}}$ 8. (i) $\frac{1}{a}$ (ii) a ; (iii) $\frac{1}{a^2}$ (iv) $\frac{1}{3^2}$ or $\frac{1}{9}$ (v) $\frac{1}{a^2}$
9. (i) x^4, $x^{\frac{10}{3}}$, $x^{\frac{1}{3}}$ (ii) $x^{\frac{3}{2}}$, x^{-1} or $\frac{1}{x}$, $x^{\frac{1}{2}}$
(iii) $x^{\frac{1}{3}}$, $x^{\frac{3}{4}}$, $x^{\frac{4}{3}}$ 10. 4 11. 3 12. 3 13. 1 14. $\frac{1}{2}$
15. $\frac{1}{9}$ 16. $\frac{1}{3}$ 17. $\frac{1}{3}$ 18. 4 19. $\frac{1}{27}$ 20. $\frac{1}{4}$

Ex.22 (Page 48)

1. 2 2. 1 3. −6 4. 2a 5. $3\frac{1}{3}$

Ex.23 (Page 70)

1. $5x^4$ 2. $9x^2$ 3. 5 4. -1 5. x^3
6. $3x^{-1/2}$ or $\frac{3}{\sqrt{x}}$ 7. $\frac{d}{dx}(x^{\frac{1}{3}}) = \frac{1}{3}x^{-\frac{2}{3}}$ 8. $4x$

9. $\frac{d}{dx}(2x^{-1}) = -2x^{-2}$ or $\frac{-2}{x^2}$

10. $\frac{d}{dx}(\frac{1}{2}x^{-1}) = -\frac{1}{2}x^{-2}$ or $-\frac{1}{2x^2}$ 11. $1 - \frac{1}{x^2}$

12. $-\frac{3}{x^2} - \frac{1}{2}x^{-1/2}$ 13. x^5 14. x^6 15. x^7 16. x^n

17. $3x^2 + \frac{4}{x^2}$ 18. $-\frac{1}{x^2} + 20x^{-6}$ or $-\frac{1}{x^2} + \frac{20}{x^6}$ 19. $2x + 4$

20. $6x + 2$ 21. $2a^2x - 4ax^3$ 22. $2ax + b$

Ex.24 (Page 70)

1. $\frac{1}{2 - 2y}$ 2. $\frac{1}{2y}$ 3. $\frac{1}{3y^2}$

Ex.25 (Page 73)

1. (i) 44 m/sec (ii) 12 m/sec^2 (iii) $3\frac{2}{3}$ secs (iv) $80\frac{2}{3}$ m/

2. (i) $v = 0$ $f = 6$ $t = 1$ or 2 (ii) $v = -3$ $f = 0$ $t = 1$ or 3
(iii) $v = 4$ $f = -4$ $t = \sqrt{2}$ or 0

Ex.26 (Page 89)

1. (2, 4) max 2. $(-\frac{1}{2}, \frac{3}{4})$ min 3. $(\frac{3}{2}, -\frac{5}{4})$ min
4. $(-1, -2)$ min $(+1, +2)$ max 5. (2, 4) max (0, 0) min
6. (2, 25) max 7. N = 600 £36,000

Ex.27 (Page 92)

1.(a) $9(3x-2)^2$ (b) $-8(5-2x)^3$ 2.(a) $-5(3-x)^4$
(b) $18(4+3x)^5$ 3.(a) $2(x^3-2x+1)(3x^2-2)$
(b) $3(3x^2+5x-1)^2(6x+5)$ 4.(a) $2/\sqrt{4x-1}$
(b) $-1/\sqrt{1-2x}$ 5.(a) $a/2\sqrt{ax+b}$ or $\frac{a}{2}(ax+b)^{-\frac{1}{2}}$
(b) $-a/3.\sqrt[3]{(1-ax)^2}$ or $-\frac{a}{3}(1-ax)^{-\frac{2}{3}}$ 6.(a) $1/(1-x)^2$
(b) $-3/(2+3x)^2$ 7.(a) $-3/(3x+4)^2$ (b) $-12x^3/(3x^4-7)^2$
8.(a) $-3x^2/(x^3-a^3)^2$
(b) $2[x-(1-x^2)^{\frac{1}{2}}][1+x(1-x^2)^{-\frac{1}{2}}]$
9. $n(x+\frac{1}{x})^{n-1}(1-\frac{1}{x^2})$

Ex.28 (Page 95)

1. $2x+5$ 2. $3(x^2+5x+1)^2(2x+5)$ 3.(a) $\frac{1}{2}(x+3)^{-\frac{1}{2}}$
(b) $(2x+3)^{-\frac{1}{2}}$ (c) $-t(1-t^2)^{-\frac{1}{2}}$ or $\frac{-t}{\sqrt{1-t^2}}$
4.(a) $\frac{1}{3}(x+1)^{-\frac{2}{3}}$ (b) $\frac{4}{3}x(2x^2+1)^{-\frac{2}{3}}$ 5. $30x+7$
6. $4x^3-2x-2$
7. $3(x+1)^5+15x(x+1)^4=3(x+1)^4(6x+1)$
8. $4x(4x+1)^3+24x^2(4x+1)^2=4x(4x+1)^2(10x+1)$
9. $2(x+1)(4x^2+2x+7)$
10. $\frac{1}{2}(x^2-3x+2).x^{-\frac{1}{2}}+x^{\frac{1}{2}}(2x-3)$
11. $-\frac{2}{(x-1)^2}$ 12. $\frac{6x^2-8x-12}{(3x-2)^2}$ 13. $\frac{2a}{(a-x)^2}$
14. $-\frac{1}{4t^{\frac{3}{2}}}$ 15. $\frac{-2x^2+4x}{(x^2-x+1)^2}$
16. $2(1-t^2)^{-\frac{1}{2}}+2t^2(1-t^2)^{-\frac{3}{2}}=\frac{2}{(1-t^2)^{\frac{3}{2}}}$
17. $\frac{2t(1+t)^2-2t^2(1+t)}{(1+t)^4}=\frac{2t}{(1+t)^3}$ 18. $-\frac{a}{2}(ax+b)^{-\frac{3}{2}}$

Ex.29 (Page 100)

(The constant of integration is omitted below but must be included in your answers)

1. $\frac{x^7}{7}$, $\frac{x^{11}}{11}$, $\frac{x^{10}}{10}$, $\frac{x^3}{3}$, $\frac{x^2}{2}$, x, constant, $\frac{x^{2.4}}{2.4}$, $-\frac{5x^{-0.4}}{2}$
2. $\frac{x^{-2}}{-2}$ or $-\frac{1}{2x^2}$, $\frac{x^{-3}}{-3}$ or $-\frac{1}{3x^3}$, $-\frac{1}{4x^4}$, $-\frac{1}{5x^5}$
3. $\frac{2}{3}x^{\frac{3}{2}}$, $2x^{\frac{1}{2}}$, $-\frac{5}{x}$
4. $\frac{x^3}{3} + \frac{x^2}{2}$, $\frac{x^4}{4} - a^3x$, $\frac{ax^3}{3} + \frac{bx^2}{2} + cx$
5. $x^3 + x^2 - x$, $5x - \frac{x^4}{4} + \frac{2x^3}{3} - \frac{x^2}{2}$, $\frac{10x^{\frac{3}{2}}}{3} + \frac{4x^{\frac{5}{2}}}{5}$

Ex.30 (Page 105)

1. $10\frac{5}{12}$ Yes, a combination of $15\frac{3}{4}$ square units and $-5\frac{1}{3}$ square units. But this does not give the area between the curve and the x axis.
2. $\int_{-1}^{2} y\,dx = -4\frac{1}{2}$ $\therefore$ Area = $4\frac{1}{2}$ square units.
3. $\int_{1}^{3} y\,dx = 14$ square units 4. $\int_{-1}^{+1} y\,dx = \frac{2}{3}$ square units
5. First loop = $\int_{-1}^{0} y\,dx = \frac{5}{12}$ square units

   $\int_{0}^{2} y\,dx = -\frac{8}{3}$ $\therefore$ Area of second loop = $+\frac{8}{3}$ square units.

Ex.31 (Page 113)

1. $\frac{56\pi}{3}$ 2. $108\frac{2}{3}\pi$ 3. 625π 4. $\frac{\pi}{30}$

Ex. 32 I (Page 131)

1.	$-\sin 30^\circ$ or $-\frac{1}{2}$	16.	$-\cos 70^\circ$
2.	$-\sin 30^\circ$ or $-\frac{1}{2}$	17.	$-\cos 10^\circ$
3.	$+\frac{1}{2}$	18.	$+\cos 10^\circ$
4.	$-\frac{1}{\sqrt{2}}$	19.	$-\cos 85^\circ$
5.	$-\sin 35^\circ$	20.	$-\cos 75^\circ$
6.	$\sin 20^\circ$	21.	$-\tan 60^\circ = -\sqrt{3}$
7.	$\sin 80^\circ$	22.	$\tan 0^\circ = 0$
8.	$\sin 0^\circ = 0$	23.	$\tan 45^\circ = 1$
9.	$-\sin 10^\circ$	24.	$-\tan 45^\circ = -1$
10.	$-\sin 80^\circ$	25.	$-\tan 30^\circ = -\frac{1}{\sqrt{3}}$
11.	$-\cos 60^\circ = -\frac{1}{2}$	26.	$\tan 80^\circ$
12.	$\cos 60^\circ = +\frac{1}{2}$	27.	$-\tan 38^\circ$
13.	$\frac{1}{2}$	28.	$-\tan 46^\circ$
14.	$-\cos 45^\circ = -\frac{1}{\sqrt{2}}$	29.	$-\tan 9^\circ$
15.	$-\cos 70^\circ$	30.	$-\tan 4^\circ$

Ex. 32 II (Page 131)

1.	$\sin \Theta$	5.	$-\cot \Theta = -\frac{1}{\tan \Theta}$
2.	$-\sin \Theta$	6.	$\cot \Theta = \frac{1}{\tan \Theta}$
3.	$-\sin \Theta$	* 7.	24.8 m.
4.	$\sin \Theta$	8.	$a = 10, T = 5\pi$

Ex. 32 III (Page 132)

1. 10 cm. 2. 11π rad/sec 3. $\frac{5\pi}{2}$ rad

Ex. 33 (Page 141)

1.	$3 \cos x + 4 \sin x$	7.	$4 \cos \frac{2}{3} x$
2.	$8 \cos 8x$	8.	$2\pi n \cos 2\pi nx$
3.	$-\frac{1}{2} \sin 3x$	9.	$-2 \cos x. \sin x$
4.	$2 \cos (2x + 5)$	10.	$2 \cos \frac{1}{2}x$
5.	$\sin (\frac{\pi}{6} - x)$	11.	$\frac{d}{dx} (\sin x)^{\frac{1}{2}} = \frac{1}{2} (\sin x)^{-\frac{1}{2}}.\cos x = \frac{\cos x}{2\sqrt{\sin x}}$

6. $9\cos(3x-2)$ 12. $\cos x - \frac{1}{2}\cos 3x$

Ex. 34 (Page 141)

1. $(1+2x)^{-\frac{1}{2}}$ or $\dfrac{1}{\sqrt{1+2x}}$
2. $-24x(1-3x^2)^3$
3. $-6x^2/(1+x^3)^3$
4. $-n(a-x)^{n-1}$
5. $\dfrac{a}{2\sqrt{ax+b}}$
6. $\dfrac{v}{\sqrt{1+v^2}}$
7. $-24(3-41)^5$
8. $-4t/(1+t^2)^3$
9. $-8x/(1+4x^2)^2$

Ex. 35 (Page 142)

1. $\sqrt{x}.\cos x + \dfrac{\sin x}{2\sqrt{x}}$
2. $2\cos x\cos 2x - \sin x\sin 2x$
3. $4x\cos 3x - 6x^2\sin 3x$
4. $\frac{1}{4}\sqrt{(1+x)} + \dfrac{x}{8\sqrt{1+x}}$
5. $-a\cos bx\sin ax - b\cos ax\sin bx$
6. $2x\sin x + x^2\cos x$
7. $3/(2x+3)^2$
8. $16/(x+5)^2$
9. $9/(x+3)^2$
10. $(x\cos x - \sin x)/x^2$
11. $2\cos x/(1-\sin x)^2$
12. $(-2x^2-2x-2)/(1+2x)^2$

Ex. 36 (Page 151)

1. Maximum velocity $= a\omega = 5\sqrt{2}$ m/sec
   velocity $= 3\sqrt{2}$ m/sec when $x = 4$
2. $T = \sqrt{2}.\pi \quad (\omega = \sqrt{2})$
3. $T = \pi/2 \quad (\omega = 4)$
4. $\omega = 1$, $a = 5$, maximum acceleration $= a\omega^2 = 5$ m/sec^2
5. $a = 4$m $(\omega = 2)$ $v = 2\sqrt{7}$ m/sec

6. Maximum V $= a\omega = 3\pi$ $\quad a = 3 \quad \omega = \pi$

Maximum acceleration $= a\omega^2 = 3\pi^2$

Ex. 37 (Page 158)

1. $\dfrac{4}{\sqrt{1 - 16x^2}}$

2. $\dfrac{1}{\sqrt{4 - x^2}} = \dfrac{\frac{1}{2}}{\sqrt{1 - (\frac{x}{2})^2}}$

3. $\dfrac{1}{\sqrt{a^2 - x^2}} = \dfrac{\frac{1}{a}}{\sqrt{1 - (\frac{x}{a})^2}}$

4. $-\dfrac{3}{\sqrt{1 - 9x^2}}$

5. $-\dfrac{1}{\sqrt{9 - x^2}}$

6. $-\dfrac{1}{\sqrt{a^2 - x^2}}$

7. $\dfrac{3}{1 + 9x^2}$

8. $\dfrac{3}{9 + x^2} = \dfrac{\frac{1}{3}}{1 + \frac{x^2}{9}}$

9. $\dfrac{a}{a^2 + x^2}$

Ex. 38 (Page 159)

1. $\dfrac{w\,l^2}{8}$

2. $\dfrac{E^2}{4R}$ when $i = \dfrac{E}{2R}$

3. $t = \sqrt{\mu^2 + 1} - \mu$

4. 2 when the number = 1

5. $v = 40$

6. Area = 12 m^2 (when x = 2)

Ex. 39 (Page 164)

1. $1 + 6x + 15x^2 + 20x^3 + \ldots$
2. $1 - 6x + 15x^2 - 20x^3 + \ldots$
3. $1 + 8x + 28x^2 + 56x^3 + \ldots$
4. $1 - 8x + 28x^2 - 56x^3 + \ldots$
5. $1 + 8x + 24x^2 + 32x^3 + \ldots$
6. $1 - 6x + \frac{27}{2}x^2 - \frac{27}{2}x^3 + \ldots$
7. $3^5\,(1 + \frac{5}{3}x + \frac{10}{9}x^2 + \frac{10}{27}x^3 + \ldots)$
8. $1 - \frac{1}{2}x - \frac{1}{8}x^2 - \frac{1}{16}x^3 - \ldots$
9. $1 - \frac{1}{2}x + \frac{3}{8}x^2 - \frac{5}{16}x^3 + \ldots$

10. $1 + 3x + 6x^2 + 10x^3 - \ldots$

11. Answer given.

12. (i) $\frac{7.6.5}{3.2}(2x)^3$ (ii) $\frac{(-2)(-3)(-4)(-5)}{4.3.2}(-x)^4$

(iii) $4^{1/2}\frac{(\frac{1}{2})(-\frac{1}{2})(-\frac{3}{2})}{3.2}(-\frac{x}{4})^3$

Ex. 40 (Page 173)

1. $-e^{-x}$
2. $3e^{3x}$
3. $4e^{(4x-1)}$
4. $ae^{(ax+b)}$
5. $6e^{2x}$
6. $e^{(4x+2)}$
7. $-\frac{1}{2}e^{-\frac{x}{2}}$
8. $4x\,e^{2x^2}$
9. $e^x(6x + 3x^2)$
10. $e^x - e^{-x}$
11. $e^{ax}(1 + ax)$
12. $\cos x.\, e^{\sin x}$
13. $4/(e^{2x} + e^{-2x} + 2)$
14. $e^{-x}(2 - x^2)$
15. $-e^{-x} + c$
16. $\frac{1}{3}e^{3x} + c$
17. $\frac{1}{4}e^{(4x-1)} + c$
18. $\frac{1}{a}e^{(ax+b)} + c$
19. $\frac{3}{2}e^{2x} + c$
20. $\frac{1}{16}e^{(4x+2)} + c$
21. $-2e^{-\frac{x}{2}} + c$
22. $e^x - e^{-x} + c$
23. $\frac{1}{4}e^{2x^2} + c$

Ex. 41 (Page 184)

1. $\frac{1}{x}$
2. $4/(4x - 1)$
3. $4/x$
4. $a/(ax + b)$
5. $x^2(1 + 3\log_e x)$
6. $\cot x$
7. $-\tan x$
8. $2a/(a^2 - x^2)$
9. $(e^x - e^{-x})/(e^x + e^{-x})$
10. $\log_e 2x + 1$
11. $\frac{1}{2}\cot x$
12. $a\log_e bx.\cos ax + \frac{1}{x}\sin ax$
13. $\frac{1}{x}(\log_e ax + \log_e bx)$

14. (i) $\log_e(1+x)+c$ (ii) $-\log_e(1-x)+c$
15. (i) $\log_e(2+3x)+c$ (ii) $-\log_e(2-3x)+c$
16. (i) $-\frac{1}{4}\log_e(1-4x)+c$ (ii) $\frac{1}{2}\log_e(3+2x)+c$
17. (i) $\log_e(1+x^2)+c$ (ii) $\log_e(2+2x^3)+c$
18. (i) $\log_e(x^2-3x)+c$ (ii) $-\log_e \cos x+c$

19. 0.4055
20. −2.0793
21. 0.5893
22. 0.2903
23. 4.9034
24. 0.1371
25. 9.543

Ex. 42 (Page 191)

1. (i) 6623 (ii) 2.0 days
2. (i) $N = N_o e^{-\lambda t}$ (ii) $N = \frac{N_o}{2}$ when $t = \frac{1}{\lambda}\log_e 2$

Ex. 43 (Page 197)

1. $v = 26 + 3t$ $u = 26$ $f = 3$
2. Unsound reading for $t = 50$; $a = 0.34$, $b = 91.5$; 25°
3. $a \triangleq 0.16$ $b \triangleq 40$; $t \triangleq 50$; $R \triangleq 54.4$

Ex. 44 (Page 210)

1. $q = 2.57p^{0.822}$ $a \triangleq 2.57$ $k \triangleq 0.822$
2. $y = 4.2e^{-1.5x}$ (Hint: Remember $\log_{10} 0.937 = \bar{1}.9717$
$= -1 + 0.971$
$= -.0283$
3. $T_o \triangleq 2$; $\mu \triangleq 0.294$; ($T \triangleq 2e^{1.851}$)
4. $a \triangleq 1.8$ $b \triangleq 0.1$
5. $a \triangleq 0.5$ $b \triangleq 0.2$

Ex. 45 (Page 216)

1. $a = 2, b = 1$
2. $a = 5\frac{3}{4}, b = 1\frac{1}{4}$
3. $a = 1, b = 1$
4. $a = -1, b = 4$
5. $a = 1\frac{1}{2}, b = \frac{1}{3}$
6. $a = 1, b = -\frac{3}{4}$
7. $x = 1\frac{2}{5}, y = -\frac{1}{5}$
8. $y = 4, z = 1$

Ex. 46 (Page 218)

1. $x = -2, \ y = 3$
2. $x = -1, y = 2$
3. $s = 3\frac{1}{2}, \ t = 0$
4. $a = \frac{2}{3}, b = -4$
5. $x = \frac{1}{3}, \ y = -\frac{1}{2}$
6. $x = 19, \ y = -17$
7. $a = \frac{1}{12}, b = \frac{1}{8}$
8. $u = -\frac{1}{10}, \ v = \frac{1}{9}$

Ex. 47 (Page 225)

1. $\Delta_1 = -6, \ \Delta_2 = 17, \ \Delta_3 = -6$
2. $\Delta = -53$
3. $\Delta = 0$

Ex. 48 (Page 235)

1. $8 - 4j$
2. $-5 - 4j$
3. $a + c + j(b + d)$
4. 0.2
5. 0

Ex. 49 (Page 238)

1. $17 + 6j$
2. $-5 - 10j$
3. $-7 + 24j$
4. 25
5. $3 + 11j$
6. -4
7. $1.6 - 0.7j$
8. $-\frac{20}{29} + \frac{21}{29} j$
9. $-\frac{20}{29} - \frac{21}{29} j$
10. $\frac{7}{5} - \frac{6}{5} j$
11. $\frac{3125}{629} - \frac{250}{629} j$
12. $\frac{270}{117} + \frac{210}{117} j$ or $\frac{30}{13} + \frac{70}{39} j$
13. $3 \pm 2j$

Problem (Page 239)

(i) Oscillatory

(ii) Yes, it becomes direct discharge.

Ex. 50 (Page 244)

1. $(5, 53^{o}8')$
2. $(13, -22^{o}37')$ or $(13, 337^{o}23')$
3. $(17, 118^{o}4')$
4. $(83.24, 151^{o}17')$
5. $4.045 + 2.939j$
6. $-0.4 + 0.6928j$
7. $5.909 - 1.042j$

Ex. 51 (Page 248)

$z^2 = 16(\cos 60^\circ + j\sin 60^\circ)$ $\sqrt{z} = 2(\cos 15^\circ + j\sin 15^\circ)$

Ex. 52 (Page 252)

1. $\frac{1}{2}\log_e \frac{x-1}{x+1}$ 2. $\frac{1}{2}\log_e \frac{1+x}{1-x}$ 3. $\frac{1}{12}\log_e \frac{2x-3}{2x+3}$
4. $2\log_e(x+3) + \log_e(x-2)$ or $\log_e[(x+3)^2(x-2)]$

Ex. 53 (Page 255)

1. $1 + \frac{1}{2}\left(\frac{1}{x-1} - \frac{1}{x+1}\right)$; $x + \frac{1}{2}[\log_e(x-1) - \log_e(x+1)] + c$
2. $2 + \frac{16}{3(x-4)} - \frac{4}{3(x+2)}$; $2x + \frac{16}{3}\log_e(x-4) - \frac{4}{3}\log(x+2)$
3. $2x + \frac{1}{(x-2)} - \frac{1}{(x+3)}$; $x^2 + \log(x-2) - \log(x+3) + c$

Ex. 54 (Page 258)

1. $\frac{1}{x} - \frac{x}{(x^2+1)}$ 2. $\frac{1}{5(x-2)} - \frac{\frac{1}{5}x + \frac{2}{5}}{(x^2+1)}$ or $\frac{1}{5(x-2)} - \frac{x+2}{5(x^2+1}$
3. $-\frac{1}{5(x+1)} + \frac{\frac{1}{5}x + \frac{4}{5}}{(x^2+4)}$ or $-\frac{1}{5(x+1)} + \frac{x+4}{5(x^2+4)}$

Ex. 55 (Page 260)

1(a) $\frac{A}{x-3} + \frac{Bx+C}{x^2+4}$ (b) $\frac{1}{x-3} - \frac{x+1}{x^2+4}$

2(a) $\frac{A}{x-2} + \frac{Bx+C}{x^2+2x+5}$ (b) $\frac{1}{x-2} - \frac{2}{x^2+2x+5}$

3(a) $\frac{A}{x-1} + \frac{B}{x+2} + \frac{C}{(x+2)^2}$ (b) $\frac{1}{x-1} - \frac{1}{x+2} + \frac{3}{(x+2)^2}$

4(a) $\frac{A}{x} + \frac{B}{x^2} + \frac{C}{x+1}$ (b) $\frac{1}{x} + \frac{2}{x^2} - \frac{3}{x+1}$

Ex. 56 (Page 268)

1. $y = x^3 + c$; first order; 1 constant.
2. $y = \frac{4}{3}t^3 + \frac{3}{2}t^2 + at + b$; second order; 2 constants.
3. $y = 2x^{\frac{3}{2}} + c$; first order; 1 constant. (Did you say second order?)
4. No solution as yet. third order; 3 constants.

Ex. 57 (Page 269)

1. Separable $\frac{3\,dy}{\cos^2 y} = \frac{dx}{\cos^2 x}$
2. Separable $(1 + y^2)\,dy = (1 + x^2)\,dx$
3. Separable $\frac{dy}{1 + y^2} = \frac{dx}{1 + x^2}$
4. Not separable since $\frac{3x + y}{x}$ cannot be expressed as (a function of x) X (a function of y)
5. Separable $\frac{1 + y}{y^2}\,dy = -\frac{1 + x}{x}\,dx$
6. Separable $\frac{2\sin y}{\cos y}\,dy = -\frac{\sin x}{\cos x}\,dx$
7. Not separable since $\frac{dy}{dx}$ cannot be expressed as a (function of x) X (a function of y)
8. Separable $\frac{y}{1 + y}\,dy = \frac{2x}{1 - x^2}\,dx$
9. Separable $e^y\,dy = e^x\,dx$
10. Separable $\sqrt{2y}.\,dy = \frac{1}{\sqrt{x}}\,dx$

Ex. 58 (Page 270)

1. $3\tan y = \tan x + c$ 2. $y + \frac{y^3}{3} = x + \frac{x^3}{3} + c$

3. $\tan^{-1} y = \tan^{-1} x + c$

5. $\log(xy) = \frac{1}{y} - x + c$ or $\log(Axy) = \frac{1}{y} - x$

6. $\log_e \cos x + 2\log_e \cos y = c$ or
$\cos x \cdot \cos^2 y = A$ where $c = \log_e A$

8. $y = \log_e [(y+1)/(1-x^2)] + c$ or

$e^y = \dfrac{A(y+1)}{(1-x^2)}$ where $c = \log_e A$

9. $e^y = e^x + c$ 10. $y^{\frac{3}{2}} = 3\sqrt{\dfrac{x}{2}} + c$

Ex. 59 (Page 270)

1. $3 \tan y = \tan x - 1$ 2. $y + \dfrac{y^3}{3} = x + \dfrac{x^3}{3}$

3. $\tan^{-1} y = \tan^{-1} x - \dfrac{\pi}{4}$

5. $\log_e y + \log_e x = \dfrac{1}{y} - x + \log_e 2 + ½$ or

$\log_e \left(\dfrac{xy}{2}\right) = \dfrac{2+y}{2y} - x$

6. $\cos x \cos^2 y = 1$ 8. $y + ½ = \log_e \dfrac{2(y+1)}{(1-x^2)}$

9. $e^y = e^x + e - 1$ 10. $y^{\frac{3}{2}} = 3\left(\dfrac{x}{2}\right)^{½} - 2$

Ex. 60 (Page 275)

1. Yes. 2. Yes. 3. Yes. 4. No. 5. Yes. 6. No.
7. Yes. 8. Yes.

Ex. 61 (Page 276)

1. $2 \tan^{-1} \left(\dfrac{y}{x}\right) + \log_e (x^2 + y^2) = c$ 3. $\dfrac{y}{x} = \log_e x + c$

4. No solution. 5. $y^2 = x^4 - x^2$ 6. No solution.

7. $x^2 y^2 = A(y - x)^3$ 8. $\dfrac{x^2}{x^2 - y^2} = \log_e (Ax)$

Ex. 62 (Page 279)

1. $(x - y + 2)^2 + 2(x - y + 2)(x + y - 2) - (x + y - 2)^2 = A$

2. $(2x - y - 3)^3 (6x + 3y + 1) = A$

Substituting $V = \dfrac{Y}{X} = \dfrac{4x + y - 1}{x + y + 1}$ yields $\dfrac{(1+V)}{V^2 - 4} dV = -\dfrac{dX}{X}$

Ex. 63 (Page 280)

1. linear, $P = 1$ $Q = e^x$ 2. linear, $P = -\frac{3}{x}$ $Q = x$
3. linear, $P = \frac{3}{x}$ $Q = \frac{\sin x}{x^3}$ 4. homogeneous
5. linear if $\frac{dx}{dy}$ and x used, $P = \frac{1}{y}$, $Q = 1$.
6. linear, $P = \frac{1}{x}$, $Q = \frac{\sin x}{x}$

Ex. 64 (Page 283)

I 1. $y = \frac{1}{2} e^x + C e^{-x}$ 2. $y = -x^2 + C x^3$ 3. $x^3 y = C - \cos x$

4. Homogeneous 5. $x = \frac{y}{2} + \frac{C}{y}$ 6. $xy = C - \cos x$

Note: Use properties of logs:

$$e^{\log A} = A \ , \ e^{m \log A} = A^m \ , \ e^{n + m \log A} = e^n . A^n$$

II Integrating factor $e^{Rt/L}$ gives $i = \frac{E_o}{R}(1 - e^{\frac{-Rt}{L}})$

Ex. 65 (Page 284)

1. Exact. 2. Not exact. 3. Exact. 4. Exact.
5. Exact.

Ex. 66 (Page 287)

1. $\frac{x^2}{2} + xy + \frac{y^3}{3} = c$ 3. $x^2 e^y + e^x + e^y = c$ 4. $x^3 y^2 = C$
5. $x^3 + y^3 + xy + x + y = C$

Ex. 67 (Page 290)

1. Yes. 2. Yes, with $P = 0$.
3. No. Coefficient 2x is not constant.
4. Yes. Coefficient of $\frac{dy}{dx} = 0$.
5. Yes. Dependent variable x. Independent t.

Ex. 68 (Page 292)

1. $m^2 + 2m = 0$, $m = 0$ or -2 $\quad y = A + B\,e^{-2x}$
2. $m^2 + 5m + 6 = 0$, $m = -3$ or -2 $\quad y = A\,e^{-3x} + B\,e^{-2x}$
3. $m^2 + 6m + 5 = 0$, $m = -5$ or -1 $\quad y = A\,e^{-5x} + B\,e^{-x}$
4. $2m^2 + 5m - 3 = 0$, $m = \frac{1}{2}$ or -3 $\quad y = A\,e^{\frac{1}{2}x} + B\,e^{-3x}$
5. $m^2 - 4m + 3 = 0$, $m = 3$ or 1 $\quad x = A\,e^{3t} + B\,e^{t}$
6. $m^2 - 6m - 16 = 0$, $m = 8$ or -2 $\quad y = A\,e^{8x} + B\,e^{-2x}$
7. $2m^2 + 3m = 0$, $m = 0$ or $-\frac{3}{2}$ $\quad y = A + B\,e^{-\frac{3}{2}x}$
8. $m^2 - 4 = 0$, $m = \pm 2$ $\quad y = A\,e^{2x} + B\,e^{-2x}$

Ex. 69 (Page 295)

1. P.I. $= \frac{3}{8}e^{2x}$, G.S. $= A + B\,e^{-2x} + \frac{3}{8}e^{2x}$
2. P.I. $= \frac{1}{6}e^{x}$ etc. (see solutions to Ex. 68 and use G.S. = C.F. + P.I.
3. P.I. $= \frac{1}{2}e^{3x}$
4. P.I. $= \frac{1}{5}e^{2x}$
5. P.I. $= \frac{1}{4}e^{-t}$
6. P.I. $= -e^{-x}$
7. P.I. $= \frac{1}{3}e^{\frac{3}{2}x}$
8. P.I. $= \frac{1}{5}e^{3x}$

Ex 70 (Page 296)

1. $y = (A + Bx)\,e^{4x}$
2. $y = (A + Bx)\,e^{\frac{2}{3}x}$
3. $y = (A + Bx)\,e^{-3x}$

Ex. 71 (Page 296)

1. $x = A\cos wt + B\sin wt$
2. $y = e^{4x}(A\cos 3x + B\sin 3x)$
3. $y = e^{-\frac{x}{2}}\left(A\cos\frac{\sqrt{3}}{2}x + B\sin\frac{\sqrt{3}}{2}x\right)$

Ex. 72 (Page 300)

1. $y = \frac{x^2}{2} - x + A + B\,e^{-x}$
2. $y = -\frac{1}{2}x\cos x + A\cos x + B\sin x$
3. $y = \frac{1}{4}e^{x} + e^{-x}(A + Bx)$

4. $y = e^{x}(A + Bx) + \frac{1}{4}e^{-x}$
5. $y = Ae^{x} + Be^{-x} - x - 3$
6. $y = A + Be^{-x} + \frac{1}{2}e^{x}$
7. $y = Ae^{x} + Be^{-x} - \frac{1}{2}\sin x$
8. $y = e^{-2x}(A\cos x + B\sin x) + 2$
9. $y = e^{-2x}(A\cos x + B\sin x) + \frac{1}{5}x + \frac{6}{25}$

Ex. 73 (Page 301)

1. $(D^2 + 3D - 4)y = (D + 4)(D - 1)y$
2. $(D^2 - k^2)y = (D - k)(D + k)y$
3. $(D^4 + 3D^2 + 2)y = (D^2 + 2)(D^2 + 1)y$

Ex. 74 (Page 302)

1. $\frac{x^4}{4} + 2x^3 + 2x^2$ 2. $\frac{1}{4}e^{2x}$

Ex. 75 (Page 303)

$-2e^{-3x}$; $4e^{-3x}$; $6e^{4x}$; 0 .

Ex. 76 (Page 304)

1. $31\cos 2x$ 2. $-13\sin 4x$ 3. $17e^{2x} + 82\sin 3x$

Ex. 77 (Page 305)

1. $\frac{1}{5}e^{3x}$
2. $\frac{1}{3}e^{2x}$
3. $\frac{1}{2}\sin 2x$
4. $-\frac{2}{3}e^{-x} - \frac{1}{13}\sin 3x$

Ex. 78 (Page 305)

1. $y = Ae^{3x} + Be^{2x} + \frac{2}{3}$

2. $y = Ae^{-2x} + Be^{x} + 3e^{2x}$

3. $y = A\sin\frac{1}{2}x + B\cos\frac{1}{2}x - 2\sin x$

4. $y = A\sin x + B\cos x - \frac{1}{3}\cos 2x$

5. $y = e^{2x} - e^{-2x} - 4x\,e^{-2x}$

Ex. 79 (Page 307)

1. $y = -6\cos 2x - 2\sin 2x$

2. $y = \frac{1}{2}\cos x - \frac{3}{2}\sin x$

3. $y = 2\sin 2x - \cos 2x$

Ex. 80 (Page 307)

1. $y = Ae^{-x} + Be^{-2x} - 6\cos 2x - 2\sin 2x$

2. $y = Ae^{x} + Be^{2x} + \frac{1}{2}\cos x - \frac{3}{2}\sin x$

3. $y = Ae^{-\frac{3}{2}x} + Be^{-x} + 2\sin 2x - \cos 2x$

Ex. 81 (Page 308)

1. $y = -3x^2 - 6$

2. $y = x^3 + 3x^2 + 6x + 6$

3. $y = x^2 + \frac{7}{2}x + \frac{19}{8}$

Ex. 82 (Page 314)

1. 47.1 2. (a) 47.1 ; (b) the totals are the same.

Ex. 83 (Page 321)

1. (a) 3.5 ; (b) (i) None (ii) None. Equal additions in positions symmetrical about the mean make no difference to the mean, as the centre of balance.
2. 4.54
3. The working is set out below:

x	α	$x-\alpha=u$	f	f u
7	32	– 25	2	– 50
12		– 20	8	– 160
17		– 15	12	– 180
22		– 10	30	– 300
27		– 5	14	– 70
32		0	10	0
37		5	9	+ 45
42		10	7	+ 70
47		15	5	+ 75
52		20	2	+ 40
57		25	1	+ 25

$n = \Sigma f = 100, \Sigma fu = -760 + 255 = -505$

$\therefore \overline{u} = \frac{1}{n}\Sigma fu = -\frac{505}{100} = -5.05$ from guessed mean 32

$\therefore \overline{x} = 32 - 5.05$

$= 26.95$

Ex. 84 (Page 325)

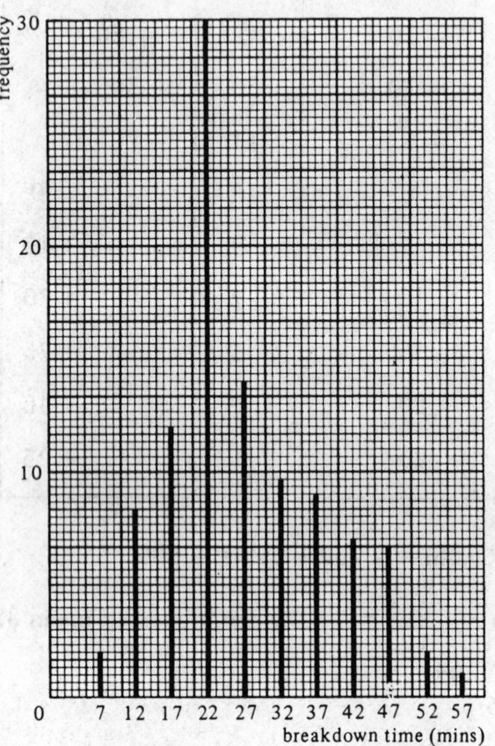

Ex. 85 (Page 328)

1. $\overline{x} = 33.9$ $s = 1.51$ 2. $\overline{x} = 162.6$ $s = 23.2$

Ex. 86 (Page 335)

1. $2^4 = 16.$ Yes.

2.

H	H	H	H	(a)
H	H	H	T	(b)
H	H	T	H	(b)
H	H	T	T	(c)
H	T	H	H	(b)
H	T	H	T	(c)
H	T	T	H	(c)
H	T	T	T	(d)
T	H	H	H	(b)
T	H	H	T	(c)
T	H	T	H	(c)
T	H	T	T	(d)
T	T	H	H	(c)
T	T	H	T	(d)
T	T	T	H	(d)
T	T	T	T	(e)

(a) $\frac{1}{16}$ (b) $\frac{4}{16} = 4\left(\frac{1}{2}\right)^3 \frac{1}{2}$

(c) $\frac{6}{16} = \frac{4.3}{2.1}\left(\frac{1}{2}\right)^2 \left(\frac{1}{2}\right)^2$

(d) $\frac{4}{16}$ (e) $\frac{1}{16}$

3. $(½ + ½)^4 = (½)^4 + 4(½)^3 (½) + \frac{4.3}{2.1} (½)^2 (½)^2 + \frac{4.3.2}{3.2.1}$

$(½)(½)^3 + (½)^4$ Yes.

4. (a) $\frac{18}{100}$; (b) $\frac{81}{100}$; (c) $\frac{1}{100}$ since $p(B) = \frac{1}{10}$

$p(A) = \frac{9}{10}$

Ex. 87 (Page 338)

1. (a) $\frac{1}{2^{10}}$ (b) $\frac{1023}{1024} = 1 - \frac{1}{2^{10}}$ 2. $(\frac{1}{6})^3$, $1 - (\frac{1}{6})^3$

Ex. 88 (Page 339)

1. (a) $\frac{19}{100}$; (b) $\frac{81}{100}$ 2. $\frac{5}{12}$ 3. (a) $\frac{191}{480}$; (b) $\frac{289}{480}$

4. $\frac{1}{32}$

Ex. 89 (Page 341)

(i) $\frac{1}{6}$ (ii) $\frac{1}{2}$ (iii) $\frac{1}{3}$

Ex. 90 (Page 342)

1. $\frac{1}{2}$ 2. $\frac{9}{200}$

Ex. 91 (Page 345)

1. $p(1,H) = p(3,H) = p(5,H) = p(1,T) = p(3,T) = p(5,T) = \frac{1}{12}$,
$p(2) = p(4) = p(6) = \frac{1}{6}$

2. (a) $\frac{171}{200}$; (b) $\frac{171}{200} + \frac{171}{4000} = \frac{171.21}{4000} = \frac{3591}{4000}$

Ex. 92 (Page 350)

1. 0.100, 0.267, 0.311, 0.208, 0.086, 0.023, 0.004, 0.000(4), 0.000, np = 6 npq = 1½

2. (i) $60/13^5$ (ii) $1440/13^5$

3. 2133/3125

4. 0.0988, 0.9805, 0.0195.

Ex. 93 (Page 351)

1. 0.6703, 0.2681, 0.0536, 0.0072
2. (i) about 496 (ii) about 4 3. 0.1912

Ex. 94 (Page 358)

1. (i) 0.6179 (ii) 0.3821 (iii) 0.5398
   (iv) 0.0781 (v) 0.4602 (vi) 0.0796
2. 1 in 1000 (p(3.3) = 0.4995)

Ex. 95 (Page 364)

1. (a) 49.50 – 50.30; (b) 49.38 – 50.42
2. $2.690 < \mu < 2.720$ 3. $693.91 < \mu < 750.09$ hours.
4. £55.14 < μ < £61.14

Index

Statistics and Operational Research

Editor: B. W. CONOLLY, Professor of Operational Research, Queen Mary College, University of London

Beaumont, G.P.	**Introductory Applied Probability**
Beaumont, G.P.	**Probability and Random Variables***
Conolly, B.W.	**Techniques in Operational Research: Vol. 1, Queueing Systems***
Conolly, B.W.	**Techniques in Operational Research: Vol. 2, Models, Search, Randomization**
Conolly, B.W.	**Lecture Notes in Queueing Systems**
French, S.	**Sequencing and Scheduling: Mathematics of the Job Shop**
French, S.	**Decision Theory: An Introduction to the Mathematics of Rationality**
Griffiths, P. & Hill, I.D.	**Applied Statistics Algorithms**
Hartley, R.	**Linear and Non-linear Programming**
Jolliffe, F.R.	**Survey Design and Analysis**
Jones, A.J.	**Game Theory**
Kemp, K.W.	**Dice, Data and Decisions: Introductory Statistics**
Oliveira-Pinto, F.	**Simulation Concepts in Mathematical Modelling***
Oliveira-Pinto, F. & Conolly, B.W.	**Applicable Mathematics of Non-physical Phenomena**
Schendel, U.	**Introduction to Numerical Methods for Parallel Computers**
Stoodley, K.D.C.	**Applied and Computational Statistics: A First Course**
Stoodley, K.D.C., Lewis, T. & Stainton, C.L.S.	**Applied Statistical Techniques**
Thomas, L.C.	**Games, Theory and Applications**
Whitehead, J.R.	**The Design and Analysis of Sequential Clinical Trials**

**In preparation*